The Badge

Memoirs of a Biologist

by

Ernest Neal

PROVIDENCE PRESS

First Published 1994

*Published by Providence Press, 38B Station Road, Haddenham,
Ely, Cambs CB6 3XD, UK.*

© *Ernest Neal 1994*

ISBN 0-903803-28-3

Printed in England by Piggott Printers Ltd, Cambridge.

Contents

The author (1994)

In gratia

In gratitude for life, for home and very special
relationships within the family covering four generations, for
rewarding friendships, experiences and opportunities to
develop a variety of enthusiasms.

For being born into such a wonderful world so rich in beauty
and variety. For eyes to glimpse its beauty, ears to catch
snatches of its music, a sense of smell to appreciate some of
the subtleties of its fragrance, and hands to explore some of
its exquisite variations of shape and texture. For the gift of
curiosity concerning some of nature's mysteries, and for deep
feelings of awe and wonder at the majesty of it all.

Introduction

When I lay under a box bush in a Cotswold wood as dusk was deepening and saw badgers properly for the first time, I was absolutely thrilled as I watched the cubs play boisterously a few yards away. Fifty-five years on, I'm still intrigued by these fascinating animals. The natural world has excited me as long as I can remember, and since those early days I have had many and varied experiences which have given me great pleasure and stimulated a variety of enthusiasms. I remember the delights of being foster parent to two small otter cubs; discovering the ways of mongooses in an African national park; struggling to the top of Kilimanjaro and gazing into its glacier-fringed crater; visiting the Forgotten Islands of the Indian Ocean; making nature films and experiencing the exciting world of the BBC when live broadcasting was the norm. Sharing experiences and enthusiasms is one of the great joys of life; hence writing my memoirs has been good fun. But life is about more than fauna and flora and visiting exotic places; so while the natural world has always filled me with awe, wonder and delight, my vocation has been teaching and my greatest satisfaction has come through rewarding relationships with people.

As a biologist I have always been intrigued by the growing-up process - how the genetic make-up is modified by environmental and cultural forces along with the power to choose, to produce that unique product, the individual. As a teacher, particularly as a housemaster in an independent school, I was intimately involved in the lives of a wide spectrum of boys, a responsibility and privilege I greatly enjoyed. Here the growing-up process was continually before my eyes.

Recent research has shed more light on the complex question of just how much genes on the one hand and environment on the other play their part in development, but clearly the influence of people and circumstances, particularly during those first few weeks, months and early years of life are of over-riding importance, and the relationships established during that formative period are of enduring significance. So perhaps these memoirs are also an attempt to show how in growing up oneself, one too has been subjected to forces which have helped shape personality and influence direction. For this reason I have included character sketches and brief reflections on the careers of members of the family as they have greatly influenced my life and development.

With a special interest in ecology and animal behaviour, I tend to see life through biological spectacles, but my early upbringing in a lively, close-knit, Christian family added a religious dimension which greatly influenced me. I came to realise more and more that biological and religious ideas were by no means incompatible, but on the contrary, greatly enhanced one another and were merely different aspects of truth about life. I'm often reminded of the old concept of the natural philosopher - science, philosophy and religion all playing a synthesising role in developing the wholeness of the person.

As an ecologist, the complex inter-relationships between species thrill me with the overall picture of life on earth. By thinking ecologically one is inevitably led towards the basic truth that all life is about relationships. This is true at all levels - between molecules, cells, tissues, organs and organisms. It is the relationships between these entities that are so significant, just as our own human relationships are all important in determining our niche in society and indeed our happiness and fulfilment.

Teaching biology gave me the chance to pursue my natural history interests. My first appointment was to Rendcomb College, near Cirencester. The school was set in superb Cotswold country - a wonderful out-door laboratory. Previously natural history had mainly been a holiday pursuit as we lived in London, now it was permanently on the door-step. My early love of butterflies blossomed; I began to study moths, beetles and aquatic life and my enthusiasm for nature photography helped to broaden my interests still further to cover birds and mammals. It was not long before badgers entered my life. This brought me into contact with so many interesting people, opened up new horizons and gave me the opportunity to carry out research.

One of the spin-offs from my work on badgers was an invitation to do some field investigations in Uganda. This I accepted with enthusiasm as from boyhood I had always been fascinated by Africa. This period proved a profound and exciting interlude in my life. I fell in love with Africa and my experiences there helped to put life into better perspective.

Many will endorse the view that wild Africa can become an addiction. Fortunately, I was able to return to East Africa on many occasions when accompanying wildlife safaris as a Guest Lecturer, so these trips helped to alleviate withdrawal symptoms.

In the chapters that follow I hope I can share some of my experiences and enthusiasms. They have brought me a lot of fun and satisfaction. Enthusiasms usually mirror an attitude to life - a philosophy of living - perhaps some of this may rub off too.

Ernest Neal   Bedford 1993

Acknowledgments

I wish to express my great gratitude to my wife, Betty, and members of our family for contributions gleaned from their diaries and reports but above all for their support and encouragement when writing these memoirs.

I also wish to thank very warmly those friends who have made most helpful suggestions after reading certain chapters and in particular Mrs Winwood Reade and Mr Doug Woods who read the whole typescript, made valuable comments and criticisms and boosted my morale.

I'm also very grateful to those who have provided illustrations. The cartoons on the cover was presented to me in 1972 by the artist Ms J. Langmuir-Lanigan. I greatly regret that all my attempts to find her present address have failed. Dr David Bygott gave me a booklet of badger cartoons when he was 17; doodling at the back of my class had its compensations! I am privileged to include a selection which are scattered throughout the book. I also thank my niece, Diana, for letting me use a photograph of the painting of the L.N.W.R. express by the Revd Ivan Lilley which was commissioned by my brother. I am also indebted to the following people for allowing me to use their photographs: Jack Beale (p.213), Peter Blomfield (p.148), Stuart Seager and The Countryman (p.136), Dr G. C. Ainsworth and The British Mycological Society (p.28). The remainder were taken by me or members of the family. I apologise if I have made any unintentional omissions.

Finally, my warmest thanks to Jim Mason of Providence Press for being bold enough to publish my memoirs. Most publishers would baulk at contemporary autobiography unless the author was a popstar, politician, sports idol or criminal. I cannot claim such notoriety.

Chapter One

Early memories and influences

My first great gift from life was to be born into a loving, highly-motivated and close-knit family. This was already well-established when I arrived in 1911 as I was the fourth child. Margaret (Marge) was 10, Grace (Bids) came next at 7 and then William Keith (Bill) 5 1/2.

We lived at The Manse in St John's Road, Boxmoor in Hertfordshire; it belonged to the Baptist Church where my father was Minister. It was a pleasant home with small front garden and a larger one behind lined on one side with mature lime trees. The garden was quite spacious and contained a few fruit trees, gooseberry and black currant bushes and an area for vegetables which my father looked after. Any crop grown was valuable as making ends meet was always a problem on a minister's meagre stipend. There was a pear tree trained against the back of the house which, in a good year, bore large and delicious fruit. My father would pick these and keep them in his study until judged to be just right. They would then appear at tea and he would ceremonially peel them with his silver-plated fruit knife and share out portions between us all-too-eager children.

Father was an ardent Nonconformist, unswerving in his belief in the Bible. St Paul's teaching was the basis of his morality and we were all brought up with strict ideas about right and wrong; no compromises were tolerated on moral issues. He was a strong advocate of Sunday Observance and a strict teetotaller, campaigning tirelessly against alcohol abuse. The only alcohol in the house was a small medicine bottle containing brandy which was kept for an emergency. It was never used. These principles remained firm throughout his life, but as time went on he became much more broad-minded and tolerant and was always eager for new understanding sought with great humility.

Beneath my father's rather serious exterior there was a very warm heart and a deep caring for Mother and the family. He was rather shy and retiring, but always outgoing when the occasion demanded.

Whenever possible he would retreat to his study where he would prepare his sermons - he was an excellent preacher. He would also write innumerable letters, many giving help, advice and support to those in need. It was routine for him to answer letters the day he received them and post them just before the last collection was made. Sometimes if he missed this post he would go on his bicycle to the station sorting office which was open until midnight.

We always considered his study to be sacrosanct and there had to be a very good reason for disturbing him, especially on Fridays when he was preparing two services for the following Sunday. In the summer, when I was two or three, I would sometimes be allowed to sit under his desk and play with the contents of the waste-paper basket, cutting off the stamps with a pair of blunt-ended scissors, but it was part of the bargain that I had to be quiet.

The study was full of books all round the walls with the large desk in the middle of the room. It was always cold in winter as heating was too expensive, but he would put on a warm dressing gown over his suit and that had to suffice. Occasionally we would hear him pacing up and down and doing exercises to warm himself up.

He would spend most afternoons visiting, as he always looked upon pastoral care as a major part of his work. He came to know a great many people intimately and was held in great respect and affection. He had the patience to listen and was able to give them friendship, guidance and support. He was out at meetings most evenings, so we saw little of him except at meals but he would occasionally take time off to take us out for walks - often on Sunday afternoons if the weather was fine. He was happy to let Mother 'bring us up', but was always supportive when needed. He had little small talk, but would discuss important issues with patience and clarity. However, I always found it easier to talk to Mother who was always understanding and much more outgoing.

Early on, I used to sleep in my parents' bedroom and would awake to the sound of a razor being stropped. My father used a cut-throat razor and I always watched fascinated as he worked away with the shaving brush to produce a good lather and applied the foam to his face and throat. Then would come the exciting part when he took up the razor and with deft strokes would negotiate curves and irregularities with considerable skill. Then it was my turn. Water from a large jug was poured into a basin and I was thoroughly 'done' by Mother. Cleanliness came a good second to godliness in our household even when there were fern-like ice crystals on the bedroom windows and ice in the water jug.

As a small child my father made a great impression on me. I was taken to chapel from an early age, and remember him then as an upright figure in black standing in the pulpit. Sitting through the long services was at first an ordeal as discipline had to be maintained, but Mother was always understanding and the reward for keeping still was a small peppermint which was made to last as long as possible. When the chapel was cold as it usually was during winter, I was allowed to put my hands in her squirrel-fur muff - it had a lovely warm, silky feel.

Religious observance was not just something for Sundays but a way of life. Grace before meals was said with conviction and thankfulness; luxuries were few and far between. War-time also brought its shortages; it was a red-letter day when we were given a large pork-pie by a farming member of the chapel who had killed one of his pigs. Cake, or jam on our bread was often limited to Sunday teas, but Mother was an excellent cook and we eagerly looked forward to her fruit cakes and swiss rolls; it was a great let-down if seed-cake turned up instead - I couldn't abide it. One memory that stands out was the unexpected and very exciting arrival of a large parcel sent by rail from Scotland where an uncle had been on holiday. This contained the first whole salmon I had ever seen - a magnificent fish resplendent in its silver scales. I watched wide-eyed as Mother expertly cut it up in preparation for a sumptuous meal. No fridges in those days, so it had to be cooked at once.

I think it was in the late winter of 1915 when there was a severe blizzard. Trees were blown across the railway line near Boxmoor station and trains were cancelled. Many passengers were stranded and my parents put up one lady for the night. The next morning she carried me across the road through the thick snow and bought me some boiled sweets from Mrs Elkin's shop. I had to choose from a bewildering selection of large glass jars on her shelves. I was not used to such luxury.

Each morning after breakfast there would be family prayers. One of the family would read a portion from the Bible, Dad might add a few words of explanation, and then we would kneel on the floor and I would press my face against the seat of the dining-room chair. These had seen much wear and I was not popular when my small fingers explored the holes that had appeared in the rexine. To this day, if I catch the smell of rexine, I'm transported back to those early days with my brother trying hard to make me giggle at the wrong moment. It was too costly to have the chairs renovated, so later on, Mother, who hated things to look shabby, bought new material and laboriously re-covered the six chairs herself. She did them beautifully.

Being the youngest, I was way down in the hierarchy and my brother would tease me relentlessly. Once, when I was about three, I had been put to bed in the brass cot and everybody had gone out except Bill. I knew Mother would return shortly, but my brother made the most of this unusual opportunity and came into my room. I had recently discovered that the many small knobs around the cot could be unscrewed and when he started teasing me I put them to good use by hurling them in his direction. My fury must have given strength to my arm as the attack was undoubtedly successful. Mother had to pick up all the knobs on her return and Bill was reprimanded, much to my delight.

Dad had a passion for butterflies and would rear small tortoiseshells and peacocks most years in a small breeding cage kept on the window sill of his study. He would show me how they were developing and the smell of bruised nettle leaves and the chomping of the caterpillars made a great impression on me. However, it was the emergence of the butterflies that was the greatest thrill. Dad's work stopped when this was happening and I was called to the study to watch the transformation as they emerged from the suspended pupal cases and miraculously expanded their crumpled wings. Then when sufficient butterflies had completed their metamorphosis the cage was taken into the garden, the door opened and they were released. Magic!

Collecting butterflies was a fashionable hobby. The supply seemed inexhaustible and there was never a thought that one day their conservation would be of major concern. My father would take me out on the back of his bicycle as soon as I was capable of hanging on safely, and when he took a day's holiday, we might go as far as Ashridge, my sisters and brother coming with us on their own bicycles. A special bunch of flowers would be brought back to Mother as she did not ride.

There was great excitement one day when somebody spotted a strange bird in the garden in one of the trees. It was large and pink! It fluttered from tree to tree and did not appear to want to go far. Closer inspection showed that it was a fine parakeet, presumably escaped from somebody's house. Dad decided to try and catch it, so his long-handled butterfly net was assembled and he tried his luck. Egged on by much conflicting advice he was finally triumphant and this splendid bird was brought into the house for inspection. Many enquiries for its owner came to nothing so a cage was bought and this endearing pet provided much interest for several years.

Mother was very fond of wild flowers. As a girl she would scour the countryside around her home in Kent for new species and try to identify them; lists were made of those found in bloom during each month of the year. She greatly treasured her well- used copy of the Revd C.A. Johns'

'Flowers of the Field', which had good colour plates for identification. When I was born, Boxmoor was no bigger than a large village and most of the land west of our home was country. Early on when she took me out in the push-chair she would choose such places as Chaldon and Swan Lane where there were plenty of flowers to find. So by the time we left Boxmoor when I was six, I knew most of the common ones by name and had acquired a love of flowers which has persisted throughout my life. By the time I was two or three, Marge was old enough to take responsibility for me in many ways and would take me out when Mother was too busy. She too had an enduring love of flowers. Looking after me was something Marge took seriously and this aspect of our relationship remained over the years. In her mind, I was always very much the younger brother who still needed to be looked after. She was a splendid sister to have and she helped me at crucial times in my life with great generosity.

Visits with my father to the Grand Junction Canal when I could walk better provided exciting possibilities. Kingfishers were seen occasionally - electric blue streaks as they flew low over the water. We would look out for the first coltsfoot flowers which could usually be found beside the tow-path. The horse-drawn barges were a delight to watch; great beasts straining at the ropes, champing their bits and trampling the tow-path with heavy feet. The barges were brightly painted and many were piled high with coal or other goods. The bargees were usually friendly, but I was firmly discouraged from calling out to them as they passed. A journey to one of the canal locks was a special treat; it was fun to watch the water levels change and the barge gradually rise, while the horses had a well-earned rest and cropped any grass within reach.

Beside the canal there were watercress beds where bunches were cut and packed into wooden boxes for market. My sisters found the beds good places for pond-dipping when the owners were not around; on one memorable occasion a large crayfish was caught, triumphantly brought back and excitedly displayed for all to see. I had never seen anything so fierce and monstrous before!

Marge and Bids were good at games and as teenagers were very lively tomboys. The lime trees in the back garden gave them much scope for climbing, but this was not enough. A rope was attached high up and fastened at the other end to the base of a small tree. The rope was taut and the idea was to slide down it on a cushion without turning upside down or falling off. I used to watch with admiration at this balancing act, but Mother could not bear to watch. However, rather than spoil their fun she would go into a front room where she couldn't see them!

Marge had already made up her mind to be a doctor and all things medical were of great interest to her. During the war there was a great need for the drug, atropine, which was extracted from the seeds of the deadly nightshade, *Atropa belladonna*. Marge knew of a place where it grew commonly and collected the berries when they had turned black. She dried them in the sun, extracted the seeds and sent them to London for processing. The plant is very local in its distribution and her contribution was valued. In this way she earned her first pocket money.

The London and North Western Railway was another source of great interest. During my early walks down Swan Lane, my mother would pause when we reached the tunnel under the railway embankment; if a train was signalled we would wait to see it pass. However, the greatest thrill was to be underneath the tunnel when a train thundered overhead. The noise was deafening, and mixed in with my excitement was a nagging fear that the tunnel might fall in under the weight of this hurtling monster.

A few years later, my brother's enthusiasm for collecting engine names rubbed off on me, and we would haunt the railway together. The names had a romantic appeal: Belleraphon, Swiftsure, Fairy Queen, Eclipse, Sir John French, Flying Fox, Pandora, Rob Roy and many others.

Painting by the Revd Ivan Lilley (1981) of L.N.W.R. express pulled by two 'Jumbos', Boxmoor embankment

The 2-4-0 'jumbos' with their long chimneys were our favourites. They were often used on 'double-headers' to add extra power for heavy expresses and were classified in the Precedent class for that reason. Hardwicke was a special jumbo which had taken part in the famous race to Aberdeen in 1895. When it was eventually retired it was said to have run over a million miles. We also liked the Webb Compounds with their double number plates and vintage look.

The Boxmoor embankment carried four tracks; we never had to wait long before a train was signalled. In those days most goods were carried by rail and passenger services were frequent. When a signal went down and we were on the wrong side, we would rush through the tunnel to be in the best position for taking the name and number. Tracks one and two were the more exciting as they carried the express trains between London and the north so there was always a good chance of seeing a new engine. Tracks three and four were less interesting as they catered for local services and goods trains and we got to know the engines rather too well - some of the drivers would even wave to us in recognition. However, very occasionally, something special would turn up such as a 2-2-2 with enormous driving wheels - a relic of the mid-nineteenth century. When we saw it, it was relegated to pulling the engineer's line-inspection coach.

On wet days, when confined to the house, we would go up to the top floor and watch the trains from there as the embankment could be seen quite clearly from the bedroom window. It was interesting to count the coal wagons, as in 1916 some of the trains were extremely long - sometimes over 100 trucks pulled by two powerful 0-8-0 goods engines belching clouds of black smoke.

The railway fired my imagination - all those wonderful far-off destinations which spoke of lakes and mountains we had never seen and cities not visited. My parents had gone for their honeymoon to North Wales and I had been regaled with stories of that beautiful countryside, in particular, the time when Dad saw his first comma butterfly, and having no net, managed to catch it in his straw-boater! This specimen was given a special place in his collection and was always pointed out when he showed anyone his butterflies. Mother's forebears were the Keiths whose ancestral home was Dunotter Castle near Aberdeen. Stories of these romantic places were made more real by the expresses which we saw heading for Wales and Scotland.

I was told by Mother that Marge, when five years old, was the youngest season-ticket holder on the line. She was put in the charge of the guard at Boxmoor station and got out at the next stop,

Berkhampstead, where she went to school. Her red umbrella was well known to the railway authorities as she frequently left it in the carriage, but when found by a porter at Leighton Buzzard or Euston it would be returned as a matter of course via the guard and would be handed to her the next morning.

During those early years at Boxmoor the First World War meant little to me, although my parents' anxieties and the extra visiting involved made me realise that something awful was happening. It became a little more real when a colonel, his wife and an orderly were billeted on The Manse when troops were undergoing training nearby. There were many horses, mules and gun-carriages in the area and periodically a contingent would be sent to France with new recruits arriving to take their place for training.

The horses and mules were fun to watch and I liked to see the soldiers drilling and saluting. Every morning the paper was delivered to our house for the colonel. This was my moment. I had a rather battered wooden horse I was fond of, and would take the paper, mount the horse, career down the hall and knock on the colonel's door. I would then place the paper ceremonially in his hand and salute. The colonel gravely saluted back, and mission accomplished, I had to remember to shut the door and retreat in good order to Mother.

Mother was born at Mussenden, an ancient farmhouse near Farningham, Kent. Her father had an ivory business which imported the product from Africa and manufactured all kinds of goods from knife handles and piano keys to elaborately carved chess sets. One of these beautiful sets was given by Mother to Dad as a wedding present. The business prospered and they moved to Ivy House in Horton Kirby, a village nearby. She had two older brothers and a younger sister.

Mother had an indomitable spirit. She had tremendous faith in the power of love, goodness and endeavour. She was always clear in her thinking over what was right and wrong, but was never severe with it; her underlying caring for people came from a very warm and understanding nature. She set high standards and was no doubt influenced by her own home background. She liked everything clean and tidy, the table neatly set, the silver and brass well polished. Good manners were important to her, but she taught us more by example than rules. She was constantly mending and ironing, made her own clothes and was always neatly dressed. How she managed to look after us all, help Dad with his church work and run a Women's Meeting was a miracle, particularly as her health was not at all good. She was a splendid mother to have and we all loved her dearly.

When Grandfather died, Gran came to live with us. Her full name was Suzanna Burleigh Keith. She looked rather like pictures of Queen Victoria with black dress and lace collar and cap. She was somewhat prim and proper and expected to be waited on. I used to take in her Bovril and a plain biscuit mid-morning, and she would dip the biscuit into the drink to soften it. She had been well educated, was an intelligent lady, and although she tried my patience to the limit on occasions with her constant corrections, I was very fond of her. She was responsible for most of my early education and gave me lessons most mornings. I was taught to read and write from an early age and her general knowledge of many subjects helped to stimulate my interests. Gran had great patience and was usually happy to play games such as draughts, ludo, halma and chess. She played chess well and it was not long before she had taught me enough to play with Dad. This was exciting as he was an excellent player and we would use the red and white ivory pieces which he kept in his study.

Gran used to go out in a bath-chair, a vehicle which was kept in the hall. It was a basket-work affair with a long steering handle. It could either be pushed from the back or the steering handle swivelled round and be pulled from in front. The chair was a cause of great delight as I would play in it surreptitiously in the hall when I thought nobody was about. Gran's presence in the home was a great asset to all of us; she also helped the family budget.

The badger is an underground animal

Chapter Two

London

When we moved to London in 1917, Dad became Minister of York Road Baptist Church in Battersea. At that time this was a slum area and much of his time was spent in visiting and social work. Whole families would live in one room and life was very tough with so much unemployment following the First World War. I remember instances, after having visited particularly dirty homes, when Dad would go straight upstairs and strip off his clothes in the empty bath in order to find any fleas he had inadvertently picked up. On Christmas Eve, he helped deliver coal to families and would return home exhausted long after midnight. It was not surprising that our presents were not wrapped up until after lunch on Christmas Day. While we waited downstairs for his study door to open, our patience was sometimes near to breaking point, but Dad would not be hurried; each present had to be carefully wrapped in clean brown paper, neatly tied with string and labelled. At last, when he appeared, doing a balancing act with a great pile of parcels, we could start guessing which was to be ours.

Christmas was our family day, but on Boxing Day various people were invited from the church to share the evening with us. We sometimes had mixed feelings about this as we were expected to entertain them. There were piano recitals, recitations, singing and many games were played including Shooting the Chute, Pickles, Magic Touches and word games.

We lived in Patten Road, Wandsworth Common. It was a tall, semi-detached surburban house with a small front garden separated from the neighbour's by a row of small ginkgo trees which Mother considered very special. The house was about a mile and a half from the Baptist Chapel. It seemed a long way for me to have to walk there and back on a Sunday, twice when I was older. We would hurry when we got to York Road as the smell emanating from Price's candle factory was revolting. We also passed Garton's factory which made honey-sugar, a sweet concoction we put on our bread during the war. There were many rumours about what it was made of, but it tasted to us like sweet saw-dust. It was sold in round cardboard containers and was so hard it was difficult to spread. Butter was severely rationed, but Mother used to mix it with mashed potatoes to make it go further.

The congregation at the chapel was very mixed. I got on best with Mr Sheppard who was a genial man with an excellent tenor voice; he under-stood people, including small boys. An extra point in his favour in my eyes was that he had in his home a glass-fronted case of butterflies which included a Camberwell beauty. I was most intrigued as this species had been extinct in Britain for some years; unfortunately he did not know the origin of the specimen. Most who attended chapel were poor, some extremely so. There was one old tramp who came regularly, but usually arrived when the service was well advanced. He would shuffle up the aisle, plonk his walking stick on the pew and take his seat near the front with loud mutterings. It was said that he never washed, but instead, used to anoint his face with walnut oil. He certainly looked well tanned.

Dad knew the other ministers and clergy in Battersea very well; they worked closely together. It was at his suggestion that once a month there should be a joint communion service held alternately at the Anglican and Baptist churches. This was a very novel idea in the 1920s, but it worked admirably and produced a feeling of togetherness among the congregations which was very valuable.

Patten Road was visited by many tradesmen and itinerants. The milkman came round every day and when sighted, somebody would run out with a jug and the milk ladled out from a large container. The muffin-man came once a week. He used to ring his hand bell to inform potential customers and kept his wares in a tray covered with a white cloth, balanced precariously on his head. As a special treat, Gran would give us money for crumpets and I would take out a plate. Then would be the fun of toasting them under the grill of the gas stove. The rag-and-bone man would also do the rounds of the streets pushing a large barrow and shouting to get attention. On one occasion he brought along some potted hydrangeas which he attempted to exchange for pairs of trousers. Occasionally a tinker would set up his grinding wheel on the pavement and we would take out knives and garden shears to be sharp-ened.

I liked to watch the lamp-lighter who came round each evening and lit the gas lamps with a spark from his long pole. The local policeman was another source of interest. He would patrol the streets at night, and if you happened to be awake, you might see the light from his torch focused on the window catch. If a downstairs window was left unfastened he would ring the bell and inform the occupant.

When we first moved to London I was sent to a small private kindergarten school called Briar Bank, in Wandle Road - a long walk from our home. I was then six. At first I was accompanied but soon was able to go on my own. I was given an iron hoop which I could bowl along at a good speed, so that helped to bring me home quickly. The hoop was a great joy, and I would spend hours playing with it. One day it snapped and I was broken-hearted, but Dad took me to the forge and I watched the blacksmith with intense interest as the iron was made red-hot and the broken ends welded together under the hammer. There were plenty of horse-drawn vehicles about and forges still did good business.

During the winter, fog would be a real problem. You could taste the pollution in your mouth and the acid stung your eyes. It was sometimes so thick that you could not see more than a few yards so you had to follow the line of curb stones. I would keep a handkerchief in front of my mouth to filter off the soot. Coming back from school down Trinity Road there was a particularly nasty cross-roads to negotiate. Both roads carried a lot of traffic, and when very foggy, the opposite pavement was invisible, so Mother or Dad would meet me on these occasions and pilot me home.

Several of the school children wore leg irons to keep their limbs straight. Rickets which caused this condition was quite common due to malnutrition. At that time, nobody realised the connection between this disease and lack of vitamin D and calcium. Children's teeth suffered badly too, due to somewhat similar causes, and visits to the dentist were frequent. Our dentist was Mr Packham. He lived in Clapham, and strangely, another dentist just down the street was a Mr Wrackham. Both names were appropriate. Mr Packham seemed to spend his time putting in temporary fillings, something we took a dim view about as it meant we had to go to see him more often.

Air raids were a new and exciting experience. When they occurred in the day-time, school was cancelled. At night the raids were more exciting as we could watch the searchlights sweeping the sky for signs of enemy aircraft. Occasionally you would see the lights converge, a plane would be spotted, and the anti-aircraft batteries would open up. I used to watch with my nose pressed against the window pane and the curtains drawn behind me, my fascination sometimes mixed with fear. I was always very glad when the bugles sounded the all-clear. Not many bombs were dropped near us, but one morning, subsequent to a night raid, Dad took me to see a bomb crater. There was a large hole in the road, a gas main had been hit and many windows broken, but no great damage had been caused. People were more concerned when the zeppelins came over. These sausage-shaped airships looked huge as they slowly throbbed across the sky. They made easier targets for the gun batteries than aircraft, but were able to carry larger bombs. During night raids the family would gather in one downstairs room which was considered safer. I would be set to draw and paint flowers while Mother mended clothes and my sisters read books or did their homework. Dad was usually outside helping.

Armistice Day, 11 November 1918, was cause for great celebration. After dark, Dad took me to see the spectacular firework display on the Common; I had seen nothing like it before. People were singing and dancing in the street, horns were blaring and there was a spontaneous expression of carnival everywhere. But during the days and weeks that followed this euphoria, the realities of the post-war era descended like a cloud and life for everybody became very difficult. Some food was rationed and all of it was in poor supply. Mother would search the shops and queue for hours for meagre supplies of butter and meat. A bright spot was the opening of one of the first branches of Sainsbury's. This was the first shop we had seen to have a long, U-shaped serving counter which made things much easier for shoppers.

The 'flu' epidemic of 1919 killed more people than perished in the war; it was a terrible scourge. Bids was very ill with it, and we were all very apprehensive. She survived to our great joy, but many of our neighbours were not so fortunate. It was the custom for blinds to be drawn over the windows if there was a death in the house and this was happening frequently along our street. I used to watch with morbid fascination as the coffins were taken away for burial. We were all kept inside as much as possible.

I think it was in 1920 that a cousin of Dad's, Sir Phene Neal, became Lord Mayor of London and we were all invited to see the procession. This was a very exciting occasion for me as I'd never seen so much pomp and ceremony before. A room overlooking the route had been booked for us, so we had a grandstand view of the horse-drawn carriages, the uniformed retinue and the bands playing as they marched. Large numbers of people lining the road waved and cheered when the procession passed. We felt very proud to have such a distinguished relative even though we knew very little about him.

I soon outgrew the kindergarten and was ready to go to Highfield School at the Trinity Road end of our road. For some time I had watched enviously the crocodiles of boys passing on their way to the Common and was now ready for a bigger school. The Headmaster was the Revd C.W.Nelson Lowe, a tall impressive figure with snow-white hair, who had rowed for Cambridge as an undergraduate. His prized possession was the oar he had used; it hung in his sitting-room.

On the day of the varsity race a bus was hired and we all saw the finish at Mortlake. It was one of the great sporting events of the year and many thousands would go to see it. We watched with eager concern the large light and dark blue cylinders, representing the two boats, suspended on a tall erection near our view point. When phone messages arrived from strategic points along the river, the cylinders would be moved to indicate which crew was leading and the distance between the boats.

On the whole the school was a happy one with kindly staff and plenty to do. Mr Austin was my favourite teacher. He combined kindness with a no-nonsense attitude and most boys got on well under his guidance. He fostered a love of reading, and as I had already read most of the books available at home which were of interest, I was glad to make use of the school library. We were encouraged to read a book a week and I saturated myself with Charles Henty, R.M.Ballantyne, Major Charles Gibson, John Buchan, Robert Louis Stephenson and many others. 'Gorilla Hunters' by Ballantyne was a favourite which I read over and over again. It sparked off my first interest in Africa. Bids too was an avid reader, and after my birthday when I had some money to spend, she took me to a bookshop in London and helped me choose. I came away with 'The Society of the Tortoise Mask' by Major Charles Gibson, a thrilling story of China which all my grandchildren have since enjoyed when it was read to them.

Dad was keen on fireworks, and we usually had a few to let off ourselves in the garden. We were drilled in the art of setting them off safely, but Bill dared me to let off a roman candle in my gloved hands. This was a great thrill as you could feel the heat and pressure with the expulsion of each coloured ball. Not to be recommended, but good fun! On one unforgettable occasion a pocketful of jumping-crackers in Dad's overcoat pocket became ignited. Dad was leaping about trying to get his coat off as quickly as possible, and as spectators, we were torn between concern and laughter. But Mother scolded him severely - not without reason, as she had to mend the coat afterwards and put in a new pocket.

Children's bicycles were not common and I was too small to reach the saddle of a larger one. However, by putting a cushion on the chain-box of Bids' bike , I could paddle along with my feet, steering from below. Later, I was able to ride with one foot pushed below the bar of Bill's to reach the far pedal, tilting the bike so I was vertical. It was tiring as I could not sit on the saddle, but it had to suffice until I had a bike of my own. I went for long journeys into the country in this peculiar manner.

Dad missed the country quite a lot and occasionally would take a day off and take me to Ewell, Epsom, Bookham Common or Boxhill. These were red-letter days as I could find flowers and butterflies and add to my collection. We would get very hot riding and Dad would take me into a dairy for a glass of milk laced with soda-water. I loved these times on my own with Dad - we were kindred spirits in many ways.

Butterflies were kept at home in wooden store-boxes, and very occasionally Dad would take me up to London to visit the firm of Watkins and Doncaster to buy another. It was an intriguing shop in the Strand with a sign outside showing a swallowtail butterfly. You went up a rickety flight of wooden stairs to the second floor and through a glass door. It was very exciting to see all the entomological paraphernalia stacked in that room, cabinets, store boxes, setting boards, breeding cages, nests of glass-topped boxes, pins of all kinds, and of course, butterfly nets. Our purchases were invariably modest, but these visits made me long for more expeditions to the country.

However, for most of the time I had to be content with local pursuits. Wandsworth Common had some interesting wild corners where you could still find butterflies such as meadow browns, gatekeepers, small heaths and coppers. There were not many kinds of wild flowers, but there were a lot of gorse bushes scattered around. However, these were very vulnerable to vandals who would set them alight just to be able to watch the crackling blaze. We were very indignant as this area was the nearest thing to the country we could find.

I also used to scour the streets for caterpillars. There were many lime trees about which were very productive. I soon learnt that trees with well-eaten leaves and caterpillar droppings below on the pavement were worth investigating, and found such species as bufftips and the occasional limehawk. The latter was always considered special with its comical curved horn near the rear end. Limehawk caterpillars were always difficult to find as, when small, they lay along the midrib of the leaf on the underside, beautifully camouflaged. I also found pussmoth caterpillars and poplar hawks on the poplars, vapourers on the apple trees and yellow underwings and ermines in the garden. All these were kept in breeding cages often made from wooden boxes with netting on top. I used to spend happy hours watching them feeding. Once they had pupated, I kept them during the winter in damp moss, eagerly waiting for the time when they were due to hatch into moths. If I caught them during metamorphosis, that was a bonus, but usually I would find them already fully formed as they would emerge at night.

I was interested in anything that moved and had already explored most of the garden habitats for woodlice, millipedes, centipedes, earwigs and spiders. On one occasion, having nothing to do, I thought I would see what lived underground, so I dug an immense hole in the garden. It was quite interesting at first as I found various beetles, worms and the like, but as I got deeper, fewer and fewer animals appeared and I began to realise that only the region near the surface was much good as a home or shelter for wildlife.

There were some ponds on the Common which sometimes got frozen over. Gulls roosted there, and as a special treat we would be given money to buy sprats for them. The gulls would go frantic when these were thrown into the air for them to catch - a welcome change from bread. The beauty of it was breath-taking as they wheeled and dived in a flurry of white wings in their excitement at such an unexpected bonanza.

We had another addition to our household when my Great Aunt Rosa came to stay. Her husband had died and she was welcomed as a companion to Gran. They shared the same bedroom. She was a kindly lady who helped us in many ways. She was particularly fond of Bill, who at that time was developing many hobbies and never had enough cash to satisfy his ambitions. She helped him with purchases on many occasions.

Around 1920 there was a good deal of army surplus material about and Bill, who then went to the City of London School, had got very keen on electrical experiments and used to haunt second-hand shops for anything useful. He came back one day with components of a wireless crystal set and put it together. To pick up signals, you needed an aerial, so a long copper wire was erected in the garden. He fiddled for hours with the cat's whisker to find the most sensitive spot on the crystal for reception. All he heard at first were morse code messages, but he soon mastered the code and what he was hearing gradually made sense. I shall never forget the thrill of hearing voices for the first time. This was when transmission was being tested prior to the first broadcasts. We listened avidly to the disembodied sentences coming from the ear-phones, 'Monday, Tuesday, Wednesday, Thursday....1,2,3,4' with endless repetitions. It was miraculous to me that sounds could somehow come through the atmosphere without wires to conduct them. Everybody had to come and listen when Bill first heard music on the air. In 1922 Daventry started regular broadcasts and listening to the wireless became part of life, but those early experiments were magical.

Bill was extremely clever with his hands and loved constructing things or taking them to bits to see how they worked. He had not been happy with the quality of wireless reception he was getting and decided to do something about it. This meant a longer and better aerial. During the war, Emmanuel School, nearby, was turned into a military hospital and many huts had been erected in the grounds. When it was closed in 1923 there was a great sale and Bill and I went along to see what was going on. He bought a telegraph pole for three shillings! This we lugged back, roped on to our two bicycles, precariously balanced on handle-bars and saddle. Somehow we got it home and down our side passage-way into the garden. Mother was staggered when she saw it! We had also bought some angle-steps, and these were soon firmly screwed to it to make it climbable. Mother gave permission for a large hole to be dug at the bottom of the garden so long as it did not interfere with her prized lemon-coloured sunflowers, and with much willing help from other boys the pole was erected and made safe with metal guys.

The idea was to make a long double aerial about 60ft long which could be attached at one end to an insulator on the pole and at the other to the house. Bill insisted that it must be as high as possible, which meant the top of the house! This he achieved by getting out of his bedroom dormer-window and running up the roof in his gym shoes to reach the row of castellated tiles along the top. The insulator was fixed firmly to these and the aerial hauled into place. When I first dared to climb to the top of the roof myself, I was very scared, but felt better when I got a firm grip on the top tiles. There was certainly a magnificent view to be had from the roof-top with the glass of the Crystal Palace gleaming in the sunlight in the far distance.

I had my own school friends, as Bill was more than five years older, but we still did much together. He acquired an old wooden lathe which was probably 100 years old. It was in poor shape, but he rebuilt it in the cellar. The lathe had a cast iron fly wheel and various other metal parts, but basically it was made of oak. It was worked by treadle and, of course, I had to work away at this while he turned out rolling pins, egg-cups, copies of insulators and the like with much skill. His constant refrain was "Come on Tiche (me) old man, come and give me a hand like a good chap". He had strong powers of persuasion and great persever-ance once he had set his mind on something. Ours was very much a love-hate relationship. I was sometimes his willing helper, at other times his reluctant slave. We were so very different. I loved sport, he hated it; I enjoyed school, but he was delighted when school was behind him (he left at sixteen); he was a loner, I was happier when in a gang. But we had many good times together and he taught me much about the practical things which he was so good at. In later years we followed very different careers, but there was always a deep love and respect for the other and I soon threw off the burden of his dominance. His great kindness shone through at all times and he carried with him to the end a great sense of family responsibility. Although we had such different philosophies and interests we remained the greatest of friends.

Bill developed a craze for collecting telegraph insulators and became very knowledgeable about them. We used to go on expeditions to look for those that had been thrown away when new posts had been erected, or the lines put underground. Many were smashed, but good ones were often found. 'Bell-shapes' were his favourites and I remember the excitement when he found some lying on the ground on a railway embankment. Unfortunately they were still attached to the arms which were too heavy to carry away. While I stayed with the bicycles, he tried to remove them with an old spanner, but they would not budge. As I watched him trying to get one off, the sight of Wandsworth Prison on the opposite side of the railway seemed to cast an ominous shadow! Bill never did get it off, but he found others of the same kind later. Many years on, his collection was recognised as the best and most comprehensive in the country and his books on the subject have become valuable collectors' items and standard works of reference.

However, old guns were his chief delight; the story of how he built up his world-renowned collection from nothing is an astonishing drama which cannot be recounted here. Enough to say that in those early days in London he gradually acquired from sales and antique shops a few pieces which I well remember. He would bring one home, soak it in oil, take it to pieces, mend any part that was faulty and re-assemble it. Then came the test - would it fire? One small percussion pistol proved very stubborn - the percussion caps were probably faulty. He tried once too often and the bullet went into his leg. We were together in his bedroom when the accident happened, so after the pain had abated somewhat, some action was called for. We decided Mother had to be told although that would take much courage as she had constantly begged him to be careful. Although she hated firearms and anything destructive, it was typical that she refused to curb his passion for them. Fortunately he was not badly hurt, and when we went to Mother she was practical as usual and took him to the doctor who disinfected the wound and had an X-ray taken. The bullet had lodged in the thigh bone and it was decided not to remove it. He had it for the remainder of his life and it gave him no trouble. He was scrupulously careful ever after, but always insisted on firing his best pieces.

By this time I was into the gang age and had a group of friends who were keen on sport, railways and to some extent natural history. I formed a club and we all contributed to the magazine we wrote each month. Expeditions were organised to my favourite London and North Western Railway, the nearer places from home being Wembley, Harlesden and Kenton. By this time we had our own bicyles. One trip to Wembley was quite eventful. We had to go along main roads with tram lines set in the cobbled surface. These were a constant hazard as you could easily get your wheel stuck in one and skid badly. We learnt, when overtaking, to cross them at a sharp angle, but on this occasion the cobbles were very slippery from rain and I skidded in front of a brewer's dray pulled by four horses. I fell off my bike in a heap and the driver had to snatch at the reins. The horses reared up on their hind legs and I felt the hot air of their breath on my neck, but mercifully I was not touched. I quickly dragged the bicycle to the side while the driver told me in no uncertain terms what he thought of my antics. This certainly taught me a lesson.

We did idiotic things on bicycles. Traffic was very light and it was commonplace to hang on to the back of lorries and be pulled along at speed. The outer side was better as you could then see what was coming, but that meant that the driver could see you in his mirror and, if unco-operative, might try to dislodge you by braking or accelerating. However we usually got away with it, and it sometimes saved us miles of pedalling. Lorries didn't go very fast in those days. Stunt riding also became popular such as sitting on the handle-bars and going backwards. When going down a slight slope if you were balancing well you could raise your feet on to the saddle while sitting on the handle bars. It was a lot of fun.

I became mad on games and in the holidays would play as much cricket, tennis and football as I could. My sisters were good at tennis and Dad would also play, so we had fun together on the new hard courts erected on the Common. In the Easter holidays some of us were suffi-ciently keen on cricket to man-handle the big roller and prepare our own pitches at the Old Leysian ground. The groundsman became a good friend and was most helpful.

Dad had been an excellent games player when at College and was glad of any opportunity to watch good matches. On one occasion he took me to Crystal Palace to see the Corinthians. They were the best amateur soccer team in the country and were exempt from playing in the first two rounds of the the FA cup. He also took me to the Oval to see England play Australia during their first tour after the war. At that time Australia had some very fast bowlers who bowled short on the off-side with four slips and a gulley and few people had the patience to play safely. Frank Woolley would have none of it, and by using his bat horizontally would slice the ball over the heads of the slips to the boundary. Dangerous, but most effective.

When I was a bit older I used to go to the Oval quite frequently with Tim Williamson. We would go by tram from Balham. Trams were fun to ride in, especially if you went upstairs and sat in the front where it was rather like being in the bows of a ship. County matches attracted large crowds and we used to sit on the ground just behind the ropes which marked the boundary. The pitches were not covered when it rained, and on a drying wicket the spin bowlers would come into their own. Bowlers like Tich Freeman would take 100 wickets by the end of May. Hobbs and Sandham used to open for Surrey and I always enjoyed watching Woolley when Surrey was playing Kent, and Hendren in the Middlesex game. They always went for the runs - something very necessary as they were 3-day matches. When a team left the pavilion, the amateurs came out of the door in the centre and the professionals from one at the side and met on the field. We were very incensed by this distinction, particularly because all our heroes were professionals. You could get into the ground for a shilling, the 'card o' match' was twopence, and if you were in cash, you could buy 'Caddy's milk chocolate at three bars for six' from the man who came round with a trayful of goodies.

By the time I was 10, Marge had completed her schooling at the City of London Girls School, done her 2nd MB at University College and had gained a place at the London Hospital Medical School. She was in the last batch of women students to be admitted. The hospital had taken in women during the war, but closed its doors to them soon after. Marge lived in a hostel in London, so we saw little of her except at week-ends. I was much intrigued by her medical stories and she was good fun to be with. At that stage, I wanted very much to be a doctor too.

Bids did well at Clapham High School. She was artistic and had a flair for literature and painting. She probably had the most sensitive nature of the four of us and played a quiet, but very effective role in our family life. She provided the feminine touch which was very valuable to me, although at that stage I did not realise it. It was probably on my twelfth birthday, that on coming down to breakfast, she put a crown of laburnum flowers which she had prepared, on my head. I had never been singled out before by such a gesture and it made a great impression on me. Looking back, I believe this probably made me conscious for the first time that I was an individual in my own right, that I had discovered my identity. Bids was like that, she was always doing kind and thoughtful things which helped my growing-up process. However, during term time all the family were so busy doing their own thing that we saw very little of each other.

On one occasion Bids took me to the Strand Theatre to see 'The Scarlet Pimpernel'. This was my first visit to a theatre and a great thrill. We had to queue for several hours to get into the gallery where the seats were cheapest, and while we waited, we played chess on a portable set. It was a great experience to be high up in the 'gods' and see the drama I loved so well unfold. Another time we went to hear the Kearton brothers speak and see their wildlife films of Africa. It is astonishing to think back to those early films where the camera had to be cranked by hand. Captain Knight was another film-maker whom we heard lecture; he made the first film of the golden eagle. This was rather a strange event because in order to make it more popular, chorus girls were brought on to the stage as an introductory entertainment. I had never seen chorus girls dancing before, and somehow this item didn't quite mix with golden eagles! Bids loved the theatre, but Mother and Dad never went, as far as I can remember.

One day Bids roped me in to collect money for the Save the Children Fund. She had acquired two collecting tins and to save time she took one side of the road and I, the other. I was met with much kindness, but not from everyone. At one house, when I explained my errand I was met with a torrent of abuse to the effect that she wasn't going to help German children after all the Germans had done to us in the war. Then the door was slammed in my face. I was speechless; it was so unexpected. But it had the salutary effect of shattering my 'do good' attitude towards collecting for charity, and in retrospect I was grateful to the lady. It made me realise for the first time how much others had suffered through the war. Our family had been so fortunate.

A year or so later I helped collect for the Red Cross, this time in the City. It meant getting up at dawn and going by tram. There were special fares for workers if you went before six. When I arrived, the streets were being swept and charwomen were on their hands and knees busily scrubbing the steps of offices. It was quite an experience to see the City at that time of the morning when a small army of people were preparing for the day ahead. They were generous with their gifts even though they had little to spare. Then came the great influx of office workers and London really woke up.

Family holidays were very special. This was the only time when dad had a few weeks to do things with all of us. We made the most of it. We would always go to the sea. Deal was a favourite (it was the place where Dad first met Mother), but we also had good times at Ventnor, Felixstowe and Ilfracombe, putting up in rented accommodation. Mother took a dim view of Ilfracombe as the landlady was not at all co-operative and Mother felt that hard-earned money had not been well spent, but I enjoyed it in spite of poor weather as this was the first occasion I saw grayling butterflies. My memories of Ventnor are of adonis blues on Boniface Downs and large numbers of humming-bird hawk moths hovering in front of the red valerian flowers. It was a good year for migrants and these 'hummers' from Africa would visit those valerian plants which still caught the late afternoon sun.

At Deal, each day was filled with activities and we could all choose in turn what the family would do. There would be bathing from the pebbly beach most days. One, two, three and you were in! The water always seemed terribly cold and we had to run up and down afterwards to get our circulation back. Then would be the good bit - eating sticky buns bought specially for the occasion. I always hoped for sunny weather as that meant Dad would take me around the clover and lucerne fields inland looking for clouded yellow butterflies.

I have many vivid memories of these trips. Dad would wear a somewhat shabby pepper-and-salt sports jacket, expertly reinforced by Mother with leather at elbows and cuffs. One large pocket bulged with an oval zinc pocket-box for keeping the butterflies, and in another were nests of glass-topped boxes for examining them before keeping or

My father catching butterflies.
Deal 1937

releasing. When we came to a likely spot, he would assemble his large kite-net and start searching for butterflies. He rode a large-framed Raleigh bicycle which he mounted from a step attached to the rear hub. Punctures were commonplace; on many occasions I would have to wait impatiently as the bicycle was turned upside down and the inner tube mended.

There were special days at Deal when we walked or cycled as far as Dover and Folkestone searching the Downs and Undercliff. These were studded with a great variety of flowers, such as bird's foot trefoil, kidney vetch, milkwort, scabious, thyme and marjoram. Here we would look out for brown argus, chalk-hill, and adonis blues. In the scrubby hollows where the thistles grew we would keep our eyes open for dark green frit-illaries and perhaps a painted lady. Isolated patches of brambles were also examined as the small blue - always so local and restricted in its flying range - might sometimes be found there. That corner of Kent was an excellent place for butterflies, particularly the migrants which crossed the Channel from France. We were there when a large migration of painted ladies arrived. They were exhausted and settled in great numbers. On one clover field, I counted 12 within a square yard. On another occasion we were astonished to see a swallowtail flying swiftly over the cliff tops and settling spasmodically on wild carrot flowers. It must have come from the Continent as at that time the nearest breeding British ones were in Norfolk.

Cricket on the green outside Walmer Castle, visiting the Castle dungeons and seeing the cannons, listening to the band of the Marines nearby, or going for long walks along the cliffs, were activities we fitted in as opportunities arose. Bill would fish for codling from the pier and would occasionally bring one home for lunch in triumph. We were not a family for lying about on the beach. A special trip was to the other side of Sandown where there was an excellent beach for shells. These would be identified and mounted on card for the collection. We were always collecting something.

Sometimes we would hire a boat if the sea was calm and Dad would teach us how to row. If we were there at the time of the Deal regatta, that was an extra attraction. I always liked to watch competitors trying to walk the greasy plank. Watching the lifeboat being launched was another thrill, particularly in rough seas; the crew would all be wrapped up in their yellow oilskins and there was much excitement as waves broke over the bows as they set off. The list on the lifeboat house of all the people rescued greatly impressed us. Those were happy days at Deal as the whole family was together and there was lots for everybody to do.

Chapter Three

Boarding school

I was sent to boarding school when I was 13. A small number of bursaries were available at Taunton School for the sons of Baptist ministers and Dad had put my name down for one. However, nothing was available for the time being, so I was sent to Bethany House School near Goudhurst in Kent as an interim measure. How my fees were paid I do not know, but the school had a Nonconformist foundation and I may have had a bursary. It is also possible that Aunt Rosa helped.

I had never been away from home on my own before; early on it was a shattering experience. I was extremely lonely and home-sick and would wander around the corridors aimlessly, pretending to be busy. However, the staff were kindly and I soon made a few friends. The school was a strange set-up with two headmasters, Messrs Kenyon and Bennian. Mr Kenyon did the administration and Mr Bennian ran the academic side of the school. It was very much a family affair as Mr Bennian's son was an assistant master and Mr Kenyon's daughter taught music.

The food was extremely dull and portions were not generous but you could always fill up with bread and scrape. I was growing fast and continually seemed to feel hungry. Complaints to Dad in my letters brought welcome postal orders - usually for one and sixpence. I changed these at the post office which formed part of the village shop, and was then able to buy my own jam - usually raspberry, more expensive, but it went further.

The staff were uninspiring except for Mr Wilson (always known as Tort). He was a splendid schoolmaster and was a tower of strength. He taught geography and history with enthusiasm, and both subjects came to life in his hands. Suddenly, all those boring facts and dates concerning the Tudors and Stuarts which had been endlessly drummed into me at Highfield were behind me, and instead, I was taught European history. Garibaldi and Cavour, Bismarck and Napoleon became real people doing real things and the map of Europe gradually made a little sense.

Tort used to come round the dormitories to put the lights out and would usually take time to talk to everybody. Occasionally he read us stories and poems and discussed all manner of topics. I would pick his brains about Africa which was by this time somewhere I longed to visit as I had vague ideas at that time of going to the Congo as a medical missionary.

A fairly wide curriculum was taught including a little elementary science, but alas, no biology, so I had to be content with my own natural history investigations. Young Mr Bennian responded to my interest in wildlife and occasionally took me out in the evening when he went shooting rabbits. He showed me how to recognise a breeding rabbit stop where the mother had carefully closed the entrance on leaving, and putting his arm into one, brought out a nestling to show me before carefully putting it back in its downy nest.

At the end of my first year I took the Senior College of Preceptors examination. This acted as a useful rehearsal for Cambridge School Certificate the following year. One of the subjects I found interesting was book-keeping, a sensible addition to the usual curriculum.

Games played a big part in the life of the school and I spent many pleasurable hours playing soccer and cricket. I had been a large fish in a small pool at Highfield; it was splendid to play with people with much more skill. In spare moments we played an amusing game kicking a tennis ball on to the roof of the school from the asphalt playground. The ball would usually be deflected by various gables and dormer windows on the return journey, so it was difficult to predict where it would land. The idea was to get to the right place quickly enough to kick it up again after its first bounce. If you were clever with your kicking and the ball bounced evenly you could keep going for some time. It certainly improved your co-ordination and foot work.

The autumn term was enlivened by an influx of hop-pickers into the area. They mainly came from the east-end of London and looked upon their job as a fortnight's holiday in the country. There were many hop fields and oast houses near the school and the hop-pickers would set up camp for the duration of their stay and go the rounds of the fields in the neighbourhood. They were colourful characters.

We all attended church on Sunday mornings and girls from the Ladies College at Goudhurst came too. We were carefully segregated, boys on one side, girls on the other. We never met them socially but they provided a nice diversion from the long, dull sermons we had to endure. I missed Dad's warmth and expertise.

By my second year, I had settled down to boarding school life. Some of the moods and uncertainties of adolescence were giving way to greater self-confidence, work was going reasonably well and my games were coming on. However, it was always good to be home for the holidays and do things with the family and my old school friends. I saw little of Bill who was working with his uncle in London and Bids who was doing nursing.

Bids enjoyed her nursing, but not being very strong, she found it very tough going and wisely gave it up after a year; however, she had gained useful experience. Another reason for her leaving the hospital was that Mother was not at all well at that time and Dad was extremely busy with his church work. She felt she should help Mother at home for a while.

At the end of the Christmas term I came home with an invitation from Tort to go with him and another boy on a cycling tour around Yorkshire during the Easter holidays. This was a very exciting prospect; I hoped I would be allowed to go. However, by the end of the Easter term, the other boy had dropped out, so it looked as if I would be alone with Tort. This was a real dilemma for my parents because although they knew my high opinion of Tort, they did not know enough about him personally to discount possible homosexual tendencies. I knew nothing of these things and was impatient to have the go-ahead. I never knew how the matter was settled, but I suspect Dad met Mr Wilson and in his straight-forward way, expressed his concern and received a satisfactory reply. Mother explained why they had hesitated, and after giving me some relevant advice, I was allowed to go.

We met at King's Cross Station, put our bikes in the guard's van and off we went to York. It was all very exciting. I had brought my Ensign box camera, purchased from Bill when he was short of cash a few years back. It had the one fixed exposure of 1/25th of a second. I had previously used it mainly for taking photographs of engines when on trips to the London and North Western Railway.

The holiday was a great success. I had not been to Yorkshire before and Tort had worked out an excellent itinerary taking in places of historic and countryside interest. We put up in an assortment of boarding houses entirely at his expense; he was most generous. We visited Ripon Cathedral, looked in on Fountains Abbey, saw the strange church at Richmond which had a house attached to its walls, explored one of the Dales and gazed from a hill-top at two far-away accumulations of smog which indicated the positions of the industrial towns of Stockton and Darlington. I was glad to visit the railway which connected these two towns as this was the first to be constructed in Britain, and on one of the platforms at Darlington I was thrilled to see on display Stephenson's famous engine, the 'Rocket'. We visited the coast at Whitby and finally pedalled our way across the moors back to York.

York was magnificent. The Minster made an indelible impression on me; it was fascinating to follow the wall which circled the older parts of the city and see some of the ancient buildings. Near the Minster there was an antique shop, where I spotted in the window a flintlock pistol. I told Mr Wilson about my brother's interest in old firearms and he suggested we made enquiries. The price asked was twelve shillings and sixpence. The shopkeeper said it was one of a pair, but as one was damaged I could have that one for seven and six. I only had about fifteen shillings left, so I said I would only buy the good one. When I got back, Bill was thrilled with the purchase and told me it was of a type used by highwaymen and was made by a good gunmaker. He was disappointed that I hadn't bought the pair. However, I knew the address and he sent off for it at once. Fortunately it had not been sold and the parcel duly arrived. He soon had the gun to pieces, and was able to mend the broken part, so that when it was re-assembled it looked as good as the other one. He always prized that pair because of its associations, and years after when I visited him would point them out from among the large number of others in his collection.

I took my bicycle back to school for the summer term and this gave me welcome freedom. The countryside was interesting, and I was able to explore several of the large deciduous woods nearby. They were privately owned and well keepered, but that did not deter me, as when I had been out with Dad catching butterflies on many previous occasions he had shown little regard for 'Trespassers will be prosecuted' notices, always insisting that if you did no damage nobody could prosecute you. If anybody accosted you, the thing to do was to talk politely, get them interested in what you were doing and ask for permission to continue. This formula usually worked. In one of these woods near Cranbrook I was delighted to see white admirals flying along the rides with that characteristic gliding flight which is so beautiful to watch - and I met no keeper!

I left the school in December 1926 as a bursary had become available at Taunton School. It was far from ideal changing schools in the middle of the school year, but having passed my Cambridge School Certificate, and wanting to go in for medicine, I went straight into the Biology Sixth. At last I could study biology! However, things were complicated, as in order to take my First Medical examination from school I needed matriculation. I was not exempted from this by my School Certificate results as my five credits did not include a modern language, so I had to take London Matriculation in the summer. I managed to do this, but my sixth-form work suffered in consequence and I started again in the Lower Sixth in the autumn term. This was a great help to me as by then I had found my feet and could concentrate on my science subjects.

Taunton School was much larger and very different from Bethany. It mainly catered for boarders with about a third day boys. It was organised on a house basis and I was put into School House East. My housemaster was a short, stocky Welshman - Jake Morgan. Boys were rather frightened of him as he was strict in his discipline and wielded the stick with vigour when he considered the punishment appropriate. He was a bachelor, not very forthcoming and rather lacking in the human touch, but he ran the house well and was respected.

Dr Watson (1870-1960): an international authority on lichens and one of the early ecologists; he taught me biology at Taunton School, 1926-29

My form master was Dr Watson - a great character. He had joined the school in 1908 and was the senior science master. He was a rather eccentric, weather-beaten Yorkshireman with a drawling northern accent which attracted much mimicry from the boys, but was a kindly man and much liked. If you responded to his enthusiasm for plants he went to much trouble to help. He was extremely well qualified as a botanist having been awarded a Doctor of Science degree by the University of London for his work on lichens - a group of plants on which he became a world authority. His real enthusiasm was for field work. He did a lot of research on the distribution of plants in relation to habitat differences;

much of his work on lichens, mosses and liverworts was incorporated in Professor Tansley's monumental work 'The British Isles and their Vegetation'. He was one of a dedicated band of pioneers who helped put plant ecology on the map.

He would regularly take out the class, and in his quiet way would teach much without you realising it. For him, theoretical teaching was always supplementary to the living countryside. I found favour early on when he discovered I knew something about butterflies, a happy contrast to my vast ignorance of biological theory. I much appreciated his encouragement. Neither of us would have dreamt that I would eventually succeed him as biologist at Taunton School.

Taking three specialised science subjects for Ist MB deprived me of wider opportunities, but we took English classes with Mr Went as a humanising measure. Most members of the form thought this a waste of time, but I loved it. He was a most inspiring teacher. I can see him now with pince-nez spectacles in hand eloquently reciting Shakespeare with the book in front of him, but seldom glancing at it. He could recite from memory by the hour. I shall always be grateful to him for giving me a love of Shakespeare and opening my eyes to poetry. In the holidays I would sometimes go with Bids to the Old Vic and see the real thing. You could get in for a shilling and sit on wooden benches or stand at the back. We once saw Hamlet performed in its entirety - $5^1/2$ hours of it, but fortunately with a long interval!

The Headmaster, Mr Nicholson, was very keen on light opera, especially Gilbert and Sullivan, and drama was encouraged throughout the school. One play which made a great impression on me was 'Journey's End'. This ended more dramatically than was intended as the whole set collapsed on to the stage, burying the actors beneath the pieces. Not quite what was planned, but a very dramatic ending to what was intended as a protest against war.

I took piano lessons with Mr Wade who was Head of Music. He was a good teacher and I became very fond of piano playing. He was also a splendid organist. When we went into chapel for school services there would always be a lot of chatter, but he would soon put an end to that by starting to play. At first the notes were so quiet they hardly intruded on the noise, but gradually we became aware, volume was increased and he would have our attention. Occasionally he gave organ recitals which were well attended even though they were voluntary.

The organ was a very good one; occasionally he would take me into the chapel and demonstrate the scope of the instrument. I was delighted to have the chance to start learning the organ during my last year.

Although I never became proficient, it was an enjoyable experience.

On Sunday mornings the school attended services in Taunton. Dressed in our Sunday suits, white shirts with stiff collars and with straw-boaters on our heads, we assembled on the parade ground by Houses. The Second Master, Mr Record, then appeared on the steps and supervised a roll-call; we would form into squads each destined for a particular church in the town. Being a Baptist, I went either to Silver Street or Albemarle - the two Baptist churches in Taunton. I preferred the former as the sermons were usually shorter. We walked into town in long crocodiles, each accompanied by a master and prefect. These Sunday mornings were not popular; most of us preferred the school chapel services in the evening when the singing was enthusiastic and the addresses more interesting.

On free afternoons we could get an exeat to go into the town and we made the best use of this freedom. However, we were not allowed to go into the cinema. This was a temptation difficult to resist, especially if there was a good Charlie Chaplin film showing - silent, of course. Sometimes a prefect would be told to watch the entrance of the cinema at the end of the performance to catch anybody from the school as the crowd emerged, but there was a good way to avoid being spotted. The Cinema manager wanted as much custom as possible, so was most co-operative. At the end of the film the national anthem was always played; this was the signal. Before the lights went up he would open a door at the back and any schoolboys present would quickly get out into the yard. Here there was a brick wall which was easy to climb and you dropped down into a back street. It was some time before the prefects tumbled to this escape route.

Taunton was particularly keen on games, and was looked upon as the best in the south-west at that time. Alan Marshall was in charge of cricket; he and his brother, the school doctor, played for Somerset when time allowed. When J.C.White was captaining the county (he was an old boy of the school), and had just returned from England's tour in Australia, we were given a day's holiday to see Somerset play on the Taunton ground, both Marshalls being in the team.

I greatly enjoyed cricket and was pleased to play for my House, but had to make the difficult decision between work and competing for a place in a school team. I found I had more than enough to do to pass my examinations, not having studied any science to speak of at Bethany. Playing for a school team meant spending a great deal of time travelling and having nets, so I regretfully gave up ideas of playing for the school. With hindsight, this was a sound decision as I was able to take up cricket again at University and help coach when I was in my first teaching job. I continued with tennis as I loved that; it took up much less time.

Cross-country runs were frequent during the winter, and those not playing in games would be sent by a prefect on a run along a prescribed route. Few enjoyed these runs, especially in wet weather when you sloshed about through muddy fields, so every effort was made to outwit the prefect in charge who would tick off your name at the finish. The last part of the run used the main road from the Cross Keys pub up the hill to Staplegrove. It was always a grind going up that hill, but on one occasion fate smiled on the sinner and half way up the hill a bus slowed down to change gear. I managed to hop on board and the conductor, amused rather than annoyed, turned a blind eye. He put me off near the school, and to the prefect's surprise, I was one of the first to arrive.

During my first term, a senior member of the House asked me if I played chess. He gave me a game and told me I should join the chess club. I did this with enthusiasm and by the following winter term was playing for the school. I greatly enjoyed the matches, particularly against the Town as they had several county players and our team had to play to the clock - something which made us feel much more professional. In my last year I captained the team. This was good fun, but after some matches, particularly if I had lost, when I went to bed, I found it difficult to get to sleep as I would go over the games in my mind and explore alternative moves and strategies. I was obviously taking chess too seriously, so when I left Taunton I only played for the fun of it.

I had several sessions in the school hospital - mainly because of recurring tonsillitis. In some ways this was a welcome break from the relentless routine of school and was more home-like with kindly females around. On one occasion, tonsillitis changed to quinsy and I was quite ill. I was over the worst, but feeling rather groggy, when a boy came in with abdominal pains and was put in the bed next to me. He didn't seem very bad, but after Sister had gone to bed, his pain was obviously getting worse as he was moaning. As a prospective medico I felt a bit responsible and was concerned that it might be appendicitis. He seemed in too much pain to do anything himself, so I knocked up Sister and she summoned the doctor at once. The boy was operated upon the same night, thankfully before the appendix perforated.

Dr Marshall took out my tonsils near the end of the summer term. I had never had an operation before and my parents were far away, so I went into it with some trepidation. A mixture of ether and chloroform was a crude anaesthetic, and I didn't enjoy the aftermath, but I made a quick recovery - even taking part in a cricket match. However, this was a mistake, as when batting I had to run a lot between wickets and began to feel very faint. My predicament ended when I fell victim to J.C.Cameron. He was a West Indian prodigy who later played for his country during a test series against England, but at that time had just got into our Ist XI at the age of $14^1/_2$. He was nicknamed 'Snowball' because of his dark skin, and was a little wizard at bowling leg breaks and googlies.

When I got back at the end of term, Mother was not at all well; she had been working much too hard, so it was decided that she should go away for a few days and I would go too. Bids said she would look after Dad. We stayed in a cottage near Tenterden in Kent and went for walks, although Mother could not go far. The country was not unlike what she had been brought up in, and she was delighted to stroll quietly along the lanes and re-discover some of her favourite flowers. On one occasion we went into a wood and she sat on a tree trunk while I explored further. I happened to notice the earth of a mole hill move and a pink snout appear. Without thinking I plunged my hand into the earth and came out with a mole in my hands. I took it back to Mother who had never seen a live mole before. It was fascinating to observe it at close quarters before putting it back where I had caught it. We watched it disappear into its tunnel with a few rapid strokes of its spade-like limbs.

When I returned to school for my final year I became a member of the Upper Sixth and was given a study. I shared it with Bill Latham who was doing English and History. We used to cook on an old primus stove nick-named 'the red devil'. It was temperamental and needed to be handled with understanding and caution, but it was a great asset.

Bill Latham had an original mind, little respect for authority and a fondness for writing poetry. He was always getting into trouble with the authorities. Occasionally, when school would depress him, he would visit a country pub and come back slightly drunk. The problem for me was getting him to bed without anybody being the wiser. He had a great enthusiasm for reading, and on one occasion, came into the study telling me how impressed he had been by W.H.Davies' splendid book, 'The Autobiography of a Super Tramp'. Then he announced his plan. Over the Whitsun week-end, he would get permission to go home, but instead, would try out the life of a tramp for himself in the Somerset countryside. The plan worked; he got his permission, bundled up some very old clothes and a shabby cloth cap and off he went, changing once he had got clear of the school. He hid his school clothes, slept rough, begged for food and never spent a penny of his own money during that long week-end. His considered judgement on return was that the life of a tramp was not for him, but the experience had been worthwhile.

Bill at this time was working in Bath with Lambert's the Photographer. He had acquired a Triumph motor-bike and wrote to say he would come over one Saturday and take me out. I was able to get an exeat and he took me on the back of the bike along the Minehead road. There was very little traffic then, so I had a go on it myself. You had to push it, let in the clutch and get on as quickly as possible. After a few goes, we decided to try the bike out on a really steep hill to see what power it had, so we went past Minehead to Porlock Hill. The new road had not been built at that time and it was a stiff test with very steep gradients and hair-pin bends. We soon found that the bike would not take the two of us, but when Bill took a run at it he could just get to the top. I walked up!

That summer term, I was working hard for my First Medical examination which had to be taken in London in June. I stayed at home during this period and went to Imperial College each day to take the papers. I celebrated the conclusion of the exam by buying 'The Collected Poems of John Masefield'. On a previous occasion I had heard him recite some of his own favourites, and they appealed to me greatly. I still derive much pleasure from his poems, some of which I have read over and over again.

While I was at Taunton, both Gran and Aunt Rosa died. I was not brought back for the funerals, but when I returned for the holidays, our home didn't feel the same. Gran, in particular, had done much for me, and I missed them both very much.

One large room was now free, so Mother suggested we had a lodger to help defray expenses. To my surprise, the new arrival was a Japanese gentleman. He was Professor of English at the University of Tokyo on sabbatical leave, studying the English way of life. The arrangement worked well as he was out all day, and just had breakfast and an evening meal in his room. This was on the first floor, so Bids used to take up the meals which Mother had prepared.

Towards the end of his stay he wanted to show his appreciation and suggested to Mother that he should take Bids out for a special Japanese meal in London. But Mother, knowing that she had a good-looking daughter, made it a condition that I should go too. I had never been a chaperon for my sister before and thought it was an extremely good idea. The professor certainly gave us a splendid evening. We had a room to ourselves and the food was brought in on large trays, each of which contained a number of individual dishes which we were expected to eat with chop-sticks. These were more difficult to use than I had imagined. The waiter was very attentive and we quickly learned not to allow the large rice bowl which accompanied the other dishes to get too low, otherwise it was immediately filled again. The professor explained what each item was and how it was prepared and was a charming host. The whole evening was great fun and a most interesting experience. I was grateful for having a pretty sister.

I had made some good friends at Taunton School including Kenneth Soddy who was in my form and was also hoping to be a doctor. His uncle was Frederick Soddy, the chemist, who with Rutherford, put forward the theory of atomic break-down and received the Nobel Prize for his work. Ken was modest about having such a distinguished uncle, but he too was clever, and later had a distinguished career in psychiatric medicine. We left school at the same time, and while we were waiting for our Ist MB results we attended a Baptist Summer School together at Seascale in Cumbria. Bids and a friend came too.

We went by train from Euston, choosing a carriage at the rear which was to take us to our destination without changing. After several hours of travel we decided to have tea in the restaurant car, leaving all our belongings strewn about in the compartment. The restaurant car was way up the train. However, on attempting to return to our carriage we found our part of the train had been disengaged at Crewe and we were in the forward section on our way to Scotland! We talked to the guard and got off at the next stop which was some distance on, at Carnforth. Here, the station master was able to phone through to Seascale Station and arrange for all our things to be collected to await our arrival. Many hours later, we arrived at our destination having used a local train back to Crewe and another one to Seascale. We were exhausted, but very relieved when we found all our possessions awaiting us.

Unfortunately, it rained much of the time, and the mountains in the distance were covered in cloud. It was very frustrating as we badly wanted to climb Scafell. On nearly our last day we saw clear weather coming in from the west, and abandoning other plans, we persuaded a taxi driver to take us to the head of Wastwater. It was sunny and clear when we made the ascent, but the going was difficult as all the streams were in spate after so much rain. However, there was extraordinarily good visibility and from the top we had stupendous views of Great Gable with Wastwater far below us and could make out parts of England, Scotland, Ireland and the Isle of Man. Wonderful! It was extremely cold at the summit so we didn't stop long and scrambled our way down the steep mountain side to the west not bothering about paths. We were ravenous when we reached Wastdalehead, but Cumbrian hospitality, at a small cottage which did teas, exceeded all expectations. The lady was used to mud and weary climbers and gave us a marvellous feast.

Chapter Four

Higher Education

With my First Medical examination behind me, I found myself up against a brick wall - there was absolutely no money to pay for a course in medicine. I went to see the University admissions people, but no scholarships or grants were available so this door seemed to be firmly shut. I was disappointed, but not really surprised as I knew the family could not help. Marge had been very fortunate in having had her medical fees paid by the Church Missionary Society as she intended to be a medical missionary, but I had no such opportunity. However, I was determined to go to University somehow even if I could not read medicine and was confident that something would work out. I had been thinking for some time that if I couldn't get into medicine, teaching would be by far the best alternative. The more I thought about it the more I liked the idea; there was not the slightest doubt in my mind what I would like to teach - it had to be biology. The decision was made; somehow, some day I would become a biologist. This meant that I would be able to keep up my natural history interests and that would be a real bonus.

The cheapest way to get a degree was to attend a polytechnic. There were several good ones in London, and the best by reputation for science, was Chelsea, so I went over on my bicycle and asked for their advice. For a science degree, I had first to take the Intermediate examination in Botany, Zoology, Chemistry and Physics. My Ist MB didn't exempt me, but taking it had not been a waste of time as the subjects were the same, but the standard was higher. If I could get a job and earn some money by day, I could take evening classes to get my 'Inter'.

It was obvious that if I was going to teach, my best interim job would be at a school, so I went along to see the Headmaster of Highfield School, the only one I knew. I was fortunate, as he was looking for a junior master and knew me, and my qualifications appeared adequate for the job. He took me on for the princely salary of £96 per year. This sounded just possible as I could live at home.

I was expected to teach a wide range of subjects mainly to the two upper forms. This was quite a challenge as I was very rusty on those subjects I had dropped at School Certificate stage, but books were available and I managed to keep a few pages ahead of the boys. Mr Austin was still there, and I was able to make full use of his advice and experience.

I found the teaching interesting and quickly got into the way of things; after all I had just left school and knew the drill. I was put in charge of games, which meant coaching the Ist XI and taking the team for away games to various preparatory schools in the south-west of London.

Life was very full that first term, and by the time the teaching was over and games had finished I didn't feel much like getting on my bike and going to Chelsea for a three-hour session. I did four evenings a week at Chelsea, one for each of the four subjects I had to take in the examination. Each would consist of an hour of theory and then two of practical, finishing at 10 o'clock. I found a good technique was to have a meal when I got back from Highfield and then lie on the couch in our drawing room and go to sleep. It was not long before this became a habit and I was able to get to sleep at once and wake up refreshed an hour later ready for the road. I decided to spend two years teaching at Highfield and sit for the exam at the end of that period; trying to take the exam after one year would have been too much of a strain.

Mr Austin had become a good friend, and I had learnt a lot from him about teaching. He knew of my interest in butterflies, and one day mentioned that he had seen commas in a wood near his home in Northamptonshire. The only comma I had ever seen was the one in Dad's collection which he had caught on his honeymoon; they were very scarce in southern England at that time. I jumped at the chance when Mr Austin invited me down for a few days at the end of the summer term. He showed me the wood where he had seen them, and it was not long before I saw my first, sitting on a teasel head in the sunshine. That was a great moment. It was not long afterwards that this species began to spread across the country, becoming quite a common butterfly, even colonising suburban gardens.

One day, whilst casually looking through The Times, I noticed an unusual entry in the Personal Column to the effect that a barrister in Lincoln's Inn wished to play occasional chess at week-ends - phone for details. I rang him up and he invited me to his Chambers. This was an interesting experience, not least for discovering what Lincoln's Inn was like. My host was in his early fifties and a bachelor. He welcomed me to his comfortable apartments and the house-keeper brought in tea. After a chat he got out the pieces and we had a game. Fortunately, we were well matched and during the course of that winter we had some excellent games. I was very glad to keep up my chess without becoming too serious about it.

Things were not too good at home around this time. Dad felt worn out after 13 years of devoted work at Battersea Chapel. The load had been heavy and relentless, with many meetings, late nights and much visiting. There had also been a lot of anxiety over money. At the peak of his career with a London church his salary never exceeded £275 a year. Mother was also extremely tired and was not at all well; keeping the home together and looking after everybody on such a small budget had been very demanding over the years even though Bids had given invaluable help. A change was essential, and Dad was glad to accept the offer of the pastorate of two small Baptist churches in North Devon - at Croyde and Georgeham. Moving was a great upheaval; it occurred during my second year at Highfield, so I was left with nowhere to live. Fortunately, the Headmaster offered me a bed-sitter in his house by way of a rise which was an admirable arrangement.

It was very difficult for my parents to adjust to life in the country after such a busy time in London. They both loved being near the sea, but life was very different. There was no electricity at the Manse and they had to use oil lamps as of old. The only heating was by coal fires and cooking was done on a range. However, there were benefits. Life went at a slower pace, new friendships were made, the garden was fertile, vegetables could be grown once more and the countryside was beautiful. During their first spring, Mother was overjoyed to see so many of her favourite flowers on the banks outside the house: lesser celandine, sweet-scented violets, both white and coloured, primroses by the thousand, wild strawberry, herb robert, greater stitchwort and many more. It was a wonderful change from buses, trams and the dirty streets of Battersea. Gradually, her health improved.

Bids stayed in London. She had loyally lived at home to help Mother and Dad as she felt it was her duty, but it was very hard on her; she had longed to be independent. Now she was 25, and at last could strike out on her own. She wanted to take up some form of social work and took a course at the London School of Economics in Social Science.

By this time, Marge had qualified and was in India with the Church Missionary Society working in a hospital in Bangalore. She was there for seven years because, although there was no obligation for her to do so, she wanted to repay the Society for the financial help they had given for her medical training. She sent us colourful accounts of her work as a doctor among the poor of that city. Occasionally, she would take a holiday trip into the jungle to catch butterflies for Dad, sending them back, unset, each wrapped in folded paper and carefully packed in a tin box. On arrival, the butterflies were so dry, they were difficult to relax before being set. Dad was delighted to see these beautiful exotic insects as he had never had the opportunity of going abroad himself.

Bill had unfortunately contracted tuberculosis and had had a spell in a sanatorium at Midhurst, but had got much better, and to finish the cure had gone to Cornwall to work on a farm. After that, he got a job in Lambert's photographic business in Bath where he developed skills he put to excellent use later.

Bids and I went to Croyde in our vacations and loved it. It was a wonderful place for a holiday; we explored the coast and countryside together. One of our favourite places was Baggy Point where we used to do some cliff climbing. One lovely sunny day, we sat down beside the lichen-covered boulders and she read me a poem. She loved reading aloud and was very good at it. She read Coleridge's 'The Rime of the Ancient Mariner'. With the calm, blue sea and the gulls flying over, it couldn't have been a more evocative setting for such a poem. I have loved it ever since.

These holidays by the sea were an eye-opener to me. I had never before had the opportunity to observe and think about wildlife in a leisurely way. Previously, I had had to be content with quick trips into the country or family holidays. I went out for long periods with my binoculars; time was of little importance; I could just sit and watch - it was most rewarding. One time I watched a seal fishing. It positioned itself strategically at the sea-end of a long gully waiting for the fish to swim in with the tide. Another time I caught a glimpse of an otter among the rocks. The author, Henry Williamson lived in the district, and this sighting reminded me of his Tarka. No doubt, he had observed otters along that same stretch of coast.

I became familiar with the sea-shore flora and fauna, finding many exciting specimens and began to understand the preferences of certain species for particular habitats and the influences of wave action and tides on their distribution; there were no popular books to refer to.

At spring tides it was possible to get to some deep rock pools at the base of the cliffs where, if you were lucky, you might see the waving antennae of a lobster projecting from its safe, rocky retreat. I soon discovered that lobsters were territorial and had their favourite hiding places when the tide was out.

It was not too difficult to climb down the cliff to reach these pools, but from the cliff path above, it looked dangerous. On one occasion I decided to try to catch one of these lobsters and having failed before, thought I would try another technique, so I climbed down the cliff, complete with long forked stick, towel and a crab for bait. The idea was to attach the crab to the string and dangle it in front of the lobster and so lure it out of its hole. If the lobster obliged, I could then pin it down with the forked stick. All went well, but the problem was getting it out of the deep pool without my falling in. Only one arm was free, but by rolling the towel and placing it in the water until it was soaked sufficiently to sink, it could then be lowered and manoeuvred around the raised claws of the lobster. I then had to twist the towel to tighten the noose and lift the lobster clear. The operation successfully accomplished, I tied the lobster around my neck and climbed up the cliff. To my astonishment a crowd had gathered on the path above - I was not expecting a welcoming party! It was all very odd. However, I soon learnt that somebody had seen me disappearing over the edge of the cliff, and as I had not re-appeared, thought I had got into difficulties and had called the coast-guard. He had just arrived and was about to attempt a rescue when I appeared. In spite of all the fuss it had been a good expedition - the lobster weighed $3^1/2$ lbs and we all enjoyed it.

I got to know Baggy Point in all its moods. Just after Christmas the weather changed dramatically and a severe gale smote the coast from the south-west. This was a wonderful chance to see a really rough sea. Making my way along the narrow cliff path was no joke in that weather, I had certainly underestimated the strength of the wind; it was very frightening. I found myself crawling on all fours in very exposed places. However, the effort was worthwhile. The sea was spectacular, and when I reached the Point the immense waves were crashing into the rocks with staggering force and the wind was taking the spume hundreds of feet into the air and hurling it a long way inland to pattern the grass as if covered in dirty snow. I was glad to have ventured out, but quite relieved when I got back home again.

I became very interested in the flora. Baggy itself had some interesting flowers including the tiny autumnal squill. It is an insignificant little plant, not bright like its vernal cousin, and very local. I only found it flowering in one place near the cliff path. Fifty years later, when paying a nostalgic visit to the area one September, I remembered roughly where I had found it, and after a short search, sure enough, there it was. However, it was in the spring that the coastal flowers were at their best with sea thrift covering large areas with pink interspersed with the white of the sea campion and the occasional blue of sheep's bit scabious.

The birds were interesting too. Ravens and buzzards nested along that coast and interactions between them were frequent. Their aerobatics were a delight to watch. Shags, like the ravens, were early nesters and several pairs could be found on ledges above the great cave at the end of Baggy. It was inadvisable to approach too near as you might be met by an evil-smelling jet of yellowish fluid expelled with some accuracy from the stomach of the parent. Grey seals occasionally visited these caves. They probably came from Lundy Island where they bred regularly. Herring gulls made use of all available ledges on the more inaccessible cliffs, defending them from their neighbours with raucous cries and vicious pecks.

But life was not all holidays; all too soon I was back in London, teaching and swotting for my examination. I had got to know Mr Christopher Hentschel very well. He was in charge of zoology at Chelsea and towards the end of my course, advised me to apply for a Continuation Scholarship for my degree course. There were three of these given each year and I was fortunate to be awarded one. This meant that I would pay no fees for tuition until I got my degree. This was fine, but I still had to find accommodation and pay for upkeep.

I had kept in touch with Ken Soddy who was doing medicine at University College and we agreed to share a flat. We found one in Lessar Avenue off Clapham Common. The landlady was helpful and friendly. It was on the first floor and furnished quite adequately although we brought our own beds. It was just what we needed, having a large bedroom, sitting room and kitchen. We cooked our own breakfasts and suppers and any meals at week-ends and had lunch at College.

This would not have been possible without Marge's help. By this time she had moved from Bangalore and taken a job with the Women's Medical Association which was government-run. This proved to be an excellent opening, with spells in hospitals in Simla, Delhi, Agra and Allahabad before taking charge of the Dufferin Women's Hospital in Calcutta, a post she held until she retired from work in India just after the war. This work meant that for the first time she was earning a good salary and was able to send back regular amounts to help Dad and Mother. She also sent £6 a month to help me while at College. I don't know how I would have managed without it. With hindsight I find it difficult to believe how I was able to live on thirty shillings a week having paid for rent, food, College lunches and bus and tube fares when essential. Fortunately, I had saved a little from my teaching at Highfield, and that was used for rail fares when going home for the holidays and for clothes and other necessities.

At the flat, we had a coal fire in the sitting room when it was cold and our landlady would buy us a couple of sacks of coal at a time from the coal merchant who came down the street each week. Coal cost two shillings and sixpence per hundredweight. We didn't go short of good wholesome food - Mother gave me excellent advice on that. We soon got to know that Saturday evening was the best time to buy a joint. Food shops did not shut until after 10 o'clock on Saturdays and if you went out to Clapham near closing time, butchers would stand outside their shops holding joints in their hands and offering them at ridiculous prices. They had to get rid of them as there were no fridges and they shut on Sundays. We both liked cooking, but a lot of frying made everything very greasy, so every so often Ken and I would decide that something had to be done about it. This meant getting a pail of hot water laced with soda, cleaning the gas cooker and scrubbing the floor boards.

Ken was studying anatomy at that time and brought back the bones from a human skeleton to study at week-ends. On one occasion we hung up the skull above the mantlepiece with two arm bones crossed below as a somewhat original form of decoration. The next step was to put a bulb from a torch inside to illuminate it. When the room light was turned off, it was most effective. However, just as we were admiring our handiwork, there was a knock at the door and our landlady entered the room. There was a gasp of horror before more rational feelings returned. Peace was only restored after we had agreed to take it down.

Travel was very cheap. I could get from Chelsea to Trinity Road Tube Station on a 49 bus for 4 pence and take a penny ticket on the tube to Colliers Wood Station which was the nearest to the College playing fields. This I would do most Saturdays; otherwise I would go everywhere on my bike or walk.

The degree course for day students at Chelsea Polytechnic was very different from the grind of evening classes. The place became human. With teaching in mind, I took a General Honours B.Sc. You took three subjects to equal standard thus giving a wide base for any further work. So I read botany, zoology and chemistry.

Having done these subjects for 'Inter' I knew most of the lecturers and this gave useful continuity. Christopher Hentschel was an excellent lecturer in zoology, classes were small, the students keen, and we got every encouragement. He was an interesting man with a good sense of humour. His father was one of the characters in Jerome's classic, 'Three Men in a Boat' and Jerome was Hentschel's godfather. Miss Nellie Brown, who was new to the department, supported Christopher very

ably and was a great asset. She taught well, was lively and most enthusiastic - nothing was too much trouble for her. The botanists were also
very able; Mr H.B.Lacey was Head of the Department and lectured
extremely well. We were all very sad when he retired at the end of my
first year to be replaced by Dr Barnes, another excellent botanist. Dr
Turrill introduced us to ecology, a subject which was excitingly new at
that time.

I enjoyed student life and soon got into the swing of things. For the
first time I found myself surrounded by as many females as males. That
was an education in itself as my boarding schools had not been helpful
in that respect. Fortunately, Bids had been a splendid sister to me, so I
was not quite out of my depth. Social life was not a strong feature of the
Poly, partly because it was non-residential, but there were many clubs
and societies and these brought people together who were like-minded.

I found there was no Natural History Society, so I talked to Hentschel
about it and started one. With so many biology and pharmaceutical
students around, the society became very popular, and soon we had an
interesting programme of lectures and discussions, bringing in outside
speakers. On one occasion I was put in touch with a zoologist who had,
for the first time, succeeded in filming cell division under the microscope. He showed the film himself, explaining how he had overcome the
problems of time-lapse photography and vibration when underground
trains passed below the building in which he was working. It was
marvellous to see mitosis in motion - so different from the series of
diagrams we had been brought up on.

Another film we were able to show was one on gannets taken by
Humphrey Hewer and Julian Huxley. This appealed to me greatly as I
had never seen one of their breeding colonies. It was marvellous to see
these great seabirds diving spectacularly for fish. The film helped fuel a
growing interest in photography. Little did I imagine then that one day I
would be privileged to make a film myself with Humphrey and join
Julian on a radio programme.

When Dr Barnes took over the botany from Mr Lacey he brought some
of his research material with him. A lorry drew up at the main gate and
the driver went inside to get help with the lifting. It all looked easy until
the porters tried to lift the boxes - they contained a lot of coal-balls,
largely composed of iron ore! These remarkable objects, many the size of
tennis balls, had been found in coal deposits and contained fossilized
plant material. If a coal-ball was cut in half, you could make out these
plant remains. To examine them, you suspended one half of the coal-ball
so that its cut surface was in contact with a solution of dilute acid. This

dissolved the ore but not the organic remains of the plants. After some minutes you carefully washed the surface and poured on nail varnish, or the equivalent, which set firmly around the fragile plant material which had become exposed. The transparent varnish set hard and could be pealed off, mounted on a microscope slide and examined. The material was so well preserved that you could make out the individual cells of such plants as giant horsetails which existed millions of years ago. It was most exciting.

The Polytechnic had an excellent sports ground, so I was very pleased to join the soccer, cricket and tennis clubs and play at the week-ends. My love of games and the time I had given to them at school now paid off and I was gratified to represent the College in soccer and cricket and play tennis when time permitted.

Many students knew only too well what it was like to be poor; there was good support for the Social Service Association. We had a link with the Princess Club Settlement in Bermondsey and each year gave the children a Christmas party. There was always a tea followed by some entertainment. One year I was cajoled into doing some simple chemical conjuring. In the quiet of the laboratory when practising it seemed a good idea, but in the event the performance became more complicated as the children were so excited it was difficult to keep them sufficiently far away to carry out the experiments. Another time we tried to put on an impromptu pantomime, but when the lights were dimmed at one point, we found some children had joined us on the make-shift stage and were helping to develop the plot in ways quite unforeseen! However, the children had a whale of a time, and perhaps we did too.

Nellie Brown was keen on dramatics and decided that the last night of the Christmas term should be brightened up with a performance of Cinderella, followed by a party. The whole pantomime was a clever skit on life in the Polytechnic with short scenes and topical lyrics. I helped to write the lyrics and was given the part of Principal of the College. This was a tricky one to play as the real one was sitting in the front row! However, it was a wonderful opportunity to pull everybody's leg and make fun of the trivialities we all had to put up with. There was plenty of scope for improvisation and I'm sure the cast enjoyed it as much as the audience.

The Chelsea Art School occupied the top floor of the main building. We had little to do with the art students, but occasionally I was able to borrow one of their lecture rooms to show films to the Natural History Society; they had more spacious facilities. Mr Williamson was the Principal of the Art Department, and although I never met him, Henry

Moore was one of his assistants, teaching sculpture in a tiny room at the end of the corridor.

Many friendships were made during my time at College. Another student taking zoology was Jan Ikin. On one occasion Hentschel took us both and another student in his car down to the Beachy Head area to study marine life. On our return to London, he rounded off the trip by giving us a splendid meal at his flat - much appreciated by all. He cared a lot for the welfare of his students and was greatly respected. Jan was keen on sport and on Saturday afternoons would often score for our cricket team. Her father was a keen cricketer and a deacon in the Baptist church in Hampstead. Her great friend was Betty Thomson who was doing a degree in chemistry with botany as a subsidiary. Betty's parents were Scottish; she was the younger daughter of George Sutherland Thomson who had a farm at Whelpley Hill in Buckinghamshire and an office in London. For most of his life he had been a consultant in dairying and agriculture, and earlier in the century had organised the dairy industry in Queensland and New South Wales. Later, he acted as dairying adviser to the Russian Government soon after the revolution.

I got to know Jan and Betty well as we not only attended the same classes, but were members of the same societies. Occasionally excursions into the country were arranged by the Natural History Society, presumably with ecology in mind, and they attended these too. On one trip we optimistically arranged a walk of some 20 miles in the Buckinghamshire/Hertfordshire countryside. Those who survived to the end certainly knew each other better! However, I was quite amazed when Betty said good-bye and told us that she was walking back to the farm, another 5 miles!

On 11 May 1934 I asked Betty if she would marry me. We had just had a wonderful time in the countryside together and all day I had been trying to summon enough courage to ask her. I need not have worried; we were both very much in love. We decided to keep the engagement quiet, at any rate until Betty was 21 which would be in two months time. She felt that her parents might not approve, particularly as she was not taking her finals until the following year and marriage would be impossible for some time as I had neither job nor money. We were on a sticky wicket and no risks could be taken, so we thought it wise to delay my talk with her father until a more appropriate time. When we met the following day in the botany laboratory, I don't think either of us could quite believe what had happened 24 hours earlier! It was not all that easy to face up to realities and get down to hard work - I had to take my finals in a few weeks time!

Betty usually joined me in the mornings as I walked from the flat to Chelsea; we tested each other in botanical revision. She had to take her subsidiary botany examination at the same time as I was doing finals, but then had another year to go before her finals in chemistry. The remainder of the term seemed to go like the wind, the days of swotting soon passed, finals were taken and the long vacation was upon us.

Whilst waiting for my results, I decided to stay on for a time in London and do something quite different. I believe it was through the almoner at the Polytechnic, that I was asked if I would consider running the Chelsea Unemployment Centre for six weeks until they found somebody to take over in a more permanent capacity. Knowing nothing whatever about what this would entail, I was somewhat apprehensive when I was given an interview by a lady on the Borough Council. She seemed to think I could do the job, so I accepted.

The Unemployment Centre was situated in the basement of the Town Hall in King's Road, Chelsea. When I was shown around I found that there were a number of large rooms being used for leisure pursuits and workshops. The man who was more or less in charge was an old guardsman, and proud of it. Almost the first thing he said was a quotation from the Guards, "Join the navy and see the world, join the airforce and see the next, join the Guards and scrub it". He certainly brought discipline to bear, but always in a kindly way. He was a great character and I got to know him well. We hit it off over the first of many strong cups of tea and he told me what went on. The idea was to do everything possible to raise morale among the many unemployed, help organise games and get them to work on useful crafts according to experience.

Any man who was unemployed could join the Centre but had to pay one penny a week for the privilege. This was a good idea as everbody could afford that much, and they probably appreciated the faciliities more because they had to pay; it gave them a sense of belonging. Opportunities for learning certain crafts were possible. Two days a week, anybody who wished could attend woodwork classes at the Polytechnic and be given expert supervision. While I was there, the men made a number of bedside tables and some bath stools for the Chelsea Children's Hospital and a dozen or so pairs of crutches for the handicapped. Others learned to mend shoes and cut each other's hair. There was a lot going on, but life was pretty boring for most of the men and only a few showed real initiative. However, they were encouraged to look for jobs and during that July about a dozen found work as painters, plumbers, porters, window cleaners and on building sites.

Somebody had provided a billiard table, and this was very popular;

table tennis and cards were also played. There was another centre for the unemployed at World's End down Fulham way; it was treated with great suspicion as the men there had a reputation for rowdiness. One day word got around that they were going to storm our centre and attempt to remove some of the equipment. Guards were set and doors barricaded, but no attacks materialised much to my relief.

I found I could arrange cricket matches against other groups and book pitches on Wandsworth Common. I used to play too, but it was unlike any cricket I had experienced before. The pitches were bad, the bowling often fast and unpredictable; survival was the name of the game. However, the men enjoyed the change and were able to get rid of some of their pent-up frustrations. I enjoyed my time there; it provided me with useful experiences which I might never have had. It was cheering the following term, when walking down Manresa Road, to hear a voice from above calling my name. It was one of the men who had got a job window-cleaning.

Earlier in the year Dad and Mother had moved from Croyde to the Cotswolds, Dad becoming minister of two small churches at Naunton and Guiting. I went there for the remainder of the vacation. I was glad to have the opportunity to get to know another type of countryside.

Naunton was not on the railway and when I made enquiries as to how to get there I found that the last train along the branch line to the nearest station had left. However, all was not lost as two railwaymen were about to go home on one of those self-propelled trucks and I was invited to jump on. The truck which was not much more than a flat platform, got up quite a speed and I hung on grimly, clasping my case with the other hand. I was beginning to enjoy this unusual method of transport when, with a squealing of brakes, it stopped in the middle of nowhere and I was told that if I crossed several fields I would reach Naunton village. I was very grateful to the two men for giving me the ride and it was not long before I was warmly welcomed by my parents in their new home.

This visit gave me a good chance to tell them of our unofficial engagement. They were very pleased and hoped it would not be long before I brought Betty to see them. I was also able to tell them that I had graduated with second class honours over all, having got a first in zoology.

On the strength of these exam results I was invited by the Principal to continue at Chelsea and do a year's research for a Master of Science degree in zoology under Christopher Hentschel. He also asked me to do fifteen hours teaching a week in the department, which meant taking charge of a matriculation class in biology on Saturday mornings and acting as Demonstrator for Inter B.Sc and Ist MB practicals in botany and zoology. For this I would get the graduate teaching rate of £150 per year. Demonstrating involved going round the class helping with dissections, explaining what was what and interpreting slides the students were examining under the microscope. I found the work enjoyable and it gave me very valuable experience. I had got my hand in with demonstrating the previous year as some of the classes were too large for one person to cover and I had helped for five hours a week at the undergraduate rate of seven shillings and fourpence per hour less 10%. The 10% was the official cut on all teachers' salaries!

Hentschel also introduced me to Dr Cunnington at St.Bartholomew's Hospital Medical School who asked me to demonstrate during his medical practicals in biology twice a week. By these means I was able to earn enough to pay for my continued use of the flat in Clapham. Ken Soddy was now resident at University College, so I was on my own, but my landlady kindly offered to cook breakfasts, suppers, and main meals at week-ends. It saved me a lot of trouble and we got on well.

Demonstrating meant a great deal of standing and bending over students to look through their microscopes or examine their drawings and I found that my lower back ached a good deal in consequence. Dr Cunnington suggested I saw a man at 'Barts' who was good at backs and might advise me. I went to see him and he suggested a manipulation of the lower back under anaesthetic. This was becoming a fashionable treatment. Being a member of the staff I got the treatment free; it meant being in for a couple of nights. I'm very doubtful if it did much good in the long term, but it seemed to help at the time.

Betty was now over 21 so we thought it was time I spoke to her father. She picked her time very carefully to broach the subject, being a little apprehensive, but she found it difficult to assess the impact of her news as her father kept his thoughts to himself. However, the upshot was that I went to see him in his office in London. I was prepared for a difficult interview as my only strong card was that Betty and I loved each other dearly and were determined to marry, but this, of course, was not nearly enough for a no-nonsense father who naturally wanted the best for his daughter. All I could offer at that moment was a good degree and high hopes of a job before too long! He was slightly more impressed when he heard that my mother was a Scot and therefore I must have a little good blood in me. I soon realised that time had to pass before much progress could be made, so I pinned my faith on Betty who I knew was at that time telling her mother more about our hopes and plans. Her mother was much more sympathetic and soon became a good ally.

It was not long after this that Betty was able to invite me home to meet her parents in a more informal way, and the fact that we were going to get married one day was gradually accepted. I was not surprised that her parents always called me by my middle name, Gordon - it was most appropriate under the circumstances, and I think my mother, being a Scot, was pleased when she heard. It was lovely to feel welcomed and be with Betty in her own environment. She showed me all over Kenmore Farm and I made the acquaintance of the stock and the large flock of poultry her mother looked after. Betty knew a lot about farming and was able to tell me much about how things were run. The next step was to buy Betty an engagement ring and put everything on an official basis!

We both enjoyed that year. Betty was able to visit my parents at Naunton during the vacations and we had many happy hours together walking in the Cotswold countryside and making plans for the future. Bids was away in Manchester where she was working as a psychiatric social worker, but she was able to spend time in Naunton when Betty was there so they got to know each other.

We all forgathered at Naunton for our first Christmas there, Bill coming over from Bath on a new motor bike. While Bids was helping Mother over the lunch, Bill suggested we went out on the bike to try it, so I rode pillion. He had heard that a flock of several thousand geese was resident on privately-owned land near the River Severn at Slimbridge and thought it would be fun to try and see them. Although the land was heavily keepered, we thought that on Christmas morning the keepers should be busy doing other things and we might be able to get away with it.

On arrival, we parked the motor bike up a lane and wandered towards the river. This was the area that was later made famous when Peter Scott acquired it as the Headquarters of the Wildfowl Trust. We could see the mudflats with some geese in the far distance, but they were a long way away. However, we were not to be put off, so wriggling under the barbed wire fencing, we walked as far as we could without disturbing the birds and then made use of the many muddy ditches to get nearer unseen, bending low. When we thought we were near enough, we poked our heads up; the sight was magnificent. The geese were not too far away, and when they saw us, all the birds stretched their necks upright like a regiment of soldiers and took flight- all 3,000 of them, honking loudly in unison. It was a wonderful spectacle, but we did not wait as we thought the honking would have alerted every keeper for miles around. We got up and ran! By the time the keepers were out of their cottages we were off on the bike speeding back for a late lunch at Naunton. We had quite an appetite!

When I returned to Chelsea for the new term, Betty and I were very busy. She was working for her finals and I found my teaching and demonstrating quite demanding, particularly the former, as lectures had to be prepared carefully and the practicals worked out. In between teaching sessions I worked at my research project. Hentschel had put me on to a rather interesting technique for staining the nervous system of live animals which were sufficiently transparent to show their nerves. I started with Hydra using methylene blue as a stain; this did not harm them. The nerve net on the surface showed up very well, but methylene blue was soluble in water and alcohol and you couldn't make permanent slides of the preparations. So the problem was fixing the blue using other reagents. Having got some promising results, the next thing was to try the technique on different animals. Hentschel suggested I applied for laboratory space at the Marine Biological Association at Plymouth during the Easter vacation and I was fortunate to be accepted. I was able to go down for a fortnight at Easter and have a further couple of weeks in the summer.

My first spell coincided with the Easter Course in Marine Biology for undergraduates and I was able to join in many of their sea-shore collecting trips, studying the fauna from different habitats. This gave me most valuable experience and fired my enthusiasm for marine ecology - a study I much enjoyed developing later on. I also went out in the research boat, Salpa, to do some trawling, dredging and plankton collecting. The Salpa was an old North Sea drifter which had been modified for this work and consequently was not well balanced, an idiosyncrasy which earned her her name, Salpa being a marine organism which rolled in the plankton like a barrel!

Each evening I was given jars of fresh plankton to examine and I stained various specimens using the new technique. Many planktonic animals are transparent so I had plenty to do. I found that one of the best species to work on was the arrow-worm, *Sagitta*, but unfortunately it was in short supply at that season and I had to go down again in July to finish the work.

During the summer term I was eagerly looking out for possible jobs in teaching. At this stage I had not made up my mind whether to try for a university or a school post. Jobs were difficult to come by in the mid 1930s as the country was still in deep recession, those in jobs were not moving, and there was much competition for those that were available. I regularly scanned the Times Educational Supplement and other papers and put my name down with a teaching agency. It was very depressing finding so few opportunities, especially as a good job was a pre-requisite for getting married. I was best qualified for a post in a polytechnic, but nothing appeared that was attractive. I tried for two; one was a junior lectureship at Northampton and the other was at Leeds. Both were in microbiology, a subject that didn't appeal to me greatly, but I was beginning to get desperate and thought I should have a go. I was interviewed for both and felt that I had done reasonably well, but I had many doubts about the jobs outlined; it was almost a relief when I heard I had been turned down. Since then, I have given heartfelt thanks that I was not appointed. My life would certainly have taken an entirely different course.

After these abortive attempts at getting a job in higher education, my preference shifted towards school teaching. I had always valued the personal contact that teachers could have with their pupils, particularly in boarding schools and I realised from my own limited experience that university departments and polytechnics did not provide these opportunities to the same extent.

I had been notified about various school posts, but nothing appealed until I received one about Rendcomb College, near Cirencester. It was to teach biology throughout the school up to open scholarship level. The present man had a first class honours degree from Oxford, had been there 3 years and was moving on. What struck me most was the fact that the school stood in its own grounds of 500 acres amid some of the best Cotswold country. That was really something for a biologist to contemplate, especially one with predilections for natural history. The salary offered was above the Burnham scale starting at £290 for a non-resident. I wrote away immediately and with much care, enclosing my personal details. A reply came by return of post inviting me to meet the Headmaster at a Soho restaurant for lunch the following week. This looked very promising.

It was by then early August with the autumn term not far away. I was somewhat apprehensive as a great deal hung on this interview, but the Headmaster was very informal and pleasant and told me a lot about the school and its interesting and unusual features. He was much concerned to get the right man for the job as he had a most promising candidate taking an open scholarship to Oxford in December. Had I any experience of scholarship work? Of course, I had not. He told me that he had also been trained as a biologist, but had given it up when he became a Headmaster. He took me into lunch and the soup was put on the table. An unusual object was floating on the surface. I looked at it. He looked at it. "What do you think you have in your soup", he asked. "A leg of a cockroach, Sir", I replied without hesitation. As a biologist himself he was able to confirm my identification, the waiter was recalled and a fresh bowl of soup was brought. Over the main course he asked me whether I had done a teacher's training course, and when I replied that I was afraid I hadn't, he said to my grateful surprise, "Thank God for that". I felt the rest of the interview went quite well, but I wasn't too optimistic as I was told there was another applicant he had to see, but I would know very shortly.

The letter arrived. He was sorry to disappoint me but he had offered the job to the other man. That really was a blow! I was extremely disappointed as I thought the job would really have suited me and my future would have been assured. Betty and I resigned ourselves to another bout of waiting. We wondered, for how long? The answer arrived a few days later in the form of a telegram. The other man had turned down the job at Rendcomb and I was offered the post. The sun had really come out at last and we could celebrate.

The new term was starting in a few weeks' time so there was much to do. Denis Lee-Browne, my new Headmaster, told me there was no non-resident accommodation available at present, but I would join Jack Fell, the physicist, in rooms in The House - a nice building a hundred yards from the main school. He knew I was engaged and would do what he could later on to find married quarters for us, but first I must prove myself to be suitable. Meanwhile, Betty had heard that she had gained her degree, but would have to do another year's work in chemistry as she had changed from external student to internal after doing her Inter and the regulations insisted that this extra year had to be taken. This was frustrating as extra chemistry was not her first choice as a run-up to marriage and the wedding could not be for another year at least. However, it had to be done, so she did some chemistry research rather reluctantly by day and attended a course in cookery in the evenings - much more to the point!

The male badger is a boar

Chapter Five

My first teaching job -
Rendcomb College

Rendcomb College in 1935 was a small boarding school founded and endowed by Mr Noel Wills just after the First World War. It had many unusual educational features which I found intriguing and exciting, the first being its social mix. About half the boys were drawn from elementary schools in Gloucestershire and were admitted at the age of 10 by scholarship examination. Those on the short list were visited in their homes by the Headmaster and Second Master who looked as much for character and suitability as academic excellence. These Foundation Scholars paid no fees at all. The remainder were fee-payers and came from a wider catchment area. This combination resulted in a good academic mix and a wide range of qualities and interests. All the boys were treated alike, had the same uniform provided by the school and helped with domestic duties. A system of allowances applied to everybody; there was a limitation placed on pocket money.

The second unusual feature was the degree of self-government achieved by the boys. There was a General Meeting which ran much of the everyday life of the school. Ideas and problems were freely debated and decisions seen to be implemented. Minutes were kept and small elected committees became responsible for various activities. One organised the weekly rota of domestic duties, another was concerned with the running of games and athletics along with the appropriate master, others ran the school shop, the library and the school magazine. There is no doubt that the General Meeting provided an excellent introduction to the democratic process and fostered a real sense of responsibility which was spread widely among the boys. As the school was small, each boy became involved to some extent and saw himself as a necessary part of the whole. The academic side of the school was, of course, under the jurisdiction of the Headmaster, and as he attended the General Meeting sessions he was able to assess how things were going and make suggestions. However, he seldom interfered.

The third feature was the small numbers in the school - between 70 and 80 when I was there. This had advantages and disadvantages. On the credit side, the staff knew everybody intimately, so during staff meetings each could contribute his own experience of the boy under discussion and a balanced decision could be arrived at. The staff/boy ratio was high and classes small. My sixth form had only seven boys in it and teaching was more like a tutorial than a lesson. There was no need for marks; you knew how well each boy was doing. Tests were assessed in categories so boys knew how well they were progressing but not their position in relation to others. There were no prizes. The same philosophy was applied to athletics. Because everybody had different physical qualities and potential, the important thing was not beating somebody else (although that was worth attempting), but improving your own performance during the course of training and growing. Boys were encouraged to keep graphs of their own progress over time.

The disadvantage of small numbers was obvious in games, especially against other schools, but results were remarkably good nevertheless. The same problem was noticeable in plays and musical events, but on the other hand there was more opportunity for the less able to have a go - sometimes with surprisingly good results.

Every boy studied biology and physics to School Certificate stage. In the broadest educational sense this was very valuable whatever subjects were chosen in the sixth form later. Chemistry was taught only in the sixth for those needing it according to vocation.

Denis Lee-Browne made it clear that two of my priorities should be coaching a third-year biologist, Alastair Wilson, who was taking an Open Scholarship in biology to Magdalen College, Oxford towards the end of the term, and spending long periods in the biology laboratory out of school hours so that those interested could develop their enthusiasms. Boys were not allowed in the lab on their own.

At first, I was not expected to help with games, so I had plenty of time after school. An excellent series of aquaria was already installed with good aeration and lighting. Two sixth- formers were responsible for their upkeep. The chief attraction was a couple of large axolotls - one black and the other an albino. They were related to newts, but differed by becoming mature when still in the larval, external-gill stage. It was not long before they produced spawn. Early on, the tadpoles were sufficiently transparent to see their hearts beating, so it was possible to devise simple experiments to show the effect of increasing concentration of carbon dioxide in the water on the heart rate. Work on the aquaria led to expeditions to find fresh material. There was an excellent lake in the school grounds and the River Churn meandered along the valley in front of the College, so here were two contrasting freshwater habitats that could easily be studied.

A number of boys were keen on natural history, and it was not long before I was taking them out in twos and threes to see what we could find. The country practically started outside the Stable Block, so no time was wasted getting to good places. This Cotswold countryside was superb, with excellent deciduous woods, parkland with ancient oaks, rough calcareous grassland, water meadows and marshes. I had certainly come to the right place for natural history, and I revelled in it.

I had a bed-sitter in The House, a lovely building built of Cotswold stone with out-buildings. It was surrounded by a good garden with an orchard nearby. Two other unmarried staff had rooms there and some boys were also accommodated. One of my colleagues, Jack Fell, was in charge of science, and had his physics laboratories next to mine in the stable block. Under his expert guidance I soon got into the swing of things and we saw a lot of each other. Apart from being an excellent physicist he was a superb craftsman and a first-class teacher. He was also a remarkably good shot. One evening he asked me to come with him to the orchard to see if he could bag a rabbit. It was already nearly dark as we paused to survey the rough grass between the old apple trees. Nothing stirred. Then he caught sight of two ears sticking up from the grass and taking careful aim he fired from about 30 yards. No response. He fired again, but still without success, so we investigated. The rabbit he had fired at turned out to be the pointed ends of two dock leaves and there was a neat hole in each one!

It was hard being separated from Betty. We kept in touch through numerous letters, but it was frustrating not to be sharing all these new experiences together. Freda Lee-Browne, the Headmaster's wife, was sympathetic and soon suggested Betty should come down for a week-end - she would be pleased to put her up. This worked out well. It was wonderful to show her some of the places I had described in letters and introduce her to people. Staff wives were most welcoming and she was able to attend a Saturday night dance at the school which the boys arranged. This gave her a good demonstration of staff/boy relationships and how self-confident and easy-mannered the boys were. Far too soon the time came when I saw her off at the station. It had been a great boost to morale and made planning for our eventual marriage seem more real- istic.

I much enjoyed being at Rendcomb; it was a lively community and the staff were most interesting people. The senior master was John James

(Jimmy). He was an excellent historian and most successful in coaching boys for Open Scholarships; he was also in charge of cricket. He and his wife, Kathleen, lived in one of the flats in the Stable Block with their small daughter. The other flat was occupied by Granston Richards (Dickers) and his wife Margaret. Dickers was a mathematician and ran the athletics and football. He became a great friend.

There was no other accommodation available for married staff and I wondered where we could possibly live when we got married. All the cottages in the village were occupied. There was talk of building a new house for the James's in due course, and if that came about, a flat would be available for us. This uncertainty made planning for our marriage very difficult. However, we were confident and optimistic.

Meanwhile I had to have my appointment confirmed - I was still on probation! My case was much improved when the Headmaster received a telegram to say that Alastair Wilson had won a demyship at Magdalen College in botany, zoology and physics. This was a major award and we had a party to celebrate. Two other biologists were taking their Higher Certificates in the summer and if they did sufficiently well would stay on an extra term to sit for scholarships. So I had plenty on my plate.

During the Easter holidays, Dickers and Margaret invited Betty and me and a couple of senior boys to go on a walking tour around Cornwall, putting up at Youth Hostels, some of which had just been opened. We went along the north-coast path to Land's End and back on the southern path - something over a hundred miles. It was a splendid opportunity to have a holiday with Betty and for her to get to know Dickers and Margaret.

Some of the Youth Hostels were very primitive. On one farm, there was a large room for the men situated above the stable where horses were very much in evidence. We could see the animals through the cracks in the elm planking and were lulled to sleep by their shuffling and snorting. The aroma coming from below was not particularly to our liking but we appreciated the warmth emanating from their bodies. We cooked our own food on primus stoves. The weather was good most of the time, and the coastal flowers were at their best.

At the beginning of the summer term, I mentioned my interest in butterflies and moths to Jack Fell. He was rather intrigued as he knew nothing about them himself, so we decided to go moth-hunting together. Conigre Wood, on the opposite hill-side to the College with Kennel Bottom in between, was lovely in May with carpets of bluebells and dog's mercury. It seemed to be a good place for such an expedition. The idea was to attract the moths to light. This involved lugging a car battery about a mile, supported on a bicycle. We erected a white sheet vertically and suspended the bulb so that the light shone on the sheet. A number of moths came and I was interested to discover what species were about.

Towards midnight we were about to pack up when I turned round and had quite a shock - there was a man with a gun under his arm, watching us. It was the gamekeeper. Fortunately it was not difficult to persuade him that we were harmless and he soon returned to his cottage on the edge of the wood. He became a good friend and ally in later years and I learnt a lot about country matters from him. His cottage smelt strongly of ferrets as he used to breed them in one of his rooms. Needless to say he was a bachelor.

On our way home through the wood we heard a loud rustling as if something large was shuffling through dry leaves. We went over to investigate and were just in time to see several badgers rushing away and disappearing down some large holes. Neither of us had seen a badger before. I was thrilled, and what's more, I knew where they lived, so maybe, I might be able to watch them properly.

The next evening I decided to make the attempt. I went on my own, and to quote from the account I wrote up afterwards, 'I set out in high hopes about an hour before dusk. Approaching up wind as quietly as possible I crept under a box bush and lay down on the ground some 8 metres from the main holes. It was not a good vantage point as there was a ridge which obscured my view of the larger entrances, but I dared not go closer as the light was still good. Dusk was deepening when my attention was rivetted by a loud scratching going on over the ridge. I knew that at any moment I would get my first proper sight of a badger. Within a minute or so the scratching ceased and a grey form came into view. The badger was clearly visible as it set off at a steady trot.

'I hoped this was not the end, so I kept quite still, and before long had my reward. A little striped face looked over the ridge and then another; then both disappeared again to the accompaniment of a loud yelp as one cub playfully bit the other. As it was now nearly dark, I cautiously came out from under my bush and carefully raised myself on to a bough about a metre up a lime tree. This gave me a good view of the sett, and with my back to the trunk, I was not noticed. I shall never forget that scene! Instead of seeing two cubs as expected, there were five, and soon they were romping round the sett entrances and tumbling over each other as they bit and yelped. They were quite small, no bigger than large cats and as playful as kittens. An adult was there too, probably the mother; she sat on one side as the cubs played together. A new noise broke out when one cub found an old treacle tin in which a stone had become lodged, and for a long time they pawed and leapt on it, fighting hard for possession and giving out much excited wickering.

'Then the noise subsided and the work of the evening commenced. They left the sett area and started to forage. They seemed to be everywhere, and I wondered what they would do if they came my way. It was not long before I knew, as one inquisitive cub came snuffling in my direction pushing its sensitive snout into every patch of leaves. I held my breath as it passed just below my feet without an upward glance. But finding it was on its own, it ran off to catch up with the others and gradually the noises became fainter as all the badgers moved off through the wood. I came off my perch, and made for home, well satisfied.'

It had been a most exciting evening but I did not imagine then that it would start me off on a 50-year study of badgers. Of course it was not possible to keep such an experience to myself so it was not long before Jack Fell came with me for an evening's watching. Then the Headmaster heard what was going on and wished to be in on the act. By this time I was set on trying to get a photograph so I enlisted his help, as I planned to be up a tree and more than two hands would be useful.

Photography was not easy. I had a folding Zeiss plate camera taking $3^1/_2 \times 2^1/_2$" pictures. This meant focusing in daylight on the exact place you expected the badger to be that evening, and if they obliged, you opened the shutter, fired the flash bulb and closed the shutter again. The large 'flashalite' bulbs available at that time were full of magnesium foil and had a flash duration of 1/40th of a second, so you had to keep the camera very steady to avoid shake and the badger had to be reasonably still.

On this first memorable occasion, we were both perched in a tree about six metres from the sett. I held the camera and the Headmaster looked after the flash. The flash bulb was attached to a modified bicycle lamp with a reflector and batteries. The badgers were far more co-operative than I had dared hope, the sow and her five cubs were all framed in the picture; marvellous! I gave the signal, opened the shutter, there was a tiny click as the flash was switched on, and a sickening pause - the flash had failed! I closed the shutter as there was still a vestige of light about, but had no sooner done so than there was a blinding flash as the bulb really did go off! I was not fit company for anybody at that moment; I could not even blame the operator as it was obviously a loose connection and entirely my fault. It was a sad walk home, but the Headmaster had at least seen the badgers and I had learned a lesson - the flash apparatus had to be made completely reliable.

Throughout the summer I watched the badgers periodically, and the more I watched, the more intriguing I found them. Accounts in books seemed to contradict each other and there were obvious gaps in knowledge. This was a challenge; I determined I would find out all I could. However, there was much else to do and badgers at that time were not a priority, just a bit of fun.

Teaching intelligent and enthusiastic boys was a two-way process. We were learning together - it was a time of discovery. Everything found had to be identified, its habitat noted and any interesting facts about it recorded. I became more and more intrigued by ecology and animal behaviour, but good books on these subjects were scarce. However, the science library was well stocked with plenty of books helpful for identification, and general natural history was well catered for. There were also some excellent botanical books - a few written from the ecological standpoint. These were a great help for the field work I was attempting. I was grateful for Tansley's excellent first book on vegetation, to my old teacher, Dr Watson, for helping me to think ecologically and later to Dr Turrill who instilled other ideas and the basic principles of plant ecology, but comparable books about animals were largely limited to excellent accounts of the natural history of such habitats as sea shore, lakes and rivers. The material was there, but not the principles which would draw things together. I eagerly scanned the literature for good reviews of new ecology books which could be added to the library.

I shall never forget the thrill of reading Charles Elton's 'Animal Ecology'. Here at last was somebody who understood some of the whys and wherefores of interdependence within communities and could transform natural history into a science. I read it from cover to cover, thought a lot about it, and was soon able to incorporate appropriate portions when teaching my senior biologists. It made a lot of sense to me.

At that time I was probably more interested in woodland than any other habitat. I found its plant life fascinating, particularly the adaptations of plants in the herb layer to varying light conditions according to season, and the relationship between plants and animals through pollination and fruit dispersal. I had also enjoyed collecting butterflies, moths and a lot of insects from woodland and had watched with delight rabbits, stoats, foxes and badgers within this habitat. I remember on one occasion sitting down quietly in Conigre Wood and considering how those ecological principles described so well by Elton and Tansley could be applied to the fauna and flora around me. This started me off on experimental field studies with the boys over a number of years and resulted in a small book on woodland ecology for schools.

When I started teaching at Rendcomb I made up my mind to be fairly strict over class discipline to begin with and then relax later when I had got the confidence of the boys. Some of the younger boys would try out anything if they thought they could get away with it. A cane was never used in the school, and only under extreme circumstances would you involve the Headmaster. One form had several boys who were difficult; on one occasion when I was marking their work, one of them started to fool about. It was the culmination of many minor irritations and I lost my temper, clouting him on the side of the head with some vigour. He was certainly taken by surprise; I told him to see me afterwards. By that time my temper had cooled and I realised I had gone too far, so I apologised for losing my temper. Expecting further punishment, he was agreeably surprised and responded by saying that he had deserved all he got. This produced a bond between us, and from then on he tried no more foolery, worked well and went on to win an open scholarship.

By the end of my first year my appointment was confirmed and there was also good news on the housing front. The new house for the Jameses was approved by the Governors, so when that was built we could move into their flat. Plans could now be made for a wedding during the following Easter holidays and we could start to look around for furniture.

No time for buying could have been better. The slump had hit trade very badly, and if you went along Tottenham Court Road, salesmen would stand outside the shops and try to entice you in to view their stock which was priced down to almost ridiculous levels in order to sell. It was a wonderful opportunity for us. We bought our three main suites for drawing room, dining room and bedroom at Wolfe and Hollander for a total of under £60. The salesman was very accommodating and agreed to store everything for six months. These, we were able to pay for, as Betty's parents were giving us the drawing room suite as a wedding present and her aunt and grandmother were doing the same for the dining room, so it was only the bedroom suite that we had to pay for ourselves. My parents were giving us the table silver which we bought at Mappin and Webb's. It was the same rat-tail design they had had when they were married. Other things we got when we could; there was, alas, plenty of time before we would need them.

By this time Betty had finished her work at Chelsea and was living at home on the farm, helping with the poultry and getting things together for the wedding. She was also much involved with running a Lone Guide Company with Jan - something she greatly enjoyed.

Time seemed to fly by during my second year at Rendcomb. However, in marked contrast, the new house was going up much too slowly for our liking. It would not be ready by April. Nevertheless, we decided to go ahead with our wedding which was arranged for the 30th of that month. It was possible to have a fortnight's honeymoon after that as all schools were given an extra two weeks holiday due to the Coronation of King George VI. We would use rented accommodation in the village until we could move into the flat.

We hoped to have the wedding at Boxmoor Baptist Church as this was only a few miles from Betty's home and Dad would then be able to return to his old church from Naunton and take the service. We liked that idea very much; Dad and Mother were very pleased too. It would also give our parents a chance to meet each other and see other members of both families while staying with friends in Boxmoor. As neither of us or our parents lived in the parish of Boxmoor, in order to satisfy the law, Betty was obliged to leave baggage containing some of her belongings for three weeks with somebody who lived there in order to provide a Boxmoor address. This was easy to arrange.

Back at Rendcomb I was able to find a place where we could stay whilst waiting for the flat. There were some well-built stone cottages in the village, and Mrs Barker, who lived on her own was pleased to let us have two rooms and the use of the kitchen for ten shillings a week. Drinking water had to be carried in pails from the village pump, but that was not far; it was reputed to be the best place to hear the village gossip in the evening!

Betty came in for most of the preparations for the wedding, and she kept me informed with regular bulletins. I had to make very exact esti-mates of what cash we would have at critical times until the end of the year when we expected to move into the flat. I had been saving all I could, so with the salary cheque due at the end of the term, I reckoned that our total assets before the wedding would be £244. That was terrific!

In the event people were marvellous over wedding presents and a lot of things we thought we would have to buy were given to us.

A desk was a necessity, but I was told of a cabinet maker in Cirencester who agreed to make one in solid oak to my requirements for £10. This was Marge's wedding present to us. It was beautifully made and I've used it ever since. An oil stove was also essential for cooking - not exactly what Betty had been used to.

The day of the wedding duly arrived. Bids had come down from Manchester and was staying along with my parents in Boxmoor. I did quite the unorthodox thing and stayed the night at Kenmore Farm, so Bill, who had acquired an open two-seater car whisked me out of the way early the next morning and drove me around the countryside to kill time before taking me to the church. He, of course, was my best man. The service was arranged for mid-morning as we needed quite a long time afterwards to get to Rhos-on-sea in North Wales by train from Euston. We had never been to North Wales before and it seemed a romantic choice as my parents had also spent their honeymoon there.

The service was well attended and we felt it was a real family celebration with Dad conducting and both families well represented. Marge was the only member of our immediate family not able to attend as she was still in India. It was wonderful that so many of our friends were able to come, including Christopher Hentschel, Nellie Brown and some of our student friends from Chelsea. When we left the reception, Betty's brother, Ken, took us to Euston in his car and saw us off. It was not long before the train was speeding its way through Boxmoor and along the embankment overlooking the moor, passing over the bridge at Swan Lane where I used to collect engine numbers and on to Berkhampstead and beyond. Having waited nearly three years since our engagement, it was difficult to realise that we were really married at last! However, traces of confetti in the compartment helped to convince us.

We had booked accommodation at a guest-house, but only had a photograph of the place to tell us what it was like. In the event, we were very pleased, the rooms were comfortable and the landlady looked after us well. We happened to be the only guests.

We wanted to explore the countryside as much as possible. Rhos itself was a small sea-side resort without great interest, but inland the scenery was superb. We were able to buy run-about tickets on the railway which allowed us to travel as much as we wished within a radius of 50 miles during the fortnight so we planned our itinerary carefully, going to a different station each time and walking or climbing from there.

The country was looking very beautiful with the pale green of the beech leaves, just unfurled, much water in the streams so the waterfalls too were spectacular and, of course, the magnificent backdrop of the mountains just inviting us to climb - and we were together. We chose a lovely sunny day to climb Snowdon, going up by the Pyg Track and along the ridge of Grib Goch towards the summit and back by the easier route to Pen-y-Pass. Those lovely days together seemed to pass at record speed and soon we were on our way back to Rendcomb to a very different life.

Living at Mrs Barker's was very much an interim arrangement. We managed well, but we longed for a home we could call our own. The James' new house was coming on and already Jimmy was developing the garden in preparation for occupation, but there was still much to be done before the Christmas holidays when we hoped to move.

During the summer term I was pressed into service to coach cricket. John James was doing noble work, but he couldn't do it all. A new all-weather set of cricket nets were constructed near the College; strips of concrete were laid with the help of the boys and matting put on top. We were then able to have net practice twice a week. To engender further enthusiasm for the game, Charles Barnett, who at that time was opening bat for Gloucestershire and England, was persuaded to bat at the nets for an hour while the staff and boys bowled everything they could at him. Other boys had the less exciting task of retrieving balls from lofted drives into the Park! We all greatly appreciated his coming out from Cirencester to demonstrate his skills during a busy season.

Each summer, Denis and Freda Lee-Browne took a group of keen biologists camping at Rhossili on the Gower Peninsula over the Whitsun week-end. The objective was to study marine life and collect specimens. Some of the latter found their way into the laboratory museum for identification and demonstration purposes, others were brought back alive along with a carbuoy of sea-water to be kept in aquaria.

I found the marine work excellent, and benefiting from my time in Plymouth, I was able to do some useful ecology with the boys in the area between the mainland and Worms Head. We found some unusual species and attempted to work out the distribution of the flora and fauna in relation to tide and exposure. Another day we studied the fauna of the sandy beach of Rhossili Bay, and at low tide dug for marine worms, razor shells, other bivalves and heart urchins. When the tide came in we tried to sample the plankton by wading into the water allowing the waves to break gently into pond nets. In spite of the crudity of this technique, it worked very well; on tipping the contents of the nets into clean water, we found we had caught a variety of planktonic forms including some sea gooseberries. When the light caught them you could make out a succession of rainbow colours as they moved their bands of cilia - lovely to watch.

These trips to the Gower were excellent value. The boys learnt a lot and were able to study a very different habitat from what they were used to at Rendcomb; it was also good fun. Getting material back alive was difficult, but by concentrating on the hardier species such as crabs, anemones, prawns and some of the molluscs and packing them in wet seaweed, there were few losses. Then it was a matter of setting up aquaria, keeping them well aerated and feeding them regularly. It was all very well worthwhile as enthusiasm rubbed off on other up-and-coming biologists who hoped they would be included another year.

It was very unfortunate that my digestion started to give trouble during the summer term and Dr Gladstone, who was the school doctor and lived in the village, put me on a diet. This was a disappointing outcome for Betty, who naturally wanted to try out her newly-acquired skills at cooking and had to restrict herself to simple fare. When in addition, my appendix started to rumble, as I mentioned earlier, the doctor thought it wise for me to have it out, hoping that it would improve my digestion at the same time. So, during the summer holidays which we spent at Naunton, I went into a Cheltenham Nursing Home and had the operation. This was all very frustrating for both of us, coming, as it did, so early on in our married life. However, I was out and about very soon and quickly felt very much better.

There was plenty of work to do during the autumn term. I had a good group in my sixth form, and one third-year boy was trying for an open scholarship to Bristol. He was an interesting character, sufficiently clever to avoid having to work too hard, and quite charming, but difficult to motivate. However, if you did arouse his interest in a particular subject he would happily discuss it by the hour. Fortunately, he rose to the challenge and became the first holder of the Dulverton Scholarship. This delighted the Headmaster as Lord Dulverton, who endowed the scholarship, was another member of the Wills family and closely related to our Founder. Later, the boy, after obtaining a good honours degree in zoology at the university suddenly, to everybody's surprise, decided to do a postgraduate course in Chinese archaeology! I believe he became an expert in the history of Chinese pagodas.

The Jameses moved into their new house just before Christmas, so after spending a few days at Naunton we returned to Rendcomb to redecorate the flat in the stable block ready for our move. I knew little about decorating but we bought large quantities of emulsion paint for the walls and set to work on the rooms we needed most urgently.

The flat consisted of a large sitting room occupying the width of the flat with windows at both ends, a smaller dining room, our bedroom, two smaller bedrooms, kitchen and bathroom. These were all on the first floor and above the old stables, one of which we could use as a workshop and for storing coal and wood.

The large sitting room was a great boon in more ways than one. By opening the windows at both ends and having lights on the window sills as well as in the centre of the room, it could be turned into a splendid moth trap. All you had to do was to move the settee and put a white sheet on the floor, put on the lights and go to bed. In the morning the moths were settled on the sheet or walls and could be examined. There was only one snag bats learnt that this concentration of moths was much to their liking and would fly into the room, catch the moths and fly out again leaving their victim's wings on the floor to tell the tale.

In early January, with the paint barely dry, we moved in. It was snowing! However, all went well, we brought our things over from Mrs Barker's, the van arrived from Wolfe and Hollander, and at last we could see our new furniture again after being in store for so long. Term started before we were straight, but that was of little consequence, we were in our own home at last!

Betty's father kindly offered to buy us a second-hand car. This was marvellous as Rendcomb was very isolated. Betty's brother, Ken, chose a Standard for us and I started to learn to drive. A driving test had recently been introduced so I practiced on the school drives and got help from Margaret Richards. The car served us well for a couple of years in spite of its age, although going on long journeys was always something of an act of faith! On one occasion the big-end broke and the journey had to be aborted.

It was a great thrill when Dr Gladstone confirmed that Betty was pregnant and could expect the baby in late autumn. Margaret Richards had by this time had a son, so Betty was pleased to have a neighbour with experience. I had talked to Dr Gladstone about the nature of the pregnancy test and he suggested I kept clawed toads, *Xenopus*, in the lab and that we went into partnership! These toads, when injected with urine from a pregnant woman were stimulated to spawn in response to the presence of a hormone secreted by the placenta. All very interesting, but I thought it better not to get involved. .

I got to know Dr Gladstone well. He was an excellent G.P. and had a large country practice. He did much of the minor work a hospital would normally do now, and on one occasion at a remote farm, had done an emergency tracheotomy on a child with diphtheria when there was no time to get her to hospital.

Another doctor I came to know was Dr McAlister, who had retired to the Cotswolds after being a consultant physician at the Liverpool Royal Infirmary. He was interested in old herbal remedies, analysing extracts from plants for substances beneficial to medicine. He had worked on a substance obtained from comfrey, *Symphytum officinale*, called allantoin - previously known to be secreted from the allantois, one of the foetal membranes of mammals. He had discovered that allantoin, injected into the blood stream, increased the number of white corpuscles and was useful in treating pneumonia; it also helped in the treatment of sores which would not heal quickly.

He suspected allantoin might act as a growth hormone and gave me some to experiment with. I tried injecting a solution into hyacinth bulbs grown in bottles with their bases in water, treating others in the same way with distilled water. All those injected with allantoin flowered before the others! However, another experiment using frog tadpoles in two aquaria, one with allantoin added and the other without showed no effect on the rate of growth and metamorphosis.

It had been well documented that war wounds infected by maggots often cleaned up unexpectedly well. On investigation it was shown that the maggots excreted allantoin! Consequently, allantoin was used for some years in medicine, particularly in America, but with the discovery of sulphonamides and later, antibiotics, it became largely irrelevant.

During the Easter holidays I was given the opportunity to spend a week at the headquarters of the Freshwater Biological Association at Windermere and find out about some of the research being carried out there. There was an undergraduate course in freshwater ecology going on at the same time so I was also able to benefit from the field trips which were laid on. This was time well spent as it gave me ideas for more meaningful field work at Rendcomb, utilising the River Churn and the lake in the school grounds. An interesting interlude was an evening trip on Windermere with Dr Frost who was fishing for char - a deep lake species of the salmon family. Dr Frost was doing research on their ecology and knew just where to go. As a result of the evening's fishing I was able to confirm that char are far better eating than either salmon or trout!

It was part of the Rendcomb tradition for staff to take boys in the holidays on expeditions, so while two groups went to the Continent, I organised a camping trip to the New Forest to study the lepidoptera of the area. The New Forest had been a favourite place of my father's for catching butterflies and my first visit there had been when I was teaching at Highfield. On that occasion I cycled down to Brockenhurst on my bicycle travelling by night. This I found difficult, as I hadn't realised until I got away from London how dark it was on the more countrified roads, using only a standard bicycle lamp. At Dad's recommendation I had arranged accommodation over the Post Office at Brockenhurst, where he had stayed.

Now I was able to benefit from this experience, and while the four Rendcomb boys cycled, the father of one of them helped me transport the gear by road using our two cars. A permit to camp was obtained, and a site selected in what appeared to be an ideal place, not too far from the main road between Brockenhurst and Lyndhurst and near to a farm from which we could get milk and eggs. We explored many parts of the forest, visiting likely habitats for butterflies and moths and trying out all the usual techniques for attracting moths, including sugaring. For this you daub tree trunks with a vertical strip of diluted black treacle made especially attractive to moths by adding a few drops of amyl acetate which gives it a pear-drop smell. You put on this delectable concoction before dusk and then go the rounds again some time after dark to see what has come. The moths settle delicately to the side of the sticky strip, each with its proboscis extended into the mixture. On humid, mild evenings this worked well; we discovered a number of interesting species including the rare dark crimson underwing which was largely confined to the New Forest area.

Coming back in the car from one such moth-hunting expedition around midnight, a car overtook us at suicidal speed; appropriate remarks were made concerning the driver's diminishing life expectancy. However, we were not prepared to find a mile ahead, the car upside down some twenty yards off the road and blazing fiercely. The driver had obviously tried to take the bend too fast, hit the curb and spun off the road. We stopped to give help, but to our surprise there was no sign of the driver. It was not long before a police car pulled up and we had to give a statement. The mystery of the missing driver was resolved when the police told us that it was a stolen car and the driver had probably been able to climb out before it burst into flames and had run for the nearby forest to escape pursuit.

It was not a very good summer for butterflies, but there was a reasonable hatch of purple hairstreaks flying around some of the oaks, a few white admirals in the wider glades and a number of silver-washed fritillaries including some of the dark variety, *valesina*. Silver studded blues were also common on the heather. We hoped to see a purple emperor but were unlucky.

The New Forest at that time was a mecca for entomologists, but understandably, they were very loath to impart useful information about localities for the rarer species. However, there was one character who knew more about the Forest than any of the collectors; he called himself 'a snakes and adder catcher'. We tracked him down to a pub near the main road and learnt that we could always find him there after lunch. When he roamed the Forest, he always carried a forked stick which he used for pinning down adders and grass snakes before putting them in his large leather pocket. He sent them in batches up to the London Zoo to feed other larger snakes! If you got him talking he would tell you much about the Forest and its fauna.

The weather was warm and sunny except for one day when rain began to fall after lunch. It then turned into something more like a cloudburst with thunder, lightning and hail. The wind rose to gale force and it was not long before the boys' tent was flooded and everybody was soaked to the skin. I found myself hanging on grimly to the tent pole as mine was threatening to collapse and at the same time a stream of water was flowing through the tent on top of the ground sheet. The storm soon ended, but with everything soaked there was no chance at all of sleeping there that night. However, our farmer was most helpful, allowing us to sleep in his barn on the hay. It was a bit prickly, but quite as comfortable as camping! Fortunately the next day was sunny again so we spent most of it drying our things and getting ship-shape again.

Towards the end of the summer holidays I went to Interlaken in Switzerland for a week to an international conference arranged by the Oxford Group. I had become involved with the movement while at Chelsea, read some of their literature with profit and was stimulated by their world outlook and sense of purpose. The Group also brought a dynamism to the churches which I found refreshing. I did not like leaving Betty, but a friend from Cheltenham came to stay with her while I was away.

I travelled from London with several others by rail and ferry. The political situation was tense at that time as Germany was becoming very bombastic and the Munich talks between Hitler and Chamberlain were soon to take place. Nobody knew whether war would break out, and as the train went through the disputed regions of Alsace and Lorraine the military were very much in evidence guarding the railway stations. This uncertainty heightened the relevance of the conference. Sessions were addressed by people of many nationalities, the dominant theme being the moral and spiritual re-armament of the world - the basic answer to war. I found it a stimulating experience.

However, it was good to get an occasional break from the serious nature of the meetings, and as I had not been to Switzerland before, I was glad of the chance to see some of the country. One afternoon, I went with some friends up the Jungfrau by the funicular railway. The train slowly wound its way higher and higher through superb mountain scenery and the views from the summit station were spectacular. I found that change in altitude played funny tricks with your physiology. Apart from slight breathlessness when you walked quickly, I was amused to see on the way down, not just one, but a whole party of Japanese tourists fall fast asleep on the train. I found it difficult myself to keep awake. Another day I was able to explore on my own some of the upland meadows and was intrigued to see species of butterflies that did not occur in Britain along with pale clouded yellows which were quite common there, but rare at home.

The autumn term opened under a cloud of uncertainty. Everybody was talking about the possibility of war and although Munich brought a breather, we all knew that war was only a matter of time. This was a frightening possibility for the school as it would lose most of its staff, for all, including the Headmaster, were under forty, and many were under thirty. To prepare for possible eventualities, Denis Lee-Browne, John James, Dickers and Jack Fell took classes and became Air Raid Wardens, while I joined the Rescue Service in Cirencester, learnt first aid and later took classes in it for the school and people in the village.

Our first son, Keith, was born on the 1 November. We had arranged for a nurse to live in for a few weeks as Betty chose to have her baby at home. It was a good thing the nurse was there as Dr Gladstone underestimated the speed of delivery and when he came the baby had already arrived!

When the nurse left, Bids was able to come down for a short while to be with Betty; this made all the difference. The school was given a day's holiday to commemorate the birth - a very popular move with the boys and also typical of the close community in which we lived with its philosophy of interdependence.

The new arrival was a great joy to us both. Attitudes immediately changed. We had to learn the art of being parents and it was not easy to adjust at first. For me, life had to go on as usual, for Betty it was a new life, and for both of us, a great adventure and an added responsibility. We wondered what sort of a world Keith was going to grow up in ?

You can recognise an occupied sett by the flies going in and out

Chapter Six

Rendcomb - the war years

After Munich, the euphoria of a respite from imminent conflict gave way to the near certainty of war. Everybody prepared for the worst. black-out curtains were made, gas masks distributed and fire drills practised. The school dug 40 yards of trenches as air-raid shelters; they were 8 feet deep, timbered for support and covered. I became deputy superintendent of the Rescue Service in Cirencester which meant that I had to have a telephone beside my bed, go to the town in response to any call, teach first-aid and supervise practices.

Dickers had been helping with the Methodist Circuit, going around the towns and villages nearby taking services on Sunday mornings. There were not nearly enough ministers to visit these churches regularly and lay preachers were a help. He asked me if I would be interested and introduced me to the Methodist minister in charge. Being a Baptist didn't matter either to him or to me, so I agreed to help every few weeks. I found the experience interesting and preparing services was a useful discipline as it helped me sort out my ideas and beliefs. Some of the village churches were poorly attended, but the town churches were active and congregations were excellent. In fact, Methodism was very strong in the Cotswolds and the farmers in particular were loyal supporters.

I was taking the morning service at Stroud when I was handed a note during a hymn which told me that war had just been declared. It was not really unexpected, but the finality of the message was salutary as no one knew what to expect. Would there be air-raids immediately, we wondered? As it happened I had prepared an address from the text 'In the world ye shall have tribulation, but be of good cheer, I have overcome the world'. Nothing could have been more appropriate following my announcement of the news to the congregation. It was with a heavy heart that I drove back home thinking of the futility of it all, but also with a renewed sense of purpose that somehow the forces of love would triumph in the end whatever the price the world would have to pay.

In the event, of course, nothing happened immediately. Air-raid sirens went off, but there were no raids. However, preparations were made for any foreseeable eventuality and several staff were recalled to the school a week before term started to help fit black-out to the myriads of windows. There was an atmosphere of unreality when the boys returned; all went on as usual, but everybody was waiting for something to happen and for a long time nothing did in our part of the world. Only the war at sea reminded us of the realities.

Several members of staff were called up immediately, including Jack Fell, who went into the airforce and spent his time doing research on the development of radar which was then not much more than an idea. Dickers switched from teaching maths to physics, and maths was taken over by a woman teacher from Bristol University. Other ladies also joined the staff.

Boys of Rendcomb College 'Digging for Victory'. 1¹/₂ acres of potatoes dug and planted in 2 days, 1942

I was not called up then, but I knew it would only be a matter of months. Meanwhile, I was put in charge of food production with the object of growing as much as boy labour could cope with. I heard that there was a sale at the Agricultural College at Cirencester. They had been doing research there on poultry and had a flock of excellent pullets, but the research was to be abandoned. I was able to buy 50 of these young birds, a few cockerels for breeding and some poultry houses. Our total expenditure was £45-17s-3d! Betty already knew a lot about hens from working with her mother on the farm, so I got some useful tips.The boys' General Meeting elected six 'hen men' to help look after them; they worked very well. It was a great day when the first pullet laid an egg.

The enterprise flourished and we collected 6,200 eggs in 8 months. In the spring we hatched some of the eggs in an incubator and reared 60 chicks. The cockerels were fattened for the table and during our second Christmas they were the main dish for our celebratory dinner.

In the spring, a local farmer ploughed up a $1^3/_4$-acre field belonging to the school and sowed it with barley for the poultry, but this was not a success as the crop was rather poor and we were not equipped for harvesting it properly. So the following year the field was prepared for potatoes; we planted 18 cwts to give a crop of nearly 10 tons. Everything was done by the boys working in two-hour shifts. One group would dig, another group followed behind, planting, some acted as barrowers, others put on fertilizers and finally they were earthed over. It was like a production line. Later they were earthed up again and the weeds hoed. In later years, we also grew carrots, swedes and other vegetables, but gave up growing greens as the pigeons wrought havoc on them. Flocks of wood pigeons were so numerous one year that when the beech mast had fallen in the Park their bodies cast a pale grey carpet over the ground and when they flew up in heavy ungainly flight the clatter of their wings was like sustained clapping from an unseen audience. There were literally thousands of them!

The great event of the Easter term of 1940 was the weather. I shall always remember it because of the 'Ice Rain'. This followed a period of intense cold. Rain began to fall, and continued as a steady drizzle for fourteen hours with an occasional interlude of heavier rain. All that time the air temperature was at least two degrees below freezing point, although not very far up the atmosphere must have been warmer as no hail fell. As the moisture collected on the cold surfaces of vegetation, telegraph wires and railings, a layer of ice formed. This envelope covered everything and became progressively thicker as more rain fell. That evening, the small twigs began to rattle like tinkling glass when the wind brought them into contact. This continued all night.

In the morning we woke to strange sounds: great crashings at frequent intervals followed by a thousand tinkling sounds as if glass was being smashed to atoms. Every so often it seemed as if someone was sliding down the roof of the house. On peering outside a fantastic world greeted our eyes. Every tree was covered in ice, each evergreen leaf was encased in an ice-mould many times its thickness. As we watched, a large bough from the tree opposite smashed down, dislodging thousands of pieces of ice from other boughs as it fell.

To venture out was to invite disaster unless one was a born athlete as the roads were like ribbons of ice and the only sensible method was to skate. Many who did go out tied sacks over their boots as they could then concentrate on what was falling from above rather than on keeping a foothold.

As I picked my way in this wooded district, boughs crashed to the earth under the weight of the ice every few seconds. The weight must have been enormous as there was little wind, for limbs a foot and a half in diameter came crashing down. As they touched the hard earth the smaller branches broke off like matchwood, they were so brittle. Practically every tree in the neighbourhood was reft of some of its branches, the beeches, elms and sycamores suffering most, but many others presented a pathetic sight. One road bordered by a fine row of sycamores and beeches was impassable, being covered for a quarter of a mile of its length by two to seven feet of tangled boughs. No part of the road was clear.

Yew trees stood the strain well, their tough branches bent gracefully, some touching the ground; they looked like weeping willows covered with ice. Isolated chestnuts stood gaunt and broken, surrounded by a circle of branches torn rudely from them. Young birches with a diameter at the base of six inches were bent double or broken off at the base.

Every yard provoked an exclamation of amazement as some new phenomenon was revealed. The telegraph wires were ropes of ice, some with a circumference of seven inches. It was not surprising that the strain caused by many tons of ice was too much for the poles. The ground below was so hard with frost that they were not uprooted but usually broke off a few feet from the ground. The school was off the phone for the remainder of the term.

'The Icy Fingers of the Grass'. Taken during the Ice Rain and showing each blade of grass covered in ice an inch in diameter, (1940)

Unfortunately the sky was leaden so photography was difficult and the lens kept misting over, but I concentrated on getting close-ups. One area of rough pasture provided an extraordinary picture as each blade of grass was standing erect like an icy finger and as you walked through them you expected to trip up as they looked so formidable, but they broke off at a touch and fell to pieces.

I was interested to see a wych elm with its covering of ice, for I knew that the white letter hairstreak butterfly laid its eggs on its twigs every year and now they would be encased in ice. The following July this species was more common than for many years, so the ice had had no appreciable effect.

It was many weeks before things were anything like normal. The sap oozed out of the wounds left by the broken branches and later froze into long icicles. These were brought back to the laboratory and melted down to give a pleasant sugary liquid! The big trees, however, were a pathetic sight. They stood battered and lop-sided as most of the boughs on the north-east side were broken off short, but when they burst into leaf the wounds were to some extent hidden by the new green growth. However, over subsequent years when the leaves fell each autumn one was reminded of that phenomenal ice rain. For the photographer it was the chance of a lifetime, but there was no doubt in my mind that once was quite enough.

That summer I got my call-up papers. I had been wrestling with the problem of what action was right for me to take. I hated war and had discussed the matter in depth with several people I greatly respected. On the one hand I wanted to help my country in any way I could, on the other I could not see myself taking an active part in the armed forces. I decided to register as a conscientious objector with the proviso that I was perfectly willing to help with ambulance or first-aid work. At the end of June I was summoned to a tribunal in Bristol where my case was heard by Judge Wethered. I had to make a statement giving my reasons for not wishing to go into the armed services in a fighting capacity. I thought long and hard about this, because I wished to be completely honest about my reasons.

I felt deeply that Christ's life, which to me was the greatest revelation of God's will, was based on an attitude of love towards individuals. He lived a life of unselfish service, putting the needs of others before His own and overcoming evil by being constructively good. He hated evil, but loved those who caused it. As a Christian I was trying to live up to those principles and was unable to reconcile my taking part in military service with living on the basis of love towards individuals. However, I did respect the opinions of other Christians who thought differently from me, although I could not agree with them.

But now the war was a reality, I believed that not only must I continue to build up right relationships between individuals, but I must as a follower of Christ do all I could to make the present circumstances happier for those hit by them. I believed that Christ would have done all He could to relieve suffering though I could never believe He would play a destructive or unloving role, so I was quite happy to offer to do medical work. I realised that this might be looked upon by some as helping the war effort and therefore incompatible with conscientious objection, but I did not agree, as relieving suffering in peace or war was always a worth-while task whatever its repercussions.

Judge Wethered's decision was 'that if he had an unfettered decision he would direct me to continue my present work at the school and in the Civil Defence Service, but in his opinion in view of the limited nature of my objection he must direct my name to be removed from the Conscientious Objectors Register'.

The following March I was requested to attend an interview for scientific work of an unspecified nature, so I refused on the grounds that I had only agreed to do medical work. I was called for a medical examination. When I attended I was put into the lowest grade (IV) due to my history of duodenal ulcers, which meant that I was unfit to do Pioneer or Medical Corps work and was left to carry on at school and in the Rescue Department. This was a great relief to us all, not least to the headmaster, so I settled down to one of the busiest periods of my life.

The school job was full time with teaching, field and laboratory work and agricultural projects, but on top of that I had to go into Cirencester several nights a week for rescue duty where one would hang about for hours waiting for a call to action, whiling away the time with games of cards and eating marmite sandwiches. Usually nothing happened. Fortunately, they soon learnt not to call me when flights of bombers droned overhead intent on distant targets, as they did most nights, but only when bombing raids were nearby such as at Gloucester where there was an aircraft factory, Cheltenham, Coventry or Birmingham when extra help might be needed. Practices were very realistic and it was no small responsibility supervising the lowering of stretchers with people on them from the roof of the post office in Cirencester, for example. There was no room for mistakes!

Very little happened locally, although the occasional bomb was dropped harmlessly in the fields as bombers lightened their loads before speeding back to Germany. One misty morning a plane flew low over the Cheltenham Drive with guns firing harmlessly as it went. It was probably the same one that machine-gunned a street in Cirencester, fortunately without causing casualties. Another flew just over the laboratories, obviously in trouble. It was finally shot down near Coates.

I had bought another car, a Rover 14, from somebody working in the aeroplane factory in Gloucester as I needed something more reliable. I paid £40 for it. Petrol rationing was then in force, but I got extra coupons for my rescue work; petrol cost 1/- a gallon!

Going in at night was no fun as headlights were fitted with masks so that no light could be seen from the air. You could only use the near headlamp and the side lights. Fortunately, there was practically no traffic, so the technique was to drive on the wrong side, hanging your head out of the window and watching the edge of the road. You inevitably went slowly, and if a car did come in the opposite direction you quickly took avoiding action!

The most difficult journey I had to make was in October when Betty was due to have our second baby. We had booked a place in a nursing home in Cheltenham. Labour started after dark, and knowing how fast Keith had arrived, I had to get her in as quickly as possible. It was ten miles, but they seemed very long ones, and on a lonely stretch of the road I suddenly saw a dark shape in front of the car. I jammed on the brakes and narrowly missed a horse standing in the middle of the road, presumably fast asleep. We got to the nursing home in time, and our second son, David, duly arrived. It was not a very peaceful occasion as a few nights afterwards bombs were dropped on Cheltenham, one in the next road to the nursing home. Not nice at all! We were glad when Betty returned to the flat where things were more restful. We had a nurse for the next few weeks. When she left Betty had to cope, although we had a girl who lived in. Eileen had been found for us by Bids; she had just been bombed out of her home in London and was glad to be somewhere more peaceful, but she was not used to the country and was rather lonely. However, she did quite well and we were glad of her help.

Bids had moved to London and had been very hard at work dealing with the evacuation of children to safer areas of the country, escorting, finding suitable homes and following up to see if all was going well. Later, when London was badly blitzed she took her turn fire fighting, using stirrup pumps to deal with incendiaries dropped on buildings in her area.

Marge was still in India carrying on with her medical work and helping with evacuated troops from the Burma war, transported to Calcutta for after-care. This kept her exceptionally busy as many had dysentery, cholera and the like, and were in a very poor state. We heard from her regularly, but she mentioned few details about her many activities during that hectic time. One letter, carried by air, arrived with the stencil on the envelope, 'salvaged mail'. The plane had been shot down over the Mediterranean, but the mail was salvaged and this letter was quite legible.

Bill was disqualified from joining the armed forces due to his history of tuberculosis and was engaged in secret work, travelling to America several times from 1940 onwards, before America entered the war, with shipments of antique firearms. He sold them for currency for the Ministry of Economic Warfare, the money being used to buy modern hand-guns for use in intelligence work. Britain was then making bombs rather than concentrating on the manufacture of automatic pistols and revolvers. On one occasion his boat was torpedoed, but he was rescued and landed in West Africa from where he eventually got back to Britain. He spoke very little about his adventures during the war and we knew nothing about what he had been doing until after hostilities had ended. He was always modest about his achievements.

I became an examiner in biology for London University School Certificate. Three or four hundred scripts had to be marked over a period of a few weeks. The method was very thorough. You attended a meeting in London with the chief examiners and when a mark scheme was agreed, each examiner marked a few papers and they were then passed around the table, each giving his own assessment. If there was a discrepancy you continued until each was marking to the same standard. You then went home and marked a number and sent samples back to the chief examiner to check. I sometimes found a note attached by the supervisor to one of the scripts saying, for example, that the candidate had been interrupted by a bombing raid during the exam, could this be taken into account? The chief examiner would consider this if results were marginal.

On one occasion I arrived at South Kensington for an examiners' meeting only to find that the night before, a huge bomb had demolished a large building just behind the Victoria and Albert Museum a few hundred yards from where we held our meeting. Debris was all over the place. This was the quickest meeting I attended as everybody wanted to get back before dark when the next raid was expected. The meeting was held in the basement of Imperial College.

It was also a very busy time for Betty with Keith now two and the new baby needing lots of attention. Eileen had gone back to London as she missed her friends and preferred the uncertainties of bombing raids to a quiet life in the country. Katherine took her place. She was a German Jewess and a very intelligent girl, but she was extremely depressed by the war situation and was very lonely. She gave us help, but her heart was not in it. Over Christmas, she was allowed to invite a German prisoner of war from a camp nearby to spend the afternoon and have a meal with us; it was good for her to be able to speak some German again.

Feeding the family with strict rationing was easier in the country than in towns as there was more scope for supplementing. I dug an allotment out of a field overlooking Kennel Bottom and later took on the garden of a cottage which became vacant. It was particularly fertile as the farmer allowed me to clear out an old cow-shed deep in dung and straw litter which I dug in. The greens were doing particularly well until some of the farmer's sheep found their way into the garden and devastated some of the crop. After that we kept the gate firmly tied up!.

Wood for fires was easily obtained after the ice rain, but it had to be sawn up and split and brought home in a trailer attached behind my bicycle. It all took time, but was good exercise. Mercifully, the school had good holidays and much of this kind of work was done then.

Holidays also gave me the chance to keep up with my natural history and photography. I had taken to nature photography with enthusiasm before the war started and continued it whenever I could. I used a hide for bird photography concentrating on peewits, willow warblers, dippers and kingfishers. Dippers nested by the waterfall at one end of the lake and kingfishers used to fish from a bough overlooking a pool where minnows abounded. I used a box bush as a hide and had king-fishers actually perching a few feet from me. They are glorious birds to see at such close quarters. I did not confine myself to birds, but took anything of interest: butterflies, moths, caterpillars, beetles, flowers, fungi and of course badgers. I was particularly interested in examples of protective resemblance having obtained a copy of that marvellous book by Hugh Cott, 'Adaptive Colouration in Animals'. Fortunately I could still get films for my film adapter, but it was not long before this source dried up and all I could get were boxes of panchromatic plates. One boy's father worked in Boots and kindly got some for me whenever he could so I had a modest supply throughout the war.

Working with a folding plate camera was not easy for such things as butterflies that would not keep still, as you had to use a focusing screen first and quickly substitute the plate holder. Often as not, by this time, the insect had moved away, but it was a challenge. By the end of the war I had accumulated sufficient photos to bring out a small book on photog-raphy, 'Seeing Nature with a Camera', which was published by Paul Elek. I also supplied various magazines such as 'Lilliput' with photographs. There was not much competition then, and I was fortunate to have an outlet for some of my pictures. This paid for all my photographic needs and I did all the processing and enlarging myself in the school darkroom.

Field work with the boys went on whenever there was time. There were some very keen naturalists who were a pleasure to go out with. The most outstanding was Ian Menzies. He later took up medicine as a career, becoming a chemical pathologist at St Thomas' Hospital. He continued his natural history interests to the present time and we have kept in touch ever since. Ian was very observant and his enquiring mind asked just the right questions. We did much together.

One incident always stands out in my memory. It was Founder's Day when parents visited the college and some celebrity was invited and speeches made. Each year I had put on some show in the labs to illustrate such themes as marine ecology, protective resemblance or nature photography. On this occasion, after the parents had collected for tea, Ian sidled up to me in a conspiratorial manner and excitedly whispered "I've discovered the large blue!" I knew this butterfly was supposed to occur in the Cotswolds, but it was reputed to be extinct. I knew Ian didn't make mistakes over things like that, so I quietly left the gathering. He slipped into my car, and off we went to Withington, a village not far away. He led me over a field to some rough grazing dotted with ant hills, and sure enough there were several of these rare butterflies flying over the patches of thyme! It was thrilling! It was not long before he discovered several other colonies in the neighbourhood and was studying them in detail. One thing that became apparent after several years was that emergence was very variable and in one year was as early as the third week in May.

On one occasion I counted forty of these butterflies on one afternoon and had the pleasure of following a female from ant hill to ant hill as she laid one egg at a time in the terminal cluster of leaves of selected thyme plants. The life history of this butterfly had been worked out by Frohawk who showed that the caterpillar, after it had moulted three times went off its food and an ant would find it and drag it down into the ants' nest where it would be fed on the ant's larvae! It would then pupate and the butterfly emerge the following year, crawling out of the nest and expanding its wings.

I thought I would try to photograph the stages of its life history, so I collected three females and enclosed them in a muslin tent on a root of thyme I had potted up. They laid a number of eggs. Would they hatch? Each morning I looked at the eggs with a magnifying glass and sure enough, I found one morning that each egg had a neat hole in it where the caterpillar had gnawed its way out. But could I find those caterpillars? I methodically went over each piece of thyme with the magnifying glass and could see no sign. It was all very queer as I was most systematic and careful in my search. Then I saw a portion of one of the pale buds move. It was the last segment of the caterpillar which was inside feeding on the stamens. Having bored its way in, it had left its back-end filling the hole it had made and was just about invisible. I was thrilled, for as far as I knew this observation had never been made before.

The caterpillars grew quickly and I watched them moult, but I knew the test would come after the third moult. How could I get ants to take them to their nest? I thought the best way was to establish an ant colony in a formicarium. Collecting a sample of earth from the large blue locality containing eggs, larvae and pupae I put it into a large shallow box having two sheets of glass a few millimetres apart with a deeper area for the main ants' nest. The ants soon established themselves and took some of the earth between the glass sheets, so their activities became easily visible. The whole thing was covered with a dark cloth when observations were not being made. All was ready for the crucial moment when the caterpillars could be transferred into the nest. Much to my disappointment, the experiment did not work and the caterpillars died. I found out later, that the ants I had collected were of the wrong species; the kind I needed did not make ant hills! I never got a chance to repeat the experiment.

There was another boy who was very keen on natural history, but when he first came, knew very little about it. One day he came back to the laboratory dripping wet and clutching a struggling feathered object. "I've caught a foreign bird", he said, "I saw it in the river, dived in and caught it!" It was a moorhen! He was rather crestfallen when he had to take it back and release it at the spot where he had caught it. On another occasion he brought back an adder in his pocket, and I discovered him testing how it moved on the smooth surface of the bench. When it got to the end, he would turn it round and start it on another journey. Why he was not bitten I never discovered; he was fortunate - he had presumed it was harmless.

Several members of the herbarium staff at Kew were evacuated with the collections to the Cotswolds and I got to know Ken Airey-Shaw very well. He used to come to our flat each day and spend his lunch hour with us. He was not only a fine botanist, but was very keen on entomology, particularly beetles and bugs. We went out together on numerous occasions and he taught me much. I had found it difficult to identify beetles from the books we had and he persuaded me to buy a second-hand copy of Fowler's *'Coleoptera'* in six volumes. This is a wonderful book with hand-coloured illustrations of most of the British forms. I became very keen on beetles and bugs and as Ian Menzies came out with us whenever possible, this enthusiasm rubbed off on him. He has since specialised in beetles and has become a real expert on the group.

In the summer of 1944, I took a party of boys to Newent woods in the Forest of Dean, taking our bikes on the train from Gloucester. Accommodation on the train for bicycles was very limited, but by re-stacking the Royal Mail bags in the guard's van during the temporary absence of the guard, they were safely stowed away. We had heard that the wood white butterfly occurred in the Forest of Dean and I had never seen one. The day started with a shower and we sheltered under a tree. Glancing around, a specimen of the food plant of this butterfly was noticed and Ian turned the leaves over. There under a leaf was a single egg, undoubtedly of the wood white! Later, we examined many plants, but never found another egg! However, the butterflies were not uncommon. We also discovered specimens of the white-barred clear-wing moth, *Sesia spheciformis*. This was a rarity which had not been recorded before in the county.

You don't as a rule get plagues of insects in this country, but one day in June we witnessed an extraordinary sight. There had been a phenomenal hatch of garden chafers near Withington. They were in their tens of thousands. Each grass blade was weighed down with beetles, and other vegetation was crawling with them. These small chafers lay their eggs in the ground and the larvae feed on grass roots. If badgers discover a colony they have been known to 'plough up' the field in order to get at the grubs. We never saw another hatch like this one.

An interesting plant discovery was a specimen of the twayblade orchid which had regular flowers instead of the usual orchid shape. I sent it up to Kew and they were very interested, keeping the specimen for the herbarium. Each year the same plant produced other inflorescences of the same regular type. Many of the woods were of ancient origin, and Clifferdene wood was a favourite. It butted on to the Rendcomb School estate and we were allowed to explore it. Amongst other interesting plants it contained wild Solomon's seal, lilies of the valley, and in September, the autumn crocus was common. Nearby there was a good patch of green hellebore with one root with white flowers, very much like the garden Christmas Rose.

Christmas term 1944 was memorable for the roosting of tens of thousands of starlings in the laurels along the back drive. The majority of the birds were probably migrants from Europe. About three quarters of an hour before dusk, the first small flocks arrived, then others joined them until they seemed to cover the sky. It was an amazing spectacle to see them flying in perfect formation, wheeling and gliding as if controlled by some unseen leader, but in reality reacting at incredible speed to the slightest variation in movement by those that happened to be in the lead at the time. The reactions are so quick that the human eye registers them as instantaneous.

A few favourite trees were used as temporary resting places, and one old elm in front of the College, gaunt and dead, seemed to burst into full leaf as hundreds of birds landed on it. When they settled they broke out into a flood of song that was almost deafening. Each bush was full to capacity by dusk and late arrivals wheeling overhead would dive almost perpendicularly to join their companions.

There were a good many casualties each night, and it was not unusual to pick up five or six dead in the morning; after a frosty night, many more. Each morning they flew off to their feeding grounds, mainly in a southerly direction. The structural damage to the laurels was considerable and their droppings formed a layer of odoriferous manure which greatly affected the growth of the bushes in later years. Trying to take photos of the invasion in the half-light was difficult and the smell very off-putting.

Being a biologist in war-time meant that you were sometimes expected to do the work of a vet. My most demanding patient was a marmoset monkey which was languishing. It belonged to the daughter of Sir Noel Wills. I could not refuse, but one could do very little except suggest vitamins and a more varied diet. Pet dogs and cats were brought for putting down when too elderly or ill to cope, something I disliked heartily and of course the usual spate of fledgling birds in May which I was expected to nurse until they could fly; largely a waste of time as they should have been left where they were found to take their chance.

When sallow or ivy were blooming, the flowers attracted moths to the abundant nectar and if you examined them with a torch it was intriguing to see their golden eyes caught in the light as they fed. On one occasion I went to a mass of ivy covering one of the stone walls bordering the main road and was engrossed in watching the moths when I was accosted by a policeman on a bicycle who thought I was using my torch for sending messages to the enemy!

I was becoming more and more absorbed with the badgers. Early watching expeditions had been exciting and I had taken a few sixth-formers out to see them too. This led to a search through the available literature to find out more about them. There were many gaps and

Photographs of badgers at Rendcomb taken by open flash before 1945; the first is referred to in the text (p.85)

ambiguities in the accounts and clearly, not a lot was known of their ecology and reproduction. I decided to try and fill those gaps.

The first thing to do was to get to know the badgers of Conigre Wood better and find out how many there were. Counting them was very difficult as they were often spread between several setts and you could not be in several places at the same time. This was solved by doing periodic counts when a sixth-former would be posted near each sett, watches would be synchronised and every emergence and departure would be noted. Afterwards over cocoa and biscuits we would piece together the night's activities and make a count. In this way we at least knew the minimum number present and by repeating the performance several times it was soon clear how many there were. We did this accurately for three years including the number of sows that bred and the cubs they produced.

Of course it was not possible to use the boys for this work very often however keen they were to do it, but I supplemented the counts with my own observations. Times of first emergence were very regular during the summer and I had reduced watching them to a fine art so that no time was wasted. I swept the main paths to remove sticks and by using shoes with crêpe soles I was able to move undetected, quickly and silently from sett to sett so long as the wind was in my favour. I would get on my bicycle, leave it outside the keeper's cottage and be in position with about ten minutes to spare before the first badgers were expected above ground. I would then do a count and move quickly to another sett and with luck count them before they dispersed. I was back home again within a couple of hours at most.

In class I was able to keep the seniors up to date with events and discuss how more could be found out about other aspects of badger ecology. A certain amount was already known about their food, but no systematic work had been done, so every opportunity was taken to add to this knowledge. Occasionally, a dead badger would come to our notice and the stomach contents analysed. It soon became clear that the range of items eaten was large, but that after wet weather especially, earthworms predominated. Their droppings were also analysed on numerous occasions and this gave an excellent idea of the frequency of non-digested material such as beetle and other insect exoskeletal remains, mammalian fur, cereal husks and other plant material. Over a few years a good idea of a badger's diet was obtained. In later years more rigorous analyses were carried out with more emphasis on detailed investigations of stomach contents.

Much controversy existed about the time of mating, so we were on the look out for any signs of this. With boys so keen on watching and being able to observe several setts on the same night, our chances were enhanced and before long this event had been witnessed on four occasions, all in July, so it looked as if this was the mating season. However, my conclusions were premature as later, various people saw mating in other months, particularly in the spring and it eventually became clear that mating could take place during every month of the year. As births were restricted to the spring, this was very strange as you would expect mating to be similarly restricted. The explanation was the phenomenon of delayed implantation, discovered to occur in badgers by Fischer in Germany. This meant that whenever fertilization took place, there followed a period of delay when the tiny blastocyst remained free within the uterine cavity until the November-December period when implantation took place. A placenta was then formed and normal gestation proceeded. But why should mating take place over such a long period? What sort of reproductive cycle did badgers undergo? What caused implantation to occur just when it did? It was to these aspects of reproduction that I later devoted much time and research.

It was around 1945 that I first got in touch with Dr Harrison Matthews who was then based at Bristol University. He had specialised in mammals and was particularly interested in their reproduction. This contact developed into a friendship which I greatly valued; he helped me considerably. I shall always remember him coming to Rendcomb for the first time when I showed him the badgers at Eycott. We climbed into an oak tree outside the sett and were absolutely thrilled to see twelve badgers come out from the only hole. It was like watching the stage of a theatre from eighteen feet away and seeing the play unfold with the actors making their entrances and exits, playing their parts, interacting and eventually leaving the stage bare as they went off to their feeding grounds. What an evening's entertainment it had been!

One thing I badly wanted to do was to get a photographic record of badger behaviour. I had taken a number of photographs, but their quality did not satisfy me. However, I only took my camera occasionally as my primary objective was observing their natural behaviour and flash disturbed them to some extent.

On one occasion I went up to one of the Conigre setts well before dusk to allow plenty of time to focus on the place I thought the badgers might use. I was sitting on the ground with the camera and flash on a tripod in front of me and a bush at my back to eliminate my silhouette. I had a long wait and the mosquitoes were paying me far too much attention, but I managed to keep reasonably still. Around dusk, when I was expecting emergence, a rabbit came out of the wood, sat behind the main badger hole and started to pound with its hind feet. This is bush telegraph between rabbits. If a fox is spotted, the rabbit thumps and disappears down its hole promptly, then others do the same as the message is passed on. This time, the rabbit went on thumping and did not go down any hole. I was annoyed, as I thought the badgers would not emerge with all that commotion going on; I couldn't understand why it went on thumping until I realised I was sitting near its burrow and it wanted to go home!

Another time I was taking some boys to Marsden Woods. These were private, but the owner had given me permission to explore. There were badger setts there and a good marshy area with lots of devil's bit scabious. This was the food plant of the marsh fritillary and the elusive narrow-bordered bee-hawk. On our way, we skirted a coniferous plantation where I saw a hen pheasant caught by the foot in a wire snare. Something had to be done about this, so I climbed the barbed-wire fence and rescued it. I had the bird in my hand and was going to show it to the two boys before releasing it when a man seemed to appear from nowhere. He thought he had caught a poacher red-handed! He snatched the bird from my hand, wrung its neck and demanded an explanation. It turned out that the estate had changed hands and he was the new owner. It took some explaining that I had had permission from his predecessor to go on his land. He was eventually convinced and became quite intrigued when I was able to tell him a lot about the flora and fauna of his new acquisition, so he gave permission for us to continue.

On reaching the marsh we were pleased to find a tiny caterpillar of the bee-hawk sitting on the mid-rib of a devil's bit leaf. You can recognise it instantly by the horn at its rear. We also discovered several webs of marsh fritillary caterpillars. They live in clusters within a silken tent spun around themselves for protection against predators and parasites.

We did some experiments on these caterpillars to see what effect parasites had on successful emergence. We reared one set of larvae obtained when in the silken tent stage and collected others in the early spring after hibernation when they were feeding solitarily. We found that those collected from webs hatched normally, but over 50% of those collected as fully-grown larvae were parasitised. Ichneumons appear to be a main factor in causing wide fluctuations in numbers of this species from season to season.

From time to time we studied the ecology of the River Churn and occasionally discovered a crayfish, but being largely nocturnal, and by remaining hidden during the day, we had no idea of their prevalence.

They were also good to eat! We organised an expedition to find out more about them.

We constructed rings of wire on which wire netting was placed with fish remains tied to the centre. Three pieces of string were attached to each platform for lifting it out of the water and another was fastened to the bank as a marker. Several of these were lowered carefully into the water at dusk and we hoped the smell of the fish would attract the crayfish. A few hours later with the help of a torch we inserted a stick below the triangle of string and gently raised the device. There were three crayfish feasting on the fish remains! The whole exercise was a great success; we caught fifteen over a quarter-mile stretch of the river. They made a welcome addition to our war- time diet.

In 1944 we were expecting our third child. No nursing home this time; our experience with David's birth was quite enough to rule that out. We were able to get a nurse to live in for a few weeks over that period and Andrew duly arrived. Early on, he developed serious earache and had to be taken to Cheltenham for specialist advice and treatment. This was an anxious time, but to our great relief he gradually got better and began to make good headway.

By this time Keith was nearly six and David four. The problem of schooling had already been solved when the headmaster's wife employed a lady to act as a governess for her small daughter, Hermione. Miss Spiridion (Spriddy) was an excellent teacher, and it was not very long before staff children were invited to join Hermione in what turned out to be an excellent little school. All the small Jameses, Richards and Neals benefited from this arrangement.

The courtyard of the stable block was a splendid playground for our children and those of the Richards. It was relatively safe being largely enclosed, and the boys could rush around on their tricycles. These were handed down from boy to boy as they outgrew them. There was no possibility of getting new ones in war-time. All toys were left-overs from before the war or else we had to construct them from anything available.

It was around this time that the College was established as a staging post for artillery units on their way to or from the artillery range at Senny Bridge in Breconshire. On Saturdays large convoys of army lorries and guns would arrive, fill the courtyard and be parked all down the two drives. Some officers and men slept in houses in the village, but the majority used their vehicles in which to bed down. Then on Sunday they would depart and the next convoy would arrive from Brecon. Immense quantities of petrol were used and the empty four-gallon tins would be left on Monday morning to be disposed of later. By going round the tins you could usually find enough petrol left to be worth keeping. The tins were a joy to the children as they could be used as large building blocks to construct all sorts of architectural masterpieces in which they could play. Being so light and of uniform size, the tins were easy to manipulate and gave endless pleasure and plenty of scope for imaginative games in conjunction with the cycling.

During the period before D-Day a force of 5,000 American troops with huge earth-moving machines camped in the Park, and the skies were full of glider trains practising for the invasion of Europe. At night large convoys of tanks made their way towards the coast, smashing most of the remaining cat's eyes on the main road. Things were indeed hotting up.

The invasion of Europe brought to a head the massive preparations that had been so evident everywhere. Then followed a very anxious time as fortunes fluctuated, but soon it was clearly only a matter of time before success would be achieved. When it did come our local celebrations of VE Day were euphoric; 1939 seemed a long time ago and wartime had been such an ever-present reality that we had almost forgotten what it had been like without it. There was joyous and prolonged pealing of church bells and an enormous bonfire was constructed near the school and ceremoniously lit by an incendiary bomb. The school made a human chain around it and there were heartfelt songs of thankfulness and jubilation. However, a heavy price had been paid and we all knew it would be a long haul before normality returned. But what was normality? No doubt it would turn out to be something very different from the pre-war years. Idealism and hope were in all our hearts as we looked towards the future, but we had few illusions about the problems ahead. There was no going back.

I had been feeling for some time that it was time to move on. I felt the need for wider opportunities in a different kind of school although I had enjoyed my time at Rendcomb to the full; it had been a great experience for me. One thing I was quite determined about was that my next post would be in a part of the country where I could continue field work with the boys and introduce some of the ideas about teaching and education in general, formulated during my time at Rendcomb. Strangely, one of the first I saw advertised was that of biologist at Taunton School; Dr Watson's old job. I decided to apply and find out more about the post's potential both for developing the subject within the school and for the welfare of our growing family. There was a new headmaster, John Leathem. He was forward-looking and determined to build up the school after the wear and tear of the war years. It seemed a worth-while post, and when it was offered me, I gladly accepted.

Chapter Seven

My first years at Taunton School

When we moved from Rendcomb soon after Christmas there was not much time to get ready for the new term. There was no school property to go into and accommodation was hard to get, but we were fortunate to find a temporary, semi-furnished cottage at Rumwell, four miles from Taunton on the Wellington road. A member of the Taunton School staff who had left the previous term had been there, so it had become vacant at the appropriate time.

At Rendcomb, Jack Fell had been demobilised from the airforce and had married. He and his wife moved into our flat as soon as we left. They had no furniture to speak of and as there was no room for much of ours at the cottage, it was sensible for them to make use of what we could not fit in. This was an excellent arrangement for both of us.

Japonica Cottage was one of a row of three and appeared attractive with its thatched roof and old-world look, but it was far from ideal as it was small, rather far from both Taunton and Wellington, and being furnished, commanded a rent which was much greater than we had paid at Rendcomb. However, it was a base from which we could look around for something more suitable. By the time term started we were just about shipshape, but it was a squeeze getting our own essential things into the limited space available.

Schooling for Keith and David was a real problem. We would have liked them to go to Thone, the preparatory part of Taunton School, but with my unpredictable and varied timetable I could not ferry them, so they had to go to schools in Wellington. David was accepted at the infant school and Keith at the junior. The change from being taught in a small group to the hurly-burly of state education was considerable, and for Keith in particular it was a rather traumatic experience. It was also a poor arrangement for Betty who had to go in to Wellington twice a day to take and meet David. This was time-consuming and awkward as it meant going on the bus each time and carrying Andrew as well.

Houses for rent were very scarce, but a good many properties were in the hands of the Borough Council, so I put my name down and explained our predicament. They were sympathetic, but the waiting list was long, and they said the best chance would be a flat in one of the larger houses that had been requisitioned during the war. It was just a matter of patience and regular reminders that we needed something urgently.

In the event, we were fortunate to be offered something in the autumn and were able to move in early November. It was a spacious unfurnished flat, one of five adapted by the Council from a large residence called Bishop's Mead on the northern edge of Taunton. It was once owned by the Bishop of Taunton and had been requisitioned during the war. The house had a large and beautiful walled garden containing a superb cedar and immaculate lawn looked after by a gardener employed by the Council. We shared this with the other residents. There was also an extensive kitchen garden which was divided up between us. We were most fortunate in our neighbours who included the headmaster of the Grammar School, a general practitioner, a water engineer and a retired couple.

When at Rumwell, being non-resident, I was able to snatch time to explore the new countryside with the family; it was so very different from the Cotswolds. The Blackdown Hills were easily accessible from Rumwell, and on one of our first expeditions we went to Otterhead where there was an old mansion which was falling into ruin. The garden was full of buddleias gone wild and the land around was fast becoming a wilderness. On exploring inside the house we found the windows were covered in spider-webs and there, caught fast, was a large tortoishell butterfly with its wings tightly shut. I carefully removed it from its entanglements, and when we got home, used a camel-hair brush to remove the rest of the spider-webs. Then to my astonishment, a miracle happened: it opened its wings! I had not dreamt that it was alive. It had presumably gone into the house to hibernate and become ensnared. It turned out to be the last record of this rare butterfly for Somerset.

My first term at Taunton School was a very busy one. There was much that was new and very different from Rendcomb. The school was suffering from the effects of the war when two schools, Eltham College and King's School, Rochester had been evacuated from Kent and integrated into the system. They left just before I came and there was much re-organisation to be done.

Some parts of the playing fields had been ploughed up during the war to grow potatoes, and any boy who wanted his own allotment could have one if he looked after it properly. Having had experience of this type of work at Rendcomb, I was not surprised to be asked to supervise. One of the biggest chores was getting gangs of boys to remove the growing shoots from the stored potatoes - a most unpopular procedure. Fortunately, the need to grow vegetables soon became less, and by the end of my first year all this cultivated area was put back to grass and I was able to give more time to other things.

I wanted to develop the natural history interest within the school, but this was more difficult than at Rendcomb as there were many competing out-of-school activities which made field trips difficult to arrange. Getting to good areas also took time and involved some means of transport. However, I found there was a lot of latent enthusiasm, and to harness this, I started a natural history society. This quickly proved popular and provided a nucleus of really keen people. One of these was a day boy who knew the countryside around Taunton very well and was able to show me some badger setts on the Quantocks, so I was able to get some good watching and compare badger behaviour here with what I had found at Rendcomb.

It soon became evident that during term time field trips would have to be few and far between so I planned a biology camp for a week during the Easter holidays. We hired the village hall at Luccombe, near Porlock, which acted as dormitory, kitchen and laboratory. We concentrated on the marine ecology of the Bristol Channel and terrestrial habitats such as the combes and moors of Exmoor. The trip was planned to include the particularly good spring-tide period when large areas of excellent rock pools were exposed. One of the more exciting finds was an octopus stranded in one of the pools. On being cautiously prodded it alternately blanched and blushed, a reflection perhaps of the feelings of the one who attempted to pick it up! However, a shirt sacrificed for the occasion was manoeuvred under it and the octopus was brought back in triumph to the laboratory for study.

Another opportunity came the following year when a new Field Studies Centre was opened at Dale Fort in Pembrokeshire. The marine biology here was varied and very different from that of the Bristol Channel and we had an excellent time with a keen group of boys, some of whom had been with me at Luccombe the previous year. It was there that I first met John Barrett who was warden then.

One of the best trips we made from there was to Skokholm Island which was being developed as a centre for research. The only way to get there was from Milford Haven where a coastal boat could be hired for the day. It was quite a distance, but as long as the weather was calm it was a most interesting experience as you saw to advantage the rugged coast-line of cliffs and bays and could look out for various species of sea bird, including shearwaters, skimming over the waves.

On arrival, we were met by the warden and taken to the research head-quarters which used to be the house where Ronald Lockley lived when he was resident on the island. We were shown the main sea-bird colonies and the area where Manx shearwaters nested in rabbit burrows. One bird was under special observation, an artificial roof having been put over its burrow; we were able to see the bird sitting on its single egg in its underground nest. Mist-netting was also in progress as it was the migration season, so we got a good idea of the ringing technique used - all good experience for our party of budding biologists.

We had arranged with the boatman to pick us up in the late afternoon at the landing stage, but he had told us that if the wind got up he would be unable to stay there, and would take the boat to the other side of the island which was more sheltered from south-westerlies. We had been so interested in all that was going on that we had not realised just how strong the wind had become when it was time to leave. On reaching the landing place no boat was there which meant trekking to the other side of the island. The boatman was waiting for us impatiently as a storm was imminent. As it turned out, it was quite difficult to get on board as the dinghy was rocking about and we had to jump from the rocks. It was an extremely rough journey back and the boat seemed very small amid the huge waves. When in a trough we could see no land; on a crest we saw white horses all around us. The boatman uttered no word; there was grim determination on his face as he grasped the wheel so tightly that his knuckles showed white. He was not the only one to be glad when we reached the shelter of Milford Haven.

When I joined the staff at Taunton, biology was merely looked upon as a sixth-form subject for those going in for medicine and allied careers. At my interview I had made it clear that I was not interested in the post unless the subject could be developed. It was my conviction that biology should be an essential part of the curiculum for everybody and that the syllabus should be widened to become a truly educational subject in the best sense of that word. The headmaster had agreed that this would be a great step forward and gave me the go-ahead to plan this. I soon found that the Head of Science, Jack Finney, was in full agreement and was already planning to expand the role of science in the school, so with the Head of Chemistry, the three of us worked out a scheme. This entailed bringing in general science for the most junior forms and all three sciences up to school certificate for the subsequent streams. Most boys would take general science and possibly additional general science in their certificates, but there would be a faster, specialised form which was given more periods and would take all three sciences separately.

At present I was the only biologist on the staff, so it was essential to appoint another man to help with the extra work when the scheme was adopted. This happened with commendable speed, and in September, Bill Snee joined us to help with the biology. At this time there was only one biology laboratory, so some work had to be done in other science lecture rooms and laboratories. It was clear that this arrangement was far from satisfactory and some time in the future more laboratories would have to be built, but for the time being, improvisation had to be the name of the game.

Bill Snee was a keen naturalist and a kindred spirit; it was good to have his help in the department. On one occasion we decided to go on a mothing expedition to the Shapwick area. It was an excellent night and the moths came to the light very readily. There were many species I had not seen at Rendcomb, some being associated with wetter habitats. Returning after midnight, there was no traffic about, and rounding a bend just outside Taunton I saw a large object lying half across the road. There was no chance of braking so I swerved to the other side, just managing to avoid contact. Stopping the car and investigating, we found a man sprawled across the road with his head towards the centre. He was dead drunk and out for the count. There was little we could do except drag him to the side out of harm's way and leave him to sleep it off. He probably never knew how fortunate he was to be still alive.

The winter of 1946/7 was a very severe one. We had just moved in to Bishop's Mead and it was very difficult to keep the flat with its very large rooms warm enough. Extra fire-wood was obtained from the Quantocks with the help of a Rendcomb boy who was staying with us. I had had an S.O.S. from Denis Lee Browne asking if I would put him up for a few weeks and give him some coaching while he was working for an open scholarship to Cambridge. Apparently, Denis had lost faith in my successor who was only kept on for a year, and having taught him previously, he thought I might be able to help. It was an odd arrangement as he worked during the day when I was at school and I helped him when I had time, mainly in the evenings. However, the arrangement was successful and he got his scholarship.

The January term started with the heaviest snow storms I can remember with $5\frac{1}{2}$m drifts on the Blackdown Hills and the sunken lanes, going up the combes in the Quantocks, completely filled with snow. I wanted to find out what the badgers were doing under such conditions, but the snow lay thick for weeks and it was not possible to get there until later in the term. I made the attempt on one occasion, hoping to get a photograph of badgers in the snow. I took a blanket and hot-water bottle and settled down with camera at the ready. After a couple of hours, I was so cold I gave up. I thought I could re-trace my path back to the car in the darkness, but I was mistaken; I ended up in a deep snow drift and only extricated myself with difficulty.

When the snow eventually melted, the bodies of several badgers were found not far from the main setts in the Blackdowns. Presumably they had gone out and become entombed in drifts, or perhaps were unable to find their way back because their scent trails had been eliminated by the snow.

The summer that followed was a remarkable one. It started with fine weather with south-easterly winds which brought migrant butterflies from the Continent in numbers, and the hot weather that followed allowed successful breeding to take place over here. Consequently, by August, clouded yellows and painted ladies were common in many parts of the country including the Taunton area. By this time, Mother and Dad had moved to Walmer, on the outskirts of Deal, from Boxmoor, Dad having taken over the pastorate of Walmer Baptist church. We all went down there for a holiday, and it was great fun to have Dad with us as we made the rounds of the clover and lucerne fields in the Deal area. It brought back many memories.

Nowhere could have been better for the migrant butterflies. Clouded yellows were all over the place; you even saw them in the town gardens and on the sea front, but it was the pale clouded yellows that we hoped to see. We were not disappointed and I was able to learn quite a lot about them. They were not easy to find as they flew much less than the commoner clouded yellows. The best places to look were lucerne fields from which a hay crop had already been taken, or fields which had been harvested for wheat, but coming up between the stubble were lucerne plants for next year. The females chose these young plants for egg-laying.

It was said that this species was difficult to rear in this country as they hibernated during the winter in the caterpillar stage and were susceptible to cold. I found a female which had just mated so I thought I would have a try. I potted up some young lucerne plants and about a hundred eggs were laid, but many were infertile and only about forty hatched. The young larvae ate the cuticle of the leaf and lay motionless during the day along the mid-rib. They went off their food during October and from then until February were quite motionless. I kept the larvae during the winter in an unheated attic and although the temperature dropped below freezing on several occasions they survived, and I concluded that damp was a more important adverse factor than a low temperature. The caterpillars started to feed again in mid-February and pupated in early April. One, which formed its chrysalis among the stems of the lucerne was particularly interesting as the caterpillar, just before pupation, had made numerous silk threads about half an inch from its body, giving the impression of a loose cocoon - a possibly beneficial anti-predator device if it became widespread in the population. The butterflies all hatched out between 26 and 30 April.

That winter I had read about a 'new' pale clouded yellow species, *Colias australis*, which closely resembled the commoner species in the adult stage but had a distinctive caterpillar. Some specimens had been recognised for the first time in Britain the previous summer, having come over with the commoner species. Looking through the specimens I had collected at Deal, I was delighted to find three which undoubtedly belonged to this species.

Since coming to Taunton I had been writing up my experiences with badgers in book form. I had sent a few specimen chapters to Collins, who at that time were publishing the first of their New Naturalist volumes. Julian Huxley replied in a very encouraging way and passed on chapters to James Fisher, who was another of the editors. He was most enthusiastic and planned to make it the first of the monographs in the New Naturalist series.

One of the features of the series was the use of colour photographs. Eric Hosking, who was photographic editor, was keen for me to get a colour picture of a badger for the frontispiece. Nobody had taken a flash-light picture in colour of a wild badger at night, so this was quite a challenge. Colour film was difficult to obtain in this country, but he said he could supply me with several pieces of cut film which I could use in plate holders.

By this time I had got to know several badger setts quite well, and in March 1947 I made my first attempt. The exposure was largely guess-work, but I got a picture which I hopefully sent up to Eric. He had to send it to America for processing, but when it eventually came back we were very disappointed to find that it was greatly under-exposed. We discussed what exposure would be necessary. Eric suggested getting nearer by a metre and using two bulbs instead of one. That was all very well, but I had taken the last one from 3^1/$_2$m and getting much nearer without being detected would be a gamble. However, it was worth trying, so I made my preparations. That night no badger emerged from the hole I had chosen and I thought my luck was out, but then an adult sow came along the path from another part of the sett and just as it reached the hole on which I had focused, it caught my scent and paused. Perfect! There was a blinding flash and the badger shot down the entrance. I knew there would not be another chance that night after the fright I had given her, but I was hopeful that all had gone well. When the film came back from America, I was elated as the exposure was correct and the badger in excellent focus. The book could now go ahead.

Having collected all the badger data for the book, I thought I might as well submit a revised version to London University for a Master of Science degree as I had previously registered with that end in view. When I was called up for interview at University College, I found that Professor Watson was the resident examiner and Professor Bramble the external one. I had little idea how the viva would be conducted and attended with some trepidation, but I was immediately put at ease when Professor Watson shook me by the hand and said that before the questioning started he wanted to say how much he had enjoyed reading my thesis. In fact, few questions were asked, and the main topic of discussion was how I should continue the study, and what practical steps I needed to take towards an eventual doctorate. This had not entered my head and I was somewhat dismayed at the thought of more work in my spare time for the foreseeable future. However, I said I would consider the proposition and see how things went. Anyway it was encouraging to be told that I had gained my M.Sc.

Meanwhile, badger research had to be put on the back burner as there was much else to do. I had found that after moving to Taunton, it was increasingly difficult to make two ends meet as the cost of living was much greater than at Rendcomb, so I had always to be on the look out for methods of adding to my income. This was my main reason for getting involved with the Workers Education Association which ran courses organised by the Extra-mural Department of Bristol University. I started with a general set of lectures on natural history, and this led to a three year University course. This took place weekly at the Taunton Library. I enjoyed the work, although I found the lectures rather a tie during term time, and being in the evenings, were sometimes more than I wanted after a full day's work.

During my first course there was an occasion when I could not attend as I had caught mumps from the children. Betty nobly stood in for me. The talk was on protective resemblance - a lecture she had heard me give before, so we went over it together and assembled the necessary slides.

Tragedy struck when the lantern was found to have the condenser missing and no visual aid was possible. However, the class was sympathetic and she coped very well in spite of this considerable handicap.

I had joined Albemarle Baptist Church when we moved to Taunton and had been elected a deacon. Being non-resident at Taunton School, I had Sundays mainly free, so could attend regularly with the family, although occasionally I would be asked to give the address at the school chapel. When the minister of the church left there was quite a gap before another was appointed and I was asked to be chairman of the deacons' meetings which organised the work of the church. Among other things, I became editor of the church magazine and took services from time to time. It was a considerable relief when a new minister was appointed.

At school, I was not expected to help much with games, which I was glad about, but I missed playing them regularly myself. Fortunately there were three members of staff who were good tennis players and I was able to fit in some most enjoyable doubles with them. I also played each year in the staff match against the Ist XI at cricket. Although I was much out of practice I found playing on the school square easier than on the more lively wickets we had at Rendcomb, so I found this annual fixture rather fun.

Term time was very busy for both of us. My days were very full and the task of running the home and looking after all of us fell on Betty. With so many things still being rationed, much careful planning had to be done; clothing had to be made to last as long as possible with careful mending and shoes and garments were passed on from one son to another when they grew out of them. Betty knew a lot about diet and was very concerned to bring up her family according to her understanding of what was best for them. This was not easy with a restricted budget, but she coped amazingly well. We were both glad to have the long holidays which gave me a welcome break from routine and provided more opportunities to spend time with the family, have holidays together and visit our parents.

The post-war years enabled us to strengthen links with other members of the family. Bids had changed her job and was employed by Somerset County Council as a psychiatric social worker. She was part of a team involved with difficult children and worked closely with Dr Rae Hodge who was a neurologist with training in psychiatry. Bids was living in Taunton, so we saw much more of her. Our children were very fond of Bids and she was a great help to all of us.

Marge had returned from India in 1946. She had married Brooke Edwards whilst out there, and at that time their son, John, was about

Family, on the occasion of my parents' Golden Wedding, 1950.
Standing: Margaret(Marge), Bill (William Keith), Bids (Grace), Self and Betty.
Sitting: John (Marge' son), Dad, Mother, Keith

four. Brooke was an American. As a young man he had joined the Allied airforce in the First World War and piloted one of the first planes to take part in it. At 19 he was awarded the Croix de Guerre for his courage in those early air battles. He had been working for many years in India with Baldwin's Locomotive Company which was much concerned with the Indian State Railway system. He was a superb tennis player and secretary of the All India Tennis Club based in Calcutta. He was elected non-playing captain of the Indian Davis Cup team in spite of his nationality. He played at Wimbledon before the war in the Veterans Class and did particularly well in the men's doubles. It was after one of these events that he gave me a couple of rackets which he had only used a few times. They were quite strange to play with as their tension was so much greater than anything I had used before. The Davis Cup took him to a variety of countries and when in Egypt, Marge was able to accompany him and have a holiday at the same time *en route* for England.

Marge had had a very distinguished career in India, ending up in charge of the Dufferin Women's Hospital in Calcutta. On her return to England in 1946 she settled in Hove as a consultant gynaecologist. She had spent nearly twenty years in India. It was good having her in the country again as we had seen so little of each other recently and she hardly knew our family. There were now opportunities for visits and she could see more of Mother and Dad. We had not been entirely out of touch as we kept up a regular correspondence and she had spent various leaves in England, but she always had much to do during these visits. On one of her earlier trips she had taken the opportunity to take her

M.D. to add to her professional qualifications.

We were also able to see more of Bill. After the war, large properties were remarkably cheap and after much deliberation he had bought Bishopstrow House on the outskirts of Warminster. This was a splendid country house with extensive grounds. He wanted something large to display to advantage his growing gun collection and to entertain visitors, many of whom came from abroad to see his collection. By this time he had built up a thriving business buying and selling old firearms and other antiques. This involved frequent trips to European countries on the trail of private collections, going to sales and visiting America where he sold many pieces to collectors. His policy was to buy up anything worthwhile, keep the best for his own collection and sell the remainder.

He would usually invite us to spend Christmas at Warminster with him and his wife, Jane, and their daughter, Diana, who was about David's age, so it was good for the cousins to meet. Bill was very fond of children and always made these visits great fun for our boys. It was certainly a very different experience for them, living for a while in a gracious house with plenty of good cheer and being surrounded by guns !

My badger book came out in the late autumn of 1948; I was amazed at the interest it caused. Being the first of the monographs, Collins gave it excellent publicity and this resulted in encouraging reviews in the national press and many magazines. I was particularly pleased with one in The Sunday Times by Dr Canon Raven who was then Vice Chancellor of Cambridge University. I had always admired his attitude towards a synthesis between science and religion and his review started me off on a most interesting correspondence with him. There was also an amusing review in Punch with the title 'Brock's Benefit'.The book somehow captured the imagination of the public and although the first edition was 11,000 it was not very long before a reprint became necessary. I was extremely surprised.

Looking back on the success of this book, I realise now what a signifi-cant factor it was regarding my future. Some of these repercussions I will refer to later in a different context. Meanwhile, within a week or so I was invited to write articles for various magazines and received a very considerable correspondence. I remember one from the Chief Rabbi who told me that the translation from the Bible I had quoted about the ark of the covenant being covered by the skins of badgers dyed red, was incor-rect; it should have been the skins of dolphins or porpoises! However, what pleased me most was that the book started many people watching the animals for themselves and I received many letters later telling me of their own experiences. In this way I was able to build up a wide circle of interested people, some of whom continue to write to me even now. However, answering some of the early letters fell on Betty, because I was taken ill in January 1949.

I had been having a recurrence of duodenal trouble, had suddenly felt very ill and the doctor was called. He thought I might be suffering from internal bleeding due to ulceration and I was sent to hospital in an ambulance. On arrival at Bridgwater Hospital they gave me atropine for the bleeding and this made me feel much worse. The next day Rae Hodge came to see me. He at once noticed that the pupils of my eyes were dilated and it was obvious that I was suffering from atropine poisoning. Apparently the atropine in the medicine I had been taking over a long period had built up to danger levels. Unfortunately, unlike most people, I was unable to excrete it.

Having spent the next few days recovering from this poisoning, it was decided that I should have a partial gastrectomy operation to solve the duodenal problem. Appropriate drugs had not been discovered at that time. Marge had been kept informed about things and been in touch with the surgeon. He invited her to be in the theatre when he did the operation, so she was able to know me both inside and out!

Recovering from such a major operation took time, so I was away from school until half-term and during the second half only taught part-time. My convalescence was greatly helped by the book reviews which kept appearing and the interesting correspondence; then, during the Easter holidays we all went to Deal with Mother and Dad which completed my recovery.

Back at work again, I realised more and more that there was a great need to develop the academic side of the school. Jack Finney had left in the summer of 1948 and I had become Head of Science. I was glad of this extra responsibility as it gave me the chance to further the development of biology throughout the school and gave me more say in curriculum development. I had also been very dissatisfied with the zoology syllabus of the Oxford Examination Board as it was so archaic, and asked if they would examine our entrants on a syllabus I had devised. I sent this up for their comments. They replied to the effect that they were considering altering their syllabus anyway and would I help? This meant a number of trips to Oxford, but as they used my draft as a basis for the new one, I was glad to take part. This syllabus was used until 1967.

I continued to take the keen boys on field trips, but finding time was difficult as I had been asked to become assistant housemaster to the junior day boys' house. This was difficult to refuse as most staff were expected to do something outside their teaching, but the job was rather frustrating as I had no real responsibility within the house and it involved looking after a lot of junior games at times when I felt I could be more profitably employed doing other things. However, somebody had to do these things and it was no use grumbling about taking my turn, but it did make field work difficult to arrange.

Ecological work was now at last an important element in the syllabus as most of my sixth-formers were taking botany and zoology as separate subjects along with chemistry and sometimes physics as well. I preferred this as it was a better preparation for open scholarships to Oxbridge. Fortunately, I was able to get permission to work at Thurlbear, an area of ancient woodland owned by Crown Lands, so whenever I could, I took a few of the keen boys who were not playing games to do projects there. This work went on for several years and ended in a book for schools, 'Woodland Ecology' which was published by Heinemann in 1953. One of the keenest boys to work on this project was John Ryland. He obtained an open scholarship to Cambridge where he got a first class honours degree and is at present, Professor of Zoology at Swansea.

Another opportunity for field work came during the summer term. There was an unusually long gap between the higher certificate theory and practical papers and my sixth-formers were at a loose end, so I got permission to take them to Lundy Island for six days. We sailed from Appledore in a converted North Sea drifter which, having no ballast, rolled like a drunken sailor. Once we had crossed the bar at the mouth of the river the sea roughened considerably and so much water was shipped that we all got soaked. I found an old chair and wedged myself with my back to the bridge and my feet on the gunwale; this allowed the water that poured on board to flow beneath me, and out at the runnels. It seemed a brilliant idea until a wave hit us amidships and broke on top of me. I had never felt so wet before. The boys had the last laugh, but were not in much better shape themselves. When we arrived at Lundy we anchored in a sheltered bay and got to shore in a small boat during a driving rainstorm; this in no way increased our wetness but helped to wash out some of the salt from our clothes. The Old Lighthouse, which was to be our home for the trip, was a welcome relief from the elements and we were at last able to strip off our soaking clothes and get warm in front of a drift-wood fire.

Meat was still rationed at that time, so we were surprised and delighted to hear that we could buy as much beef as we liked if we asked at the Marisco Arms which occasionally put up visitors. On enquiry we were shown a large carcass hanging in one of the out-houses from which we could cut off what we wanted! Apparently it was customary for a farmer to bring stock from the mainland for fattening. When he came to collect them again, this animal was so wild it could not be caught. Sometime after the farmer left, it had been stalked by one of the residents and shot, providing an abundance of meat for all.

Our visit was a wonderful opportunity to explore the island and see something of its wildlife. The boys had varying interests, botanical and zoological, and each made notes about his observations which were later incorporated in a general report for the School Natural History magazine. It was interesting to watch a family of peregrines on the cliffs; the young could fly, but they were still keeping to the area where they had nested. Seals were observed from close quarters by stalking them as they basked on the rocks, and we discovered to our surprise a small herd of sika deer. Seabirds were much in evidence although most of them had finished nesting, but puffins were still around their burrows at the far end of the island.

One of the most fascinating experiences was a night visit to the area where Manx shearwaters were nesting in their underground burrows. By day, nothing could be seen except the burrows. On arrival, nothing happened for some time and we thought we were going to be disappointed, but then the adults started to come in from the sea to feed their young. Soon, dozens were wheeling around our heads making their weird cries. You could just make them out in the darkness silhouetted against the lighter sky. It was a strange experience to be surrounded by these half-seen birds as they wheeled and dived towards their burrows.

On my return from the island, I was surprised to receive an invitation to give an open lecture on badgers to the British Association for the Advancement of Science at their annual conference in Birmingham. This was quite an awesome occasion as I had never before addressed such an academic audience. Betty was ill at the time so I could only go for the day, travelling by train from Taunton. The meeting took place in the Great Hall of the University, a most unsuitable venue as it was enormous, with such a large stage that the screen was a long way from the rostrum. If you wished to point anything out on the screen you had to remember to stop talking while making your way across to where there was another microphone. Apparently, no other room of reasonable size was available. In the event, about 150 people turned up; an audience that looked absurd in a hall that held several thousand. However, the talk had interesting repercussions.

The invitation to lecture had come from the general secretary of Section D (Zoology), Professor Humphrey Hewer. He had made some excellent nature films with Julian Huxley, and after the lecture, asked me what the chances were of filming badgers? Filming wild mammals at night by habituating them to light had never been attempted before as far as we knew, but it was well known that given time, some nocturnal mammals would tolerate light to some extent. Whether badgers would accept the very bright light needed for filming was anybody's guess. We decided to make the attempt.

The first thing to choose was the location. Humphrey and I lived 150 miles apart; we needed a place which was free from interference and near a mains supply of electricity. If possible, the sett should be among trees to support the overhead lights and be sufficiently open to give good views of the animals. Rather a tall order! Then I remembered that Bill had badgers in the grounds of Bishopstrow House, ideal in every way and roughly half way between our two homes. I rang him up and he was most enthusiastic and helpful. This was marvellous as he was also happy to switch on the lights each night during the long period we thought would be necessary for habituating the badgers.

I made a survey just after Christmas and found there were many badger holes in the wood at the back of Bishopstrow, mainly dug into an ancient long-barrow, but new signs of bedding outside one group of holes in a different area suggested that breeding was likely to take place there. Although there were many alternatives the badgers could use if they disliked the lights, I thought the sow would be unlikely to move very small cubs when the lights first came on, and when older, would be sufficiently habituated not to want to do so.

We calculated that four 1,000-watt bulbs about 3 metres feet above the ground would be needed for the main light source with supplementary 500-watt bulbs for certain areas. Even with this apparently dazzling light the fastest possible film available at that time would be needed to give sufficient depth of focus. It was a scramble to get the apparatus made in time. Aluminium bowls from Woolworths were adapted as lamp holders and thoroughly water-proofed, and in one hectic week at the beginning of March we installed the overhead supporting wires, lamps and fuse-box and ran the cable back to the house. The idea was to put 25-watt bulbs in for the first few weeks, change them for 60-watt and by early April use 200-watt. Bill said he would switch on just before dusk each night and leave them on for a couple of hours.

As luck would have it, I caught a bad cold which turned into pneu-monia and I was rushed into hospital as penicillin was not helping, but thanks to the pathologist, a newly-developed antibiotic was tried and that worked wonders. After a week's recuperation at Hove under

Marge's care, Bill invited Betty and me to spend a week in Paris at his expense to complete the cure. We had a wonderful holiday and I was quickly fit again.

Incidentally, this attack of pneumonia might also have affected our future. Out of the blue, I received a letter from the Headmaster of Winchester College asking me if I was interested in the job of Head of Biology? He was making the appointment for the following September. This was a very tempting offer as academically it was probably the best school in the country, so I felt I should at least find out more although I had my reservations. He asked me to come for an interview in March, but pneumonia prevented this. He was very sympathetic, but was seeing one other candidate and could not wait more than a week or two. It was impossible for me to attend, so the other man got the post. He happened to be a good friend of mine, Bunny Dowdeswell, who was in charge of biology at Blundell's School. I think he would have been chosen anyway as he was better qualified and an excellent biologist both academically and as a field worker. He was at Winchester for many years and later became Professor of Education at Bath University. In retrospect, I am glad I was not offered the job as I do not think I would have been so happy in such an elite school, not being a traditionalist at heart, and I would not have had the opportunity to be a housemaster and do some of the things I was able to at Taunton.

But to get back to the filming. It was not until late April, just before term started, that Humphrey and I allowed ourselves an inspection of the Warminster badgers. How were they responding to the 200-watt lighting? We waited anxiously, full of hope at first, rather despondent as time passed. Then to our delight there was a striped face at the entrance and we were thrilled to see a boar and sow coming out in light conditions as never before. Every hair, every twitch of the nostrils were visible! However, their behaviour was not normal, they seemed to be doing nothing in particular and soon they went down again. Once more they emerged, but they just sat about. They looked as if they were waiting for something. Were they waiting for the lights to go out, we wondered? If so, they were going to be disappointed because from then on we decided to keep the lights on all night! At this stage we linked up with the lights a small motor which made a whirring sound like that of the camera.

We hoped to start filming at a week-end in mid-May by which time the cubs should be active. So much for our plans. The sow thought differently, and we discovered that she had moved her cubs some 80 metres away to the long-barrow and had excavated about a quarter of a ton of chalk to make their new home comfortable!

How could we get them back again? We decided to wait until they had all left their new home, then block those holes and I would stay near for the remainder of the night so that my scent would cause them to return to the lighted sett. This worked, and the sow and her cubs came back. Today, of course it would be illegal to interfere with a sett in this way without a licence.

All our hopes were now centred on the Saturday night, but that afternoon there was a severe thunderstorm and the rain continued throughout the evening. In desperation we rigged up a large umbrella over the camera and braved the elements. A cub did come out, and we took our first few feet of film, but that was all. We had only one more night before we had to get back to our teaching. It was a fine night, but now it was the wind that was the problem; it had changed right round, and was now behind our one possible filming position. Cubs did come out but they were suspicious and the noise of the camera caused them to shoot back. The night before, the torrential rain had probably obliterated the sound. It was imperative to do something about the noise.

During the next week, Humphrey encased the camera in a box which was heavily blimped to reduce noise and with a plate-glass front, so when we returned on the Friday evening we were full of hope. However, we were not very surprised to see that the badgers had re-opened some of the other holes! Nevertheless, a little shepherding in the pale light of dawn sufficed to ensure that at least four badgers were in the lighted area.

During the following two nights we had considerable success, but only with the cubs. They could still hear the camera, but they got used to it. The lights attracted many insects, including maybugs, which fell into the vegetation below, and on one occasion a cub systematically worked over the sett area foraging for these insects for three-quarters of an hour giving us excellent chances for filming. This was the last week-end we could spare, but when the film was processed we found there was enough good material for an eight-minute film which we were invited to show at a meeting of the Zoological Society in London.

Bill and Jane had been wonderful hosts. We were not exactly ideal guests, being up most of the night and sleeping for part of each day, but we were given every facility. I remember the embarrassment of coming back wearily in the middle of the night to make a hot drink and letting the milk boil over on to the Aga hot plate. The resulting smell seemed to permeate the whole house! However, in spite of all the problems we caused, Bill and Jane could not have been more helpful about everything.

We hoped to film the adults the following spring. More preparations were made to habituate the badgers to light and sound, particularly the latter, as camera noise seemed to be the major problem. Bill once again carried out the routine preparations for us. Unfortunately, the badgers had other ideas and quickly switched to different holes, and although some did return, we got no film at all. To add to the difficulties, my father became seriously ill, so after several abortive week-ends we abandoned the scheme for the year.

It was then that we heard from Major Maxwell Knight about a sett he knew near Camberley which he thought might be suitable. It was only 25 miles from Humphrey's home, the badgers had not been interfered with, and some of them used to feed on scraps from a house nearby.

Our plans were laid afresh. This time we built a raised stand from which to film, and food scraps were put out regularly in the area where we planned to film. The badgers quickly appreciated this addition to their diet, and once the lights were installed, food was only put out when they were switched on. When they had got used to this, we started to habituate them to the sound of the camera. To do this we planned to put food down the entrances and listen for signs of eating, then we would run the camera without film. In this way we hoped the badgers would associate something pleasant with the camera noise. This worked, and when we watched in early April we saw several adults feeding under the 200-watt lamps and they took no notice when we ran the camera. This was very promising, so we hoped when the full 6,000 watts of illumination was turned on they would behave naturally.

The sett had many entrances, and the main problem now was getting them to use the ones in the lighted area. From our observations we deduced that the badgers tolerated the lights, but did not prefer them, so some gentle persuasion was necessary. We decided the best way was to block some of the other entrances with loose vegetation which would not put them completely out of action but would deter them from using them.

It is usually about the middle of April when the sow brings her cubs above ground, so we aimed to make all-night vigils for ten consecutive nights from 18 April. Keith, who was now an experienced badger-watcher, helped with the first three nights and Humphrey and I did the rest. We each did four-hour stints. It was a great success. Towards the end of the spell the badgers were taking no notice of either lights or camera noise and we got some excellent sequences.

I shall never forget the first time the cubs came above ground. I was

Set-up for filming badgers at Camberley, 1954

fortunate to be on camera duty when a small snout appeared at an entrance, quickly followed by another. When these small cubs emerged fully, I was so excited that I went on filming until the 100ft spool ran out! We soon found that there was a third cub in the litter, and after a few nights we saw them regularly; their antics were a delight to watch.

We were unable to return to Camberley until the end of May when we had some extra holiday due to the Coronation, and by this time the cubs were well grown and very playful. It was again rather a battle of wits to keep the badgers under the lights but we were able to get good shots of both sow and cubs and record different aspects of their behaviour. We were even able to do some filming on Coronation night in spite of the local firework display; the badgers paid little attention.

One night there was a fierce fight between two sows when one tres-passed on the territory of the other. Unfortunately we could not film it as the badgers were just outside the lighted area; they made a tremendous din as they bit and snarled at each other. After several minutes, the fight ended when one chased the other out of the area. As it happened, Eric Simms from the BBC was making sound recordings of the badgers and had placed a microphone near where they were scrapping, so he was able to record the whole incident.

We had been amused by the side effects of the continuous lighting. A field mouse had its hole under the lights and became habituated and we were able to film its antics during dull moments when no badgers were about. It was also strange to see bumble-bees visiting the rhododendron flowers all night long and hear a robin singing at 2 o'clock in the morning.

Pressure of work made further filming impossible, but we were well satisfied. Although the film had taken three years to make, working only at week-ends and holidays, we had broken new ground. For the first time, nocturnal wild animals had been filmed by training them to tolerate strong light and an unusual noise and an extremely interesting record had been made of badger behaviour. It had been a rewarding partnership; Humphrey's technical skill and filming expertise had made the whole project possible, and I was able to contribute some knowledge of badger behaviour. We learnt a great deal from each other.

As I mentioned earlier, in the spring of 1952, Dad became seriously ill. He had always appeared so well and had not had a day in bed due to illness since he was a youth, so it was a great shock to us all when he had a severe stroke. He never recovered consciousness and died on the second of May. He was greatly loved and it was so sad for Mother to be left on her own after they had spent 52 years together. Fortunately, all the family were now settled in England, but we were widely scattered. Marge and Bill had bought the house in Walmer for Mother and Dad, so there was no problem there, but Mother's widow's pension was quite inadequate. As usual, Marge helped financially, and Bids found somebody to live in and keep Mother company. From then on, we all visited her whenever possible, and in the summer holidays, Betty and I brought the family to stay for a time. Mother looked forward to these visits enormously. However, she managed wonderfully well in spite of loneliness and poor health. She was never demanding and lived very positively and philosophically.

I missed Dad very much. He had been a splendid father to me and had influenced me greatly, much more by example than by what he said. He was always there when there were things to discuss and he seldom interfered unless there was very good reason. He was always a very private person, and apart from Mother, seldom really opened his heart to any of us about his innermost feelings other than his deep beliefs. His work as a Christian pastor was his life, and all else was secondary. It was typical that he took the services at Walmer as usual on the Sunday before he had the stroke from which he died. His legacy was the gratitude of so many for his understanding, friendship and guidance, and a wife and family united in their love for him and for each other.

Chapter Eight

Becoming a housemaster

It was in 1953 that I was offered the housemastership of Foxcombe at Taunton School. John Wilkins, who had been housemaster for a number of years, was retiring after a distinguished career. I was delighted to accept this post as it brought me in closer contact with the boys and gave me the opportunities and responsibilities I enjoyed. However, I realised this would limit the time for field work which would in future have to be done mainly in the holidays. A housemaster is technically on duty 24 hours a day during term time, but with a good assistant it is always possible to make arrangements for regular times off. I found this was essential as otherwise the school became your world and you lost all sense of perspective. I found that it was a wonderful help to get right away from the school atmosphere, meet adults other than colleagues and pursue my other interests. I was extremely fortunate with my assistants who could be trusted to take responsibility and cope with any eventuality.

Foxcombe was the largest of the junior houses, having 70 boys between the ages of 11 and 14^1/$_2$. It was a boarding house standing in its own grounds and isolated from the other school buildings by a main road. At that time, it could have been said to have been on the edge of the country as school playing fields were out at the back, and these led to farm land. On one occasion, when umpiring a cricket match, seated on a shooting stick at square leg, I could hear a nightingale singing from the copse at the edge of the field. Another year, a pied flycatcher stayed a fortnight in and around our garden before continuing its migration.

Foxcombe did its own catering and employed its own staff of matron, housekeeper, cook, sewing ladies and cleaners. Brian Hastilow, who ran the school cricket, was assistant housemaster when we arrived, but he soon got married, no longer lived in, and John Wright took his place. We were quite a large community and had a considerable degree of autonomy.

We moved from Bishop's Mead in late August after a most enjoyable family holiday at Salcombe. This was our first visit to Salcombe, but by no means our last as it proved to be an ideal place for a holiday and I found the sea-shore flora and fauna so varied and interesting that I later had several biological field courses there. Our boys were in their element as it was their first chance to do much in boats. Our host had a motor-boat and knew the best places for fishing, and we were soon sufficiently proficient to hire our own boat and explore the estuary ourselves. The boys loved it. I even discovered a badger sett on the headland where we could watch the badgers emerge against a backdrop of sea and cliffs and with the cries of gulls in our ears. This was very different from anything I had experienced before.

We looked forward with keen anticipation to the new term. Before it started we were able to get to know the staff. Betty was now able to play a significant role within the school, keeping an eye on the staff, seeing that the domestic side ran smoothly, welcoming parents when they brought their sons back and giving hospitality to staff and boys. She also provided that indefinable quality of caring that helped to maintain a happy and secure feeling of home for me and our boys. The catering side alone was a headache, as some rationing was still in force and although there was a housekeeper, it was necessary to see that the boys had a healthy diet within the rigid financial limits imposed by the bursar, no easy matter as Betty had advanced views on what was best for the boys, and both bursar and the boys themselves were very conservative in their thinking.

Being in loco parentis to 70 boys was no small responsibility. To deal with such a large and varied family effectively meant that you had to know as much as possible of their backgrounds. Some had parents who were abroad, some came from broken homes and others from single parent families. A few were there because both parents were working, or they had no brothers or sisters and the parents wanted to give them greater companionship. However, the majority just felt that boarding school was the best environment for a teenager in which to grow up.

The first day of term was important for all of us. Those parents who accompanied their sons wanted to make the acquaintance of the new housemaster and his wife, and we were anxious to get to know them. There was never enough time to see everybody on that first day, but priority was always given to those new to the school. The attitudes of the parents towards their sons was always a good clue to what the boys were like, and later on when you got to know some parents quite well you could see only too clearly why the boys had particular problems.

Some parents were very co-operative, looking upon education as a partnership between home and school, others with a sigh of relief made it quite clear that their son was now our responsibility. That was what they were paying for!

All the dormitories were small and it was important to arrange that those new to the house settled down quickly and happily. As one of my main biological interests was animal behaviour, I found it fascinating to see how members of a dormitory soon worked out a sort of hierarchy. The one who became the dominant member of the group was usually the one to watch for any sign of bullying, while the lowest in the peckorder often needed extra attention and understanding. I was glad now of my own experience of loneliness and home-sickness when I first went to Bethany; those memories helped me to understand.

Some of the older boys in the House were quite ready to take responsibility and were given prefect status. We regularly met to discuss House problems and individual boys; usually they responded with common sense and enthusiasm. They were made to feel that we were running the House together, and if somebody was having problems that I did not know about, they would alert me to the situation. Some, of course, were better than others, some had problems of their own, but as a group they were invaluable in fostering a sense of family within the House.

My predecessor had given me excellent tips as to whom I could trust with such responsibilities, and also mentioned a few who were difficult. Discipline in the House had become slack and I knew the first few days would be crucial. There are always a few rogues in every House and one boy in particular had a reputation in Foxcombe for being a thorough nuisance. One story that reached me was, that in the changing room after a game, he suddenly shouted at the top of his voice, "Chaps, I've not been beaten for a fortnight", and picking up a football, kicked it through the window. He then went up to his housemaster's study, knocked on the door, and said, "I'm so sorry, Sir, I've just broken a window".

It was this boy who on my first day was caught climbing high up on Foxcombe roof (fortunately in gym shoes) to the encouragement of excited onlookers. When I called him into my study, he was expecting a caning as a matter of course. I asked him whether he had ever thought why he wanted to show off in front of others? I soon got him talking about his home background and what he did in the holidays. I found he was an only son with little to do and with parents who were too busy all day and showed little interest in him. His main haunt was an amusement arcade where with some dubious companions he spent his considerable amount of pocket money. I gave him the stark choice of war or co-operation, and told him I wanted people like him to take responsibility within the House and show us all what he was worth rather than what an ass he was. He was always a tricky customer, full of roguishness, but with a good sense of humour. As time went on, there was a gradual change in attitude, and we developed a good rapport. The real problem was not the boy, but his parents!

When you take up a new job you tend to be idealistic with clear ideas about objectives and procedures. In reality, you learn by your mistakes and successes and respond to circumstances as they arise. However, I found it essential to keep basic principles and aims constantly in mind, otherwise I got bogged down in the minutiae of a very full job without enough time to think. Why was I doing this job anyway? What was education really about?

In some ways the responsibilities were frightening. You were expected to know each boy well; sometimes you got to know them even better than their parents, especially when they lived abroad. You had to be readily available to them as foster parent, padre, schoolmaster, careers adviser, interrogator, or Justice of the Peace as the occasion demanded. You had to be an expert in human nature and be trusted by everybody and seen to be fair. In other words you were expected to be superhuman, so of course you fell far short of what was needed and at times failed altogether. However, you learnt that failure can have useful consequences so long as you were willing to admit to the boys when you had been wrong or made mistakes in judgement. This helped to give them the feeling that you were a fellow human being, not just a schoolmaster, still learning how to live, still failing like everybody else. However, humility was not my strong point and I found the principle hard to live up to!

One thing of enormous benefit to me as a Housemaster was that I had three sons of my own, two of them just having been through the typical experiences of boys in the age range within the house and one of comparable age. Without them knowing it, they had helped me to understand the feelings and needs associated with that stage of growing up and reminded me of my own emotions, desires and frustrations when I was their age. At the time I did not realise this, but with hind-sight I'm sure it was of the greatest importance. It helped to bridge the age gap which can be such a hindrance to mutual understanding

Basically, I felt that a House was a laboratory for learning how to live together, and that everybody concerned from housemaster to the youngest boy should understand that that was why they were there. In the biological sense a House was a community within the larger ecosystem of the school, a testing ground where each boy could discover his unique niche within the confines of a small community and so become responsible eventually for taking his place in the larger world outside. All fine in theory, but when faced during an assembly with such a motley gang, showing such varying abilities and interests and coming from such varied backgrounds, you knew that theory and practice were poles apart. The comforting thought was that in reality the boys were bringing each other up; it was their inter-relationships which mattered most and it was for you to try and provide the right environment for their development and help them to see themselves as they were and also give them the vision of what they could be. One of the fascinating aspects of the job was that you were dealing with boys covering the puberty period; they arrived as youngsters and left as young men, and you could watch them develop and establish their individual identities.

One of the things I wanted to establish within the House was trust. Each boy had his own locker in the prep room in which he kept his few personal things. His locker and his desk were sacrosanct; they were essential symbols of individuality, and his territorial instinct was to defend them as private and precious, so lockers were kept locked. Within a House containing such a variety of boys, you are very fortunate if there is no petty thieving from time to time. The problem was discussed during assembly and I made the suggestion that perhaps it might be a good idea to trust people more and leave lockers unlocked. I asked them to think about it. It was unanimously agreed to give it a try, and padlocks were removed. Of course, there were occasional problems, but on the whole it worked well and the boys soon took it for granted.

One term, mistrust took hold because money was being stolen from clothing left in the changing room during games. It occurred on several occasions and created a lot of bad feeling. Boys started blaming particular people whom they suspected might be the culprits, and the whole atmosphere within the House changed. Somehow I had to find out who was doing it. I discussed the matter with the prefects and devised a plan involving marking coins with invisible ink and leaving them in pockets in the changing room. I soon discovered who was doing it and we had a talk. I gave him the chance to admit that he was the culprit, but he repeatedly denied it as he thought he would be expelled. Eventually, when I presented him with the evidence he broke down and admitted that he had been stealing regularly. He was extremely frightened, particularly about what his father would say and do as he was very strict and a pillar of his local community. I tried to show him how his action had poisoned the atmosphere within the House, let down his parents and himself, and destroyed the trust that was slowly being built up within the House. I gave him a few hours to decide what he thought he should do to restore that trust.

When he saw me again, he told me what he thought he should do. He had decided to write to his parents, tell them all about it without making excuses, and apologise for letting them down. He also said he would like to apologise to the House if I would give him the chance, and restore the money to the people he had robbed. I said he could make a statement at House assembly that evening. This he did with enormous courage. He stood up in front of everybody, asked their forgiveness and left the room. I then told the House how much I admired his courage, and asked how many of us had at one time or another stolen something and not been caught? I did not have to say anything more, but I knew the battle had been won and the boy would be accepted back into the community without further recriminations.

The next night I had a telephone call from his father who was furious and devastated by his son's letter. He told me he would come down at once to take him away. I told him that was unnecessary, but he said that he was so ashamed of his son that expulsion was the only answer and his son could then make a new start somewhere else. I told him I had not the slightest intention of expelling him and that I thought he would come through all right. However, he insisted on coming.

When I saw him, he was still angry and determined that he should take the boy away. He said that his son had ruined the family reputation and should be sent to another school where his story was not known. I told him of his son's courage in apologising to the House and their response, and asked him whether he was really considering his son's future or his own personal reputation? He did not like that as it was too near the mark, but agreed to see his son on his own. He was a different person when he came back, and the boy stayed on. I don't know what was said, but I believe it was the start of a new relationship between the boy and his father. A few years later he left school as a person of integrity who commanded trust and respect.

If only all problems would end as happily! Unfortunately, the opposite so often occurs, and you are left with a sense of failure and despondency, but in most instances you never know whether anything constructive has come out of an incident. It is just a case of plugging on and maintaining your faith in human nature even when common sense tells you it is a waste of time. To me that is what housemastering is all about.

Another instance of thieving was very different. Boys had complained to the housekeeper that food was regularly stolen from cupboards in the dining-room where boys kept their extras. Boys did not appear to be responsible and strong suspicion fell on one of the cleaning ladies who came each day. It was difficult to prove without searching their bags when they left, and this would be very embarrassing, so I thought I would try a different technique. I placed a notice in each of the cupboards which read 'Stop stealing'. The stealing stopped!

But thankfully, housemastering is not all problems. There are many things which create togetherness and are enjoyed by everybody. It used to be a tradition that Foxcombe had a bonfire and fireworks on Guy Fawkes night, the evening ending with hot-dogs around the glowing embers and a very popular sing-song led by John Wright. There was also a House party at the end of the Christmas term which, apart from the food which was much appreciated, gave scope for a series of comic sketches which the boys performed with varying degrees of success. But it was probably the many inter-house competitions that engendered most enthusiasm and sense of community. However, not all boys were good at sport, and one of the most difficult things was to discover alternative interests which could be encouraged so that nobody felt left out. Fortunately, there were school activities such as music and drama and many societies which catered for a variety of interests; boys were encouraged as much as possible to take part in these.

It is also the housemaster who is best able to monitor how a boy's work is going in the context of all his other activities. Fortnightly assessments by the form masters were passed on, and this provided a good means of seeing each boy for a few minutes individually. It was often on these occasions that you were able to get him talking about some of the problems he would otherwise have kept bottled up. Once you had got his confidence and he knew you tried to be impartial and would listen, there was a chance of being of some help. This applied particularly if he was worried for any reason about parental quarrels or illnesses; things he would not talk about to his friends.

Betty enjoyed taking part in House activities, but with family responsibilities as well, she carried a heavy load. She had done so much in the aftermath of my operation and our growing family was a full-time occupation in itself. To add to the burden, during our second year in Foxcombe, she was not at all fit, and the upshot was a major operation. At Marge's suggestion this took place in Bristol as she knew the good reputation of the surgeon there, but in retrospect it would have been easier for all concerned if she had gone to Taunton. The operation was successful, but conditions were far from ideal. I was able to visit in the evenings or at week-ends, but she was very glad when she was fit enough to be home again.

The seven years I spent at Foxcombe were fruitful ones in many other ways. As Head of Science there was a lot to do. The chief project was the building of an extension to the science block. With biology being taken by nearly everybody from 11 until O-level it was essential to provide adequate laboratory space. A limited number of industrial grants were made available to schools in order to give a much-needed boost to science education in the country. The headmaster was pleased to apply for one of these and the project was approved. The plan was to build a large, two-storey wing at the back of the existing science building which would be connected to it by a bridge. It would be used for biology and contain the science library which sixth-formers could use during free periods. The whole of the original building was to be brought up to date and the upper floor devoted to chemistry except for the art room and a small common room for science staff. The lower floor would be used exclusively for physics including a workshop and storage room for the head technician - a great character who had been with the school for many years, knew just what was needed and understood the various idiosyncrasies of the teaching staff. He was invaluable to me and became a good friend.

In the biology block there would be two large laboratories, one mainly for the sixth and specialised senior forms, and the other for lower forms. Both could double up as lecture rooms. There was also a lecture theatre on the ground floor, well equipped with visual aids which could be used for lessons and society meetings. The bridge linking the two buildings was large enough to act as a small laboratory for third-year sixth-formers and contained more specialised apparatus.

I worked very closely with the architect and was able to tell him exactly what I wanted from a functional point of view and he drew out the plans and made them architecturally attractive and sound. As always, the chief check on ideas and materials was financial as the school had to contribute towards the cost. It was opened in 1957. To have biology so well catered for in the school was a matter of great satisfaction to me.

I had previously thought out the curriculum in biology for the five years to O-level. The strategy was to start the 11-year olds with simple human anatomy and physiology so that they understood all the body systems, what purposes they served and roughly how they worked. This brought in sex education without giving it special status and before they reached puberty. It also gave a chance to give them a few basic ideas about health and hygiene, which led on to a practical study of bacteria and some of the lives of the scientists who made discoveries about them.

Most boys found the second year was great fun as we covered the whole of the animal and plant kingdoms, with many opportunities to examine living examples and study their behaviour. Each boy had a good quality notebook and was given the chance to illustrate it in any way he wished so long as the pictures were relevant to the group of animals or plants being studied and adequate notes made about them. They enjoyed doing this, and by the end of the year, some boys had produced volumes which were not only a pleasure to look through, but represented a considerable knowledge of general natural history. At 12-13, animals appeal to the majority, and it is not difficult to quicken enthusiasm and a sense of wonder and excitement. By having a junior section of the natural history society, keen boys could be encouraged further. Geoffrey Stephens took charge of that. Geoffrey had taken Bill Snee's place as assistant biologist; we got on very well together and he was an invaluable addition to the department.

With this background, most boys had no difficulty in doing the O-level syllabus during the next two or three years, and it was possible to put more into it than the syllabus required, including the application of biology to health, medicine, agriculture and social science. Human anatomy and physiology took the place of the rabbit's, and this again brought in sex education with the emphasis now more on teenage problems, responsibility, the family and the larger community. I looked upon the course as a useful bridge between the sciences and the humanities. It had the further advantage that those who specialised in biological sciences when they reached the sixth form found they had already got a broad base on which to build their more specialised work.

Many years later when the whole philosophy of the Nuffield approach stimulated science teaching so much, I was glad to incorporate some of the excellent ideas and projects from these courses, but I found that using the whole 5-year course only worked really well with the brighter boys, otherwise much time was wasted and the duller ones could not cope. I found a compromise was ideal, using the project-orientated Nuffield scheme in the parts of the syllabus where it was particularly applicable and the more traditional form of teaching for the remainder. This made the course sufficiently flexible for boys of varying intelligence.

I had become involved with the Southern University Joint Board for examinations through the biology panel, as the school had changed its allegiance from the Oxford Board. They asked me to chair a committee to bring the syllabus in biology up to date. The Board felt that it was more realistic to have as chairman a schoolmaster who was actually involved in the teaching of the subject rather than one of the professors of botany or zoology from Exeter and Bristol who were more knowledgeable, but out of touch with schools. Other school teachers from different kinds of schools were also represented. I found it an interesting assignment as it was a good chance to discuss some of the things I had learnt from my experience at Rendcomb and Taunton. It was quite hard to get a consensus as some were steeped in the academic traditions, while I wanted to widen it to include matters of more general educational importance. Fortunately, I was not a lone voice crying in the wilderness and there was a satisfactory outcome.

Following this, I was persuaded to represent the Board on the Schools Council which met periodically in London. I only had to attend sectional meetings which discussed new syllabuses, examination standards and future trends in biology. On the whole I found these meetings very depressing. They contained a number of left-wing theorists with little, if any, classroom experience and who talked most of the time, and an opposing block of die-hard conservative academics. I resigned after a couple of years as I felt I was making no useful contribution. Many years later, I was pleased, and not surprised, when Mrs Thatcher got rid of it altogether as an expensive and unnecessary quango.

I was also invited to become the external examiner in rural biology at Rowle College, Exmouth, a training college for women teachers. I found this an interesting assignment as it showed how the subject could be adapted for a wide range of ages and aptitudes. The teacher in charge of the subject was Alison Brown, who was also doing research on the aquatic life of the rhines of the Somerset Levels. She gave me some useful ideas on what field work we could do at Taunton along similar lines. As a consequence we were able to breed the great silver water beetle, *Hydrophilus piceus*. This can be as long as 45mm and is the largest of all British water beetles. Unlike the more common *Dytiscus marginalis*, it is a vegetarian. We were able to study all the stages in its life history from egg-laying to adult and the various adaptations enabling them to exist in an aquatic environment.

One of the spin-offs from being Head of Science was an invitation by Shell to visit Holland for five days and see what the company was doing. It was, of course, a publicity drive as they wanted to recruit promising scientists. They certainly gave our party of about a dozen a wonderful time, showing us everything from oil wells to refinement plants, and putting on lectures and demonstrations featuring all aspects of the company's work. Hospitality was lavish and they went out of their way to show us the country and give us a good time in between more serious matters. One of the things that greatly impressed me was the Rembrandt Exhibition which was being held in Rotterdam. Rembrandts had been collected from all over the world for this tricentenary celebration and plans were made for us to see it. However, we could only be in Rotterdam on the Sunday when it was discovered that the exhibition was closed. Nevertheless our Shell representative rang up the curator and he was pleased to open it up exclusively for our party, and personally conducted us over it, commenting on the pictures. I cannot imagine such a thing happening for a small party of schoolmasters in any other country however influential Shell might be. We felt very privileged.

Through my work on badgers I had got to know a number of mammalogists who were working on other British species, and as a group, mammals were becoming more popular. Bird societies were flourishing, but there was nothing comparable for mammals. I was very pleased when I had a letter asking if a mammal society were to be formed, would I be interested? I was enthusiastic as I thought it was an excellent way of bringing like-minded professional scientists and amateur naturalists together for discussion and fieldwork. There was remarkably little reliable information known about many of the species at that time, although after the war some zoologists, mainly at the universities, had begun scientific studies to supplement the work hitherto done by amateur naturalists. Thus the time was ripe for such a society, and the Mammal Society of the British Isles (later called The Mammal Society) was formed.

Forty of us forgathered at Birmingham in April 1954 largely due to the initiative of Jo Pickvance who worked for the Extra-mural department of Birmingham University, and plans were drawn up to attract more members and arrange conferences. It was a most enjoyable week-end with talks and field trips; I found myself voted on to Council for the first five years. It was not long before most British biologists working on mammals had become members, including Alastair Worden who became president for the first year, Leo Harrison Matthews who was chairman for many years, Humphrey Hewer who was working on seals, Mick Southern and Ian Linn (small mammals), Peter Crowcroft (shrews), Harry Thompson (rabbits), Ronald Lockley (seals) and Harry Hurrell (pine martens) who was also treasurer. After the first year, Lord Cranbrook, who was an amateur mammalogist of distinction, specialising in bats, became our president. Annual conferences were held at different universities in the early spring and many surveys were started to work out the status and distribution of our native species.

It was not long before some of us, all particularly interested in badgers formed a group within the society to pursue our studies and hold separate meetings. Arising from this, a national badger sett survey was started, and although I felt I was far too busy to act as secretary, I was happy to help initiate it. We hoped to find a recorder for each county who would map as many setts as possible and list the relevant habitat factors for each. I became recorder for Somerset. All recorders tried to enlist the help of naturalists, farmers, foresters etc as it was impossible for one person to cover anything but a very small area. Several members of the school natural history society who were day boys, helped considerably by concentrating on the countryside near their homes. The survey went on for many years and the results were recorded in Mammal Review, the scientific journal of the Society. The work continues and by 1993 over 15,000 setts had been recorded and a great deal of data accumulated about the badgers' habitat preferences and distribution.

It is a matter of great satisfaction to me that badger groups have now been formed all over the country which monitor setts, record behaviour and play a significant part in protecting setts from diggers and unauthorised interference. They are co-ordinated by the National Federation of Badger Groups - a considerable force for conservation.

I always had a great affection for the Mammal Society. The membership, early on at any rate, was fairly small, and you got to know people well; I made many good friends. There was an excellent mix between amateurs and professionals and a pleasant informality about its meetings. A sense of humour permeated its proceedings making it unique amongst scientific societies within my experience; co-operation was the guiding principle. I found it invaluable, as teaching in a school, I had few local contacts with experts in that field. I always attended its conferences whenever possible and later served as chairman for six years and president for five. I felt it a great privilege to participate in this way and watch its development from humble beginnings to a scientific society of international repute with its own scientific journal, regular news letters, a junior section to enthuse and train younger members and above all a focus for mammalian research and a provider of scientific data relevant to the causes of conservation and legislation.

Another consequence of my work on badgers was a number of invitations to lecture in various parts of the country. I had to be rather choosy as travelling took time and I limited them largely to school holidays. When I retired there was more time to devote to such activities. One particularly interesting one was at Queen's University, Belfast in the early days of 'the troubles' when the city centre came in for a lot of violence. Buses had been burned, barricades erected, and a hotel bombed. It was January and I went by plane from Bristol. We stopped at Manchester to take on more passengers and when the twin-engined plane stopped at the end of the run-way before take-off the pilot went through the routine of testing each engine separately. There was black ice on the tarmac and when the first engine was tested the plane swivelled on its axis by 90 degrees and when the second was tried, it swung back again. I was glad when the plane managed to take off without trouble.

At Belfast airport, I was met by my host who took me by a roundabout route to the university to avoid problems and we went in by a side door guarded by two men who were interested in our credentials. There were two lecture theatres in use that evening, one was crammed with an excited crowd of people, the other, which I was going to talk in, was barely half full. Apparently, the other meeting was political and was to be addressed by a well-known member of the IRA who had been smuggled into the country from the Republic. I'm afraid 'badgers' came a poor second for popularity! However, the biological society was pleased to have a speaker from England and I was glad I went.

On another occasion I was invited to talk to some of the inmates of Shepton Mallet prison. I had never been inside a prison before. I was met at reception and taken by a warder along corridors and through a number of doors which had to be unlocked and relocked after us. We eventually arrived at a small room where about twenty men had assembled. I was told they were long-term prisoners who were allowed certain privileges for good behaviour. The warder introduced me and there was another at the back of the room. It seemed to be rather odd talking about badgers and showing them slides under such circumstances. The men seemed interested in the subject and afterwards asked a lot of questions. One man in particular seemed to be very well informed and came up to me later to talk. He told me he had been a gamekeeper and there were badgers on the estate where he had worked.

It was a very different experience speaking to Cambridge University Biological Society where I was bombarded by questions on reproductive biology by people who knew more about the subject than I did and we had some useful discussions about the problems I was investigating. It was quite an experience being entertained at High Table at King's College by my host, Dr Salt, who explained what I had to do when processing to our seats and stand for the long Latin grace. I felt more at ease when I discovered that Dr Salt was an expert on the vegetation of Kilimanjaro, a mountain I had just recently climbed.

I usually found lecturing interesting as there were nearly always people in the audience who were glad to talk of their own experiences of badgers and that helped to broaden my knowledge. I made many friends in that way.

I look back with gratitude to the first talk I was asked to give. It was to the School Scientific Society during my last year as a pupil at Taunton. I had chosen as my subject 'Peculiarities of Natural History' and had collected some slides to illustrate some bizarre examples. My chairman, cleverly made use of my initials when he introduced proceedings by saying the subject was 'Peculiarities of Natural History - e.g.Neal'. It got me off to a good start and taught me that a necessary ingredient of a lecture was a sense of humour.

The black and white stripes on the face are clearly an ingenious form of camouflage

Chapter Nine

Family, Friends and Field work

These seven years at Foxcombe were significant ones for our family. Our boys were growing up fast and widening their interests. It was exciting to see their own particular enthusiasms developing and their futures unfolding. It was also an important time for me as I was at an age when I had to make up my mind if I really wanted to apply for a headship as the likelihood of getting one after 45 was far less. Did I want to remain at Taunton until retirement?

There were good reasons for staying on. I was enjoying the new challenge of being a housemaster, the boys were at critical stages of their schooling and I was far too interested in teaching biology to exchange it for a more lucrative and responsible post as a headmaster with all the administration that that would entail, so I decided not to apply unless something particularly attractive turned up.

I did apply for Dauntsey's School as that appealed more with its agricultural and biological bias, and our boys could have continued at Taunton as boarders, but I was not particularly disappointed when I wasn't appointed. After that, I felt more and more that my future lay in Taunton, and in retrospect I'm glad I did not move; there was too much worth doing where I was and my outside interests were developing rapidly.

When we moved to Foxcombe, Keith was 15, David, 13 and Andrew, 9. They were all at the school, but were members of day boy houses, so other staff had the responsibility of looking after their everyday activities. This was an excellent arrangement as they lived at home, had a degree of freedom, but had opportunities to attend evening functions with the boarders. As I was responsible for arranging teaching schedules for the science staff, I was able to see to it that I did not teach my own sons unless I chose to do so. With other staff it had caused embarrassment, so I wanted to avoid this if possible. Thankfully, there were no problems of significance as all three were popular and respected. I was very happy to teach both Keith and Andrew when they eventually opted for biological sciences in the sixth form and I taught David biology for his school certificate. It was an unwritten rule in our household that we did not discuss other boys and sensitive school issues, and there was an easy relationship between all of us.

Keith from an early age had been extremely interested in natural history, and when we were living at Bishop's Mead had formed a club of keen boys which had its own magazine, library, aquaria and museum, and many field expeditions were organised. David and Andrew also belonged. Keith's right-hand man was Roger Avery who was at Wellington School. Later on, he and Keith did much badger research together and Roger went on to a university career in zoology. They have been friends ever since.

At Bishop's Mead when Keith was 12, he organised a natural history exhibition in some empty rooms to which we had access above our flat. It was set up with great care and enthusiasm by members of the club, and in addition to friends and family, a reporter from the local paper was invited. He was probably surprised to find the event was organised by a group of young boys and amused that he was not exempt from paying the entrance fee of two pence. However, he was proudly shown the exhibits and was sufficiently impressed to write a full column about it in the local paper. The exhibits were certainly impressive, including some interesting specimens provided by an enthusiastic member who had been able to get his father's co- operation; he was the son of the Curator of the Taunton Museum! This club paved the way for more serious natural history projects when we moved to Foxcombe.

Roger Avery was particularly interested in amphibians, and in their early teens, he and Keith did three years of observations on the breeding habits of frogs and toads at Broomfield Lake. They wanted to find out what climatic factors influenced their breeding behaviour. Each year, they noted the dates of arrival of the first frogs and toads, the date of the first spawn, the period over which spawn was plentiful and when the frogs and toads left the water. From these data they were able to calculate the total time both species spent each year in the lake, the main period of spawning and the number of days the animals were in the water before spawning. Each day they measured the maximum and minimum temperature of the air and took the water temperature at approximately the same time each day. They also measured rainfall, humidity and noted general conditions such as cloud cover. This was no mean feat as it meant one or other of them cycling to the Quantocks five miles each way whatever the weather. Their results were sufficiently interesting to be published in the Journal of the Herpetological Society in 1956.

Keith's keenness on badgers spilled over to Roger, and after Keith's experiences at Camberley with the filming in 1953 (p.106), they decided to find out all they could about winter activity. They had watched a sett in the Quantocks on many occasions, and it was here that they planned to make their observations. Only occasional winter watching was feasible, but a lot could be deduced by regularly placing sticks over the entrances and noting whether they had been pushed aside the next day. Signs of bedding having been collected and fresh digging were also noted. They were able to show that during the period October-March, activity showed well-marked phases. Up to mid-November, activity was regular, but gradually tailed off as December approached. The last half of that month showed least activity, but around the New Year the badgers came out every night in spite of snow, and whenever there was a dry spell, more bedding was brought back in preparation for cubbing. The approximate date of birth was calculated from later observations to have taken place during the second half of February.

The badger-watching bug had now really got into their system and they planned much more detailed observations over the next few years to amplify the data already collected. Over a period of four years they visited the sett 1200 times, including more than 400 night watches. Data regarding times of digging, bedding collection, when cubs were first seen above ground, and various behaviour patterns were noted and correlated with weather conditions. This was the first time comprehensive data had been collected over such a long period; I was delighted to be able to make use of this excellent data in my book, 'Badgers', some years later. With so many other things going on, particularly in term time, my own badger work was limited to occasional watches as a relaxation, to take photographs, or, more importantly, to continue with laboratory work on their reproductive cycle. It was wonderful having two such enthusiastic people doing this field work so meticulously.

However, I did carry out one experiment to see how badgers reacted to strangers. At that time, little was known about territorial behaviour, and as I had been given a stuffed badger by the Taunton Museum I thought it would be interesting to see how they reacted to it. On the afternoon of the last day of March I took it up to a sett where I knew there was a sow with young cubs and placed it facing the entrance, about seven feet away.

That evening I arrived in good time. It was a clear, frosty night with a half moon and I could see details clearly from up a tree close to the sett.

An adult boar badger emerged at 8.05pm, looked straight at the stuffed badger and retired below. In a few minutes he came out again, growled menacingly, but did not attack; instead he retired once more. Soon after, he re-emerged, this time backwards, but with his head turned sufficiently to keep the stuffed badger in view. Slowly, he backed away, growling menacingly until he had gone a few metres; then, turning tail, he sped away into the wood. Immediately after, an adult sow emerged, looked at the stuffed one and immediately retired. About twenty minutes later she came out again and slowly, step by step, approached the stuffed badger. When quite near, she darted back a few paces, then approached once more keeping her head low to the ground. This to-ing and fro-ing was repeated for a full 25 minutes, the sow getting no nearer than two feet and never leaving the hole unguarded. Several times I thought she was going to attack, but she never did and eventually retired below ground. After another twenty minutes, she was out again, going through the same routine. I became so sorry for her that at 9.20pm I retrieved the stuffed badger and left her in peace.

I tried again in July when two well-grown cubs emerged first. They saw the stuffed one at once, reared up on their hindlegs and then bolted for home. Later the sow came out, followed by her cubs; she looked at the stuffed one, sniffed at it, made a detour and went off. The boar came out last, and he too avoided the stuffed one, and quickly left the area.

I got the impression that the stuffed one was recognised from a distance as a strange badger, but on nearing it, the smell was not right, or there was a lack of movement, so it was treated as a strange new object, more with fear than aggression. The differences on these two occasions suggested that the sow in particular was much more concerned when she had small cubs below.

Badger-watching can have its amusing side. Once, I was sitting on a fallen elder branch at the edge of a spoil heap, watching some badgers cautiously emerge when the bough broke with a rending crash. My feet shot in the air and I turned a back-somersault down the slope. I ruefully picked myself up, knowing that that must be the end of the evening's watching. But no; two black and white faces appeared where I had been - the roles were reversed and now it was they who were investigating.

On another occasion when watching a sett from an oak tree nearby I was poised with flash at the ready when a man out poaching rabbits passed beneath me. I resisted the temptation to take his photograph and he passed on oblivious of my presence. It is surprising how seldom poachers look up!

Another time I was visiting a favourite sett in Somerset, had parked my car in the usual place by a gate and made my way across fields to the sett. I had a rewarding watch and after a couple of hours made my way back using a small torch to see where I was going as it was very dark. On climbing the gate, two men sprang out from behind my car and shone a strong torch in my face. I expected the worst and a challenging voice asked me what I was doing on the farm so late at night. I explained my mission and added that the farmer who owned the fields knew I watched badgers there regularly. They apologised for giving me such a fright, explaining that a number of lambs had been stolen recently from farms in the neighbourhood and they were acting as vigilantes. Seeing a strange car parked made them suspicious.It was a new experience to be taken for a lamb stealer!

One year, Keith decided to try to feed wild badger cubs by hand, the bait being bread, soaked in dilute honey solution. Five cubs were present belonging to three sows, so there was much activity. The tin containing the feast was placed at the base of the tree used by Keith for his observations. The first night, the bait was approached cautiously by one cub, which was faced with conflicting stimuli - the lure of honey and the fear of the new object, the tin. Eventually it plucked up enough courage to feed and soon two others joined it. This procedure was successfully repeated for several nights. By this time the cubs were beginning to expect their meal and on emergence would quickly make their way to the tree. So far so good, but would they feed from the hand?

Keith decided to try. He crouched in the partial shadow of a bush near the tree, tin in hand, waiting motionless for their arrival. The cubs emerged and started to play. Suddenly, one caught the smell of honey, its nose twitched and soon it was making its way along the path to the tree. A metre away it stopped dead. Cautiously it moved forwards, the scent of man and honey strong in its nostrils. It stopped again, ran back a few metres, and Keith thought it would bolt, but another cub joined it, and confidence seemed to be restored as they both moved forwards together. One seemed bolder than the other, and throwing caution to the wind, buried its snout in the mixture. The second joined in and the air was full of sucking noises. The experiment was a success!

A few nights later, I tried for a photograph. I thought that there would be a better chance after dark, but the cubs usually came out in reasonable light, so Keith climbed about 2 metres up the tree, rested the tin of food on a bough and waited until it was dark enough to come down. A short ladder rested against the trunk to facilitate a quiet descent.

We arrived early and I set up my camera, focused on a pre-arranged spot below the tree and retired a few metres towards some bushes. A cub emerged in good light, and without waiting for its friends, made its way purposefully to the tree. It was amusing to watch it scenting here, there and everywhere, and even trying to climb the ladder. During its searching it soon found my camera and started wandering in and out of the tripod legs, threatening to knock everything over. Finding this new object on its home ground, it set scent on one of the legs to claim it as its own. It was still far too light for Keith to come down from the tree and for me to reach the camera, so when the cub gave up the search and wandered off, we wondered if the chance was gone. However, at dusk, the first cub returned with two others and all three searched the base of the tree. It was now or never. Slowly, Keith made the descent and I crept up to the camera. As Keith's feet reached the last rung but one, two cubs climbed up to meet him. At last he was down. He held out the tin, and all three were jostling to get their reward; one even clambered on to his knee.

Photography was difficult as the cubs were moving all the time and it was getting too dark to see details clearly. However, Keith held a red torch in his free hand, and by focusing on the cubs, I was able to see what was going on. The cubs took no notice of the light. At last, there was a moment of comparative inactivity and I took my chance. The flash startled them, but did not stop them from guzzling. I changed the bulb, put in another plate and took another. Still no problem. I then tried colour and had to change to a large blue flashalite bulb full of magnesium foil. I was only 3 metres away. There was a blinding flash, a crackling of cellophane and a smell of burning. The cubs reacted violently and retreated a few yards, but apparently the attraction of honey was greater than their fear of minor explosions and they were soon at it again.

The tin was now empty, and as Keith stretched his legs, the last cub regretfully retired. It was a matter of great satisfaction that we had won the trust, or should I say the cupboard love, of truly wild badgers. An account of this which I wrote for The Times caused much interest, and since then, other badger-watchers have used rather similar techniques and experienced the same thrill of feeding wild cubs by hand.

While we were at Foxcombe, the school natural history society was going extremely well as there were some very keen and knowledgeable members who had become particularly interested in carrying out projects and collecting data about the flora and fauna of the area. Everybody was encouraged to enter observations of interest in a book kept in the biology laboratory, so that by the end of the year they could be incorporated into the society's annual report. I was eager that members should feel they were contributing to knowledge about the wildlife of the county, not just on a school basis, so everything identified on field excursions was recorded on cards and filed, and important data sent to the Somerset Archaeological and Natural History Society for their records.

Sixth-formers were encouraged to carry out lines of research which interested them. This included more work on the ecology of Thurlbear Wood which was an on-going investigation. It was noticed, for example, that there appeared to be fewer seed capsules on bluebell plants which were growing in shady conditions, so an investigation was started to find out if this was due to less effective pollination due to fewer visits by insects during the flowering period. Another group compared the flora of two tracts of grassland adjacent to the wood, one grazed by cattle and the other only by rabbits. This gave them ideas about plant succession and how grassland would revert to woodland under certain circumstances. Nobody pretended that these projects were done thoroughly enough to provide scientific answers to complex questions, but they were invaluable in introducing boys to field-study techniques.

When myxomatosis swept the country, the effect in Somerset was spectacular. An area of the Quantocks near Cushuish was a rabbit paradise. I used to watch badgers in a wood nearby, and when I went up in the late evening in summer I could clap my hands and see as many as a hundred rabbits on the heavily-grazed slopes run for their burrows. When the disease hit them in 1954, it was a pathetic sight to see so many wandering aimlessly about, blind and helpless. Foxes, badgers, crows, buzzards and other predators and carrion eaters became satiated with this abundance of food. By April 1955 all the rabbits appeared to have died, although it was found later that a few did survive, probably because they had been living above ground and had not picked up infected fleas from diseased animals. Some of the boys helped me monitor a few of the changes that occurred as a consequence.

We were surprised that foxes managed so well without any rabbits and appeared to be in such excellent condition. Stomach analysis of foxes killed by the Hunt showed that once the rabbits had gone, they relied much more on voles, mice and beetles; also, the proportion of vegetable material eaten greatly increased. Some were even eating silage!

Rabbit hairs in the dung of badgers had previously been found commonly, but these came from young animals. However, during the epidemic, adult rabbits were their main food. I found as many as seven rabbit skins in an area of a few square metres not far from the sett I used to watch. During the last half of 1955 the badgers reverted to their normal diet which included earthworms, beetles, cereals, acorns and sweet chestnuts.

Buzzards had a very hard time. They raised very few young in 1955 and widened their feeding area considerably by frequenting farms in Taunton Vale and the outskirts of towns and villages where they were able to prey on rats.

The hill vegetation changed considerably. Instead of the close-cropped turf of the rabbit era there was six inches or more of coarse grass. Leguminous plants were more abundant and the farmers who put more sheep on the hills reaped a bountiful reward. One farmer told me that he was able to graze one extra sheep for every twenty rabbits that were there before. Perhaps the most obvious difference was the amount of ragwort present. On the hillside I kept under observation, there were previously only a few ragwort plants which flowered when rabbits were abundant, but the year following myxomatosis, the area was yellow with it. It is well known that ragwort is poisonous to most mammals, but I believe when food is scarce, rabbits will nibble the very young shoots and leaves when they first appear and before they become obnoxious, so their growth is restricted. However, without the rabbits, the shoots were able to develop and flowered profusely.

The Natural History Society ran a moth trap continuously from autumn 1951 to July 1957 apart from short breaks during the coldest months and during the summer holidays when there was nobody to man it. Moths were attracted to a mercury-vapour lamp placed at the centre of a large metal container, and fell down a metal cone from which they could not easily escape. Egg-packing cases were placed inside the contraption and the moths hid away in, or under them, remaining quiescent until looked at the next day. Each morning, two boys identified the species and counted the moths before releasing them. Results were recorded on graphs to see if there was any correlation between total numbers caught and such climatic factors as temperature, humidity, atmospheric pressure changes, rainfall and cloud cover. Similar observations were made using key species, such as the hebrew character, which were caught in sufficient numbers to give reliable results. Excellent information was obtained in this way about optimum conditions for moth flight, the succession of species throughout the seasons and their time span, and whether they were single or double-brooded. Occasionally, migrants from Africa and southern Europe turned up in the trap to add to the interest.

We were able to record two new species for the county in July 1955, the most interesting being a small moth, *Eulia formosana* which had only recently been recorded for Britain, and the double line, *Leucania turca*, of which three specimens were taken. All our records were incorporated in Mr A.H. Turner's, 'Lepidoptera of Somerset', published by the Somerset Archaelogical and Natural History Society. The data helped to give a wider picture of the distribution of moths in the county.

The trap was operated during different years from several locations in the school grounds, including the roof of the new science block, but best catches were obtained from Foxcombe, probably because it was on the edge of the country. The only problem here were the sparrows, which quickly learnt that every morning the trap provided some easy pickings. Keith, who was in charge at that time, had to get up around dawn each morning to forestall them by putting a cover over the trap.

It was during this year (1956) that phenomenal numbers were recorded. In July there were ten catches of over 800 and four over 1,000. I well remember the record night when 1,450 were caught. Counting and recording was a nightmare as any disturbance caused some of them to fly. Each piece of egg-packing material was crowded with moths and many were settled on the sides of the trap. With normal catches more moths were found on the underside of the packing than on top, their position reflecting the habits of the different species in the wild. As most are very vulnerable to predation, they hide away during the day in grass or other vegetation, so these were found on the underside. In contrast, those which are protectively coloured such as the hawk-moths and those which are bad tasting and have warning colours, like tiger moths, chose the upper side; in the wild the former settle on tree trunks where their forewings blend with their surroundings, and the latter advertise their presence by selecting conspicuous positions. In spite of the break during the summer holidays, over 32,000 moths were captured that year, representing 243 species.

One of the problems of such a project was knowing how many moths were recaptured the following night. It was thought that the figure would not be high as release was delayed until late afternoon and was carried out 400 metres from the place where the trap was sited, but to make sure, marking experiments were carried out for a test period by placing a spot of quick-drying cellulose paint on the fore-wing of each moth caught, different colours being used on successive days. It was found that on average, only about 5% were recaptured the following night, but it varied according to species.

Interest was not confined to those working the moth trap and doing the recording, as some females of rare species were kept for egg-laying, and other boys helped to breed them through. One of particular interest was the alder moth as the early stages are seldom seen in the wild. The young caterpillar looks exactly like a bird dropping as it lies quite motionless on the upper surface of a leaf, but when fully grown is black and yellow with rows of long clubbed hairs projecting on each side like oars from an ancient long-boat.

By this time, Keith had joined the Mammal Society, and at the annual conference had learnt much about research on small mammals. This was something he thought the school society might emulate. Several members of the sixth-form were interested, so for a start the school bought a set of Longworth live-traps and a preliminary project was initiated for two terms in 1956. This was to discover what species occurred in the school grounds, the best method of marking individuals and to assess the main problems and perfect techniques. Advice was willingly given by Dr H.N. Southern of the Zoology Department of Oxford University, and following a discussion with him, it was decided the next year (which was Keith's last at Taunton) to try and discover how far the three common species of small mammals moved within their habitat. This meant setting traps over a fairly large area using hedgerow sites, marking each animal caught and noting in which traps it was recaptured. To increase the scope of the project, the Mammal Society lent the school thirty traps to add to the ones already owned.

The work was carried out by a group, known to the school as the 'mouse men'. It involved a great deal of work concentrated over three selected periods of the year, leaving a long gap before public examinations claimed the group's attentions. During each period the traps were laid out three times a week and Keith and one other got up at 6.30 am the following mornings to inspect the traps. Recaptures of marked animals were sufficiently numerous to produce some excellent results, one animal being recaptured twenty seven times! It was found that long-tailed field mice, *Apodemus sylvaticus*, were the most intrepid travellers, going 50m on average, with one animal doing a marathon 230m. Bank voles, *Clethrionomis glareolus*, averaged 30m, and field voles, *Microtus agrestis*, only 20m. Apart from these results, much was learnt about population fluctuations during the year and from season to season. The project provided excellent training in this type of field work, and allowed critical discussion on the reliability of the methods used and conclusions reached.

The project ended with a memorable evening picnic on the Quantocks for which Betty did the catering. This included a celebratory cake adorned with chocolate mice! After consuming the feast with much enthusiasm the mouse-men finished the celebration by climbing some trees to watch for some larger mammals. Two badgers obliged!

During our time at Foxcombe, it became quite a tradition for boys taking biology to go to Salcombe during the Easter holidays to study marine ecology. We hired the schoolroom belonging to the Baptist church, and while Betty and I slept on a lilo in comparative comfort in the church vestry, the boys stuffed palliasses with hay to lessen the impact of the bare boards of the schoolroom. The hay also came in handy for making a hay-box in which the porridge was slowly cooked overnight.

Salcombe supplied a great variety of habitats so that we could study the differences in flora and fauna on exposed and sheltered rocky shores, sandy and muddy beaches, and mud-banks such as the Saltstone. The latter was particularly interesting as the animals did not have to cope with any wave action and this allowed some, such as sea squirts, to lie unattached on the surface of the mud. We also found that strange creature, the burrowing shrimp which has one nipper longer than the other and can be either right or left-handed.

To find the animals at low tide on a sandy shore, a spade was the most efficient tool to use, but it needed a lot of skill to capture such species as razor shells as they burrowed so fast. Heart urchins were common in some areas, and we were particularly pleased to find the highly specialised polychaete worm *Chaetopterus*. It lives in a U-shaped burrow lined by a tough parchment-like secretion and has a very delicate body. It remains in its burrow all its life, and by rhythmically flapping a series of large fan-like structures, it maintains a continuous current of water which brings it oxygen and microscopic nutriment and allows the elimination of waste. The worm is luminescent, emitting a blue-green light - a very curious phenomenon for a creature living almost all its life in the darkness of its tube.

Everybody enjoyed these work-holidays. The field investigations were sometimes quite arduous and identification of the material often difficult and time consuming, but there was always time for the boys to do what they liked. Some went boating and others explored the countryside or amused themselves in the town. On one occasion an enterprising member of the party went out fishing before breakfast and surprised us by bringing back enough pollack to give all of us an excellent meal. One wet day I was able to take a few of the senior boys to Plymouth to see the Marine Biological Association's aquaria where I had worked for a time after graduating, and this gave them a chance to see what research was going on there.

Our three boys came on these trips too, so with Betty there to organise the meals and keep everything more civilized, those from the school felt they were part of a large family. On two occasions, Geoffrey Stephens helped to run the course and brought along his wife and daughter to join us. It was good to have another enthusiastic biologist to help. His wife was able to keep Betty company and help with the catering. Another time John Wright came along too with a group who were keen on sailing and canoeing.

All these biological camps and projects within the school gave the boys an invaluable adjunct to their class work, and this was reflected by the number of scholarships they achieved. We were all particularly pleased when Keith was accepted for Trinity Hall, Cambridge to read natural sciences.

The School Scout Troop was a particularly good one and was well run by Mick Johnson, ably supported by Bill Stock and John Wright. All three were enthusiastic and imaginative leaders; Bill was a keen mountaineer and John included sailing amongst his many practical skills. Our three boys became very enthusiastic, and before they left school had all gained high qualifications, Keith getting his first class badge, David becoming a Queen's Scout and Andrew a few years later getting his Duke of Edinburgh Gold Award. In later life they profited greatly from the practical skills they learnt whilst members. They all enjoyed camping and went with the scouts to various parts of Britain and Ireland where they had some tough assignments and many adventures.

From his early days, David had shown much enthusiasm for making things. He was clever with his hands, quickly acquired skills in woodwork and from an early age showed leanings towards engineering. It was gratifying to have one member of the family who was not going to be a biologist! He was also artistic and good at games, particularly rugby, hockey and athletics.

One of his early loves was canoeing, and it was when he was 15 that he constructed his first canoe. Most of his pocket money went on materials for making it. He became a founder member of the Taunton Boating Club and took part in rallies on the River Tone. If there were rivers to explore, David always made the best of his opportunities, so when we had a family holiday with Bill at Warminster, he saw to it that the canoe came too; he was able to explore the River Wylie. Later on, during our biological camps at Salcombe, he explored the estuary while the biologists were at work elsewhere. It was a sad day when the canoe was stolen from its compound and found damaged further up the Tone, but he reacted typically by building another and better one. He used it in the holidays to explore and survey the rivers Tone, Parrett and Yeo with his friend David Peregrine-Jones.

Whenever David made one of these canoeing trips, he wrote a detailed log illustrated with his own sketches and photographs. These portrayed the construction of the bridges, camp sites and features of special interest. This meticulous recording of detail stood him in good stead when he designed engineering projects later on.

His most adventurous canoe trip was a five-day, hundred-mile journey down the Wye with David Peregrine-Jones, camping *en route*. All went well until, ahead of schedule, they arrived at Chepstow in the late evening, only to find that the tide was so far out they couldn't reach the landing stage. They had no option but to wade laboriously through the gooey mud, first carrying all their gear and then returning for the canoe. Cleaning themselves and the canoe for the journey back by train was a real problem, but they found a fire hydrant in the road, which sent up a jet of water which did the trick.

The station was not too far away, and here they were lucky enough to find a baggage truck which they commandeered to retrieve the canoe, bags and equipment they had left on the jetty. They caught a train to Bristol, but were disappointed to find that the next train to Taunton was the 1.15 am However, a parcels train went earlier and the guard kindly let them put the canoe on board and said they could travel with it. Much relieved, they went to the refreshment room until it was time for the train to depart. But when they emerged, to their dismay the train was already leaving, before the scheduled time. David just managed to shout to the guard to put the canoe out at Taunton before the train left the platform. They eventually caught the 1.15 am, and were mightily relieved to find the canoe and packs waiting for them on the platform. They left the gear at the station and wearily made for home. We did not expect David back until the next day so everything was locked up; rather than wake us, he got into the boys' side of Foxcombe through a window and went to sleep in an old armchair.

Our boys attended scout camps whenever possible, and as these took place at the end of the summer term, we often planned holidays some-where near so that they could join us for a family holiday afterwards. It was when Keith and David were camping at Braemar that we had a holiday at Coylum Bridge. They joined us there and we were able to explore the Cairngorms together. I was very surprised to meet another member of the Mammal Society, Ian Linn, at Coylum Bridge. He was setting Longworth traps on Ben Macdui to find out the distribution of small mammals on the mountain. This entailed repeated trips up this 1,300 metre mountain. All for the sake of science!

We all loved Scotland and had a number of holidays there. On one of

*Author with apparatus
for photographing
badgers, 1986*

these, John Ryland, who had just qualified at Cambridge, joined Betty, Keith and me, and we explored parts of Perthshire including the area around Ben Lawers. We particularly wanted to examine its fascinating flora. At the summit, in the shelter of a boulder we were thrilled to find a specimen of the drooping saxifrage, *Saxifraga cernua*. This relict of arctic alpine flora is found nowhere else in Britain. It seldom flowers on Ben Lawers, relying on red bulbils in the axils of the upper leaves for vegetative reproduction. By great good fortune, our specimen was actually flowering and was growing within a few inches of another rare species, the alpine saxifrage, *S.nivalis*. The light was bad, but by giving an exposure of 1/8th of a second, I was able to get a colour photograph of the two species together. I still have the photo to remind me of that day.

Another find which excited us was a wild cat lair in a patch of alpine lady's mantle. The burrow was high up Meall nan Tarmachan, a nearby mountain west of Ben Lawers. Its owner was not at home, but it had left a few tell-tale hairs behind which made identification possible.

One summer, David and Andrew were camping with the scouts at Bray in Ireland while we stayed at Clonmel with the Reverend William Dawson. They joined us for the last two days before going on a camping holiday together in Kerry and then north to Achill. William had corresponded with me about badgers for some years and asked if I would come over and give a talk. He and his wife warmly invited us to stay with them and offered to show us that part of the country. They were a delightful couple and great characters. William loved to tell Irish folk stories, which he did with great charm and humour, and was well known for telling them in dialect over the radio. He was an Irish Protestant in an area predominantly Catholic, and was much respected by the people of Clonmel. He loved horses, and was an excellent rider, liking nothing better than to help exercise racehorses from stables nearby.

The cattle market in Clonmel was held in the High Street. It seemed to us a good example of organised chaos, with milling crowds and cattle all over the road and the shop windows boarded up to prevent damage. There was a lot of clearing up to do afterwards.

William was a splendid historian. He showed us the wonderful ruins of Cashel, the famous round towers, ancient crosses and many places of historic interest in the area. Knowing his history so well, we couldn't have had a better guide. He also showed us the local badger setts!

It was quite an experience giving the lecture on badgers - the original reason for our visit. It took place in the school hall in Clonmel. An ancient projector was conjured up from somewhere, dusted and set up on a box in the middle of the room; a sheet was pinned up to act as a screen. I hoped fervently that everything would work; in the event it did. The audience, who sat on wooden benches, was a remarkable mix of Clonmel society, with the local Count in the front row sitting next to his gamekeeper and dog.

The Count had badgers on his land and invited us to see the estate. The gamekeeper showed us around, but time seemed of no consequence and we were late back to the ancestral home for tea. The Countess had already had her's with our boys who were being shown the river, so we were left to have tea on our own in the enormous baronial hall surrounded by trophies, suits of armour and oil paintings of the Count's ancestors. It seemed rather incongruous to us, coming straight from a badger sett survey, having shed our gum-boots, to sit in state, use the family silver and be waited on by a servant in black dress and white apron!

Our camping trip was most eventful and interesting. All our gear and the two boys were crammed into the somewhat ancient Morris A40 shooting brake, and at Killarney station we met Keith. He had completed his first year at Cambridge and had come back from a short trip to America. We had to pitch tents in pouring rain and I was glad to have a family of three scouts to do the job for me! We were soaking wet, the ground squelchy and the outlook unpleasant. However, out of the nearby house came the local priest, who warmly invited us to pitch our tents on his lawn which was less waterlogged, and use his kitchen. Understandably, putting up the tents all over again was not a popular move, but everybody was glad in the end as the rain was relentless and the priest, kindness itself.

We spent a week exploring the Ring of Kerry and the Dingle Peninsula. We had one large tent and two very small ones, so accommodation was tight for the five of us. Sometimes, Betty and I slept in the car, with the boys in the large tent. On a beautiful camp site overlooking Dingle Bay, which we thought we had to ourselves, we were awakened by shouts from Andrew. He was in his pyjamas brandishing a bottle menacingly and yelling at some cows which were threatening to chew the tent's guy ropes.

We climbed Mount Brandon and explored the point, where we were thrilled to see our first large flock of choughs. Being so rare in Britain, it was good to be able to see them at close quarters and watch them feeding with their long, curved, red bills. We would have loved to visit the Blasket Islands which were tantalisingly close, but it was impracticable, and we had to be content with watching a small boat loading sheep destined for the islands.

We were very interested in the flora of Kerry which is greatly influenced by the high rainfall and mild winters due to the Gulf Stream. Montbretia and fuchsia were growing in profusion beside the roads, and it was interesting to see woods of oak and holly which also contained large specimens of the wild strawberry tree, *Arbutus*. The latter is a true Mediterranean species. In a gully near the sea we found our first St Patrick's cabbage, the wild form of the London Pride of our gardens. There was also a profusion of ferns, mosses and liverworts in these damp places.

It was not possible to leave the area without attempting to climb Carrauntoohil, the highest mountain in the Macgillycuddy's Reeks at 1,052 metres. We were fortunate in having reasonable weather and decided to tackle it via Mount Caher and along the ridge that separated the two mountains. During the ascent, Betty found a splendid specimen of the great grey slug, *Lomax maximus*, a local rarity which reaches a length of six inches.We had wonderful views from the ridge towards the Dingle peninsula with Lough Eagher far below us. When we at last reached the summit, there was a large cross to mark the spot and a visitors' book, well protected from the weather. Having added our names, we read down some of the signatures. To our astonishment we found that one of the most recent was that of a Taunton School prefect. We had missed him by a few days.

As this was our first trip to Ireland we wanted to see as much as possible before returning, so we went north as far as Achill and spent a few days camping on the 'Island'. My chief memory of that trip was climbing Croaghaun. It was not high, just over 609 metres, and the ascent was just a hard slog and of no great significance, but on reaching the summit, without any warning, we suddenly found ourselves on the edge of a spectacular cliff which dropped precipitously to the sea far below. It was as if the mountain had been sliced in half with a giant knife and one half removed. It was a dramatic experience and quite breath-taking.

It was hard to leave this wild and beautiful area, but we had been away a month and we all had much to do before the new term, so we headed across Ireland for Rosslare. We underestimated the time it would take on Irish roads, but we arrived just in time for the ferry. A crane picked up our car in a sling and deposited it in the car-well of the ship and we were on our way back to Fishguard.

It was this same year (1958) that Betty's father became very ill after a long life of excellent health. He was confined to his bed and Betty spent the last five weeks of his life helping her mother with the nursing. He had lived a remarkable and adventurous life, and as a dairy expert, advised governments in Australia, Romania and Russia and pioneered many practices in dairying which we take for granted today. He had formidable strength of character and was a real fighter for what he thought was right, something which Betty greatly admired and has always had in common with him.

Betty's mother did not survive him long; she died the following year. She had loyally supported Betty's father through good times and bad and brought up her family with love and dedication. She always gave me and the family a warm welcome whenever we could visit. Our children were very fond of her.

My mother too was becoming very frail over this period. She found standing very difficult and would carry around a light folding stool which Bill had made for her so that she could rest at intervals when going out for short walks. However, she remained cheerful and was overjoyed whenever a member of the family visited her at Walmer. In 1957 we were thrilled when she managed the journey by train and visited us. She was very fond of her grandchildren and interested in all their doings. I was so glad she was able to come, as she had not been to Foxcombe before and it proved to be the last time she was able to leave home. She was well looked after by her companion at Walmer, but age and poor health were taking their toll and we knew that her time was running out.

It was a very sad time for us all when she died on the 5 March 1959 at the age of 83. I felt her loss terribly;, she had been so very special, but it was comforting to know that there was no more pain and ill-health and I felt full of gratitude for all her love. She endeared herself to so many by her fearlessness, simple faith and devotion. She understood the needs of people and did her utmost to supply those needs. Her life was one of triumph over difficulty, poverty and ill-health and she took sunshine with her wherever she went. That sunshine remains. The funeral was at Boxmoor where she was buried with Dad.

Within a short span Betty and I had lost our parents and our children their grandparents. One generation had gone, now it was up to us to attempt to carry the torch. More and more I saw life as a continuum with our lives such ephemeral episodes in the drama of human evolution. At this time of loss, it was a wonderful boost to our spirits to see our three boys already beginning to play their part in the on-going pageant of human endeavour.

The following summer was David's last term at school and we planned to spend a month in Scotland with him and Andrew. Keith was unable to join us, but Bids came for the first fortnight and Marge brought John for the second. There was just room in the cottage for Bids to stay with us; Marge and John preferred rooms at the Gairloch Hotel. We rented a cottage at Melvaig on the headland, five miles west of Gairloch. It was in a marvellous situation, with spectacular views of the sea and rocky coast-line, and sheep as our nearest neighbours. The cottage was sturdily built to withstand the storms but at first we found it rather disconcerting when the wind was strong as the wooden panelling of the rooms made ominous creaking sounds.

We all needed time to unwind after such a hectic year, and this was the perfect place to do it. It was a wonderful spot from which to explore that part of Wester Ross, taking the car to different areas and then walking or climbing. At odd times I liked to fish for saithe from a rocky headland quite near the cottage; I found it was always best to choose evenings when there was a wind as the midges were terrible.

It was great to explore Scotland at a period when there were few good main roads and holiday-makers were less evident. It was a long journey from Taunton, but we took it in stages, stopping for the night just over the border. The Preston bypass - the first part of the M6 - had just been opened, and this provided me with a good opportunity to see how fast our little car could go. It managed very well in spite of being loaded up with family and gear, but going up Shap was a different matter - it did just get up!

Andrew joined us after his scout camp in Braemar. He had suffered a nasty scald on his leg and was not as mobile as usual, so early on he couldn't do much climbing, but that did not deter him for long. Meanwhile, David and I climbed An Teallach together and saw a number of ptarmigan. They were difficult to see on the rock-strewn slopes due to their wonderful camouflage. Stalking them with a camera was quite a challenge; they let you get to a certain critical distance, but beyond that point, they took flight. There was a lot of cloud on the top, but a brief break came just at the right moment and we were able to get photographs of the summit with the mist swirling around.

I had never seen a pine-marten in the wild. I had been told they were not uncommon on the lower slopes of Ben Eighe and would cross the road at night towards Loch Maree to feed. We searched the area, and found what appeared to be a lair and some droppings containing rowan seeds; this was a good start. Andrew was as keen as I was to see one, so one evening we set off for Loch Maree. We parked in a passing-place beside the loch with a good view of the road for about a hundred metres. We thought the most likely time would be around dusk and were prepared to put on the headlights if we saw anything.

Everything was quiet and no other cars were about. We settled down hopefully. The weather was cloudy but it was not actually raining. We watched the road with great concentration, but no pine-marten appeared. By 10.45 pm it was too dark to see far with the naked eye so we took it in turns to watch with 7x50 binoculars for five minutes at a time, ready to turn on the headlights if we saw anything. Still nothing. At 1 am the rain started to fall in torrents and we could hardly see more than a few metres. The headlights did not help at all. However, we had come a long way and there was always the hope that the rain would soon stop, so we stayed on. Our luck was out; it rained continuously and we saw nothing, so we had to console ourselves with an extremely early breakfast which Betty had provided. Never before or since have we eaten hot porridge straight from a thermos flask! To us it was the height of luxury as by then we were both ravenous and very cold. Soon after dawn a car went slowly by. The driver gave us a very suspicious look as he passed, apparently debating in his mind whether we were poachers, but he did not stop, and probably decided with some justification that we were merely wrong in the head to be out so early on such a morning.

During our second fortnight, when Marge and John were with us, David got his examination results. He had previously had an interview with the Civil Engineering Scholarship Trust and been awarded a scholarship with the proviso that he obtained the necessary grades in his Higher Certificate. His results were excellent, so he now had the necessary qualifications and could take up his place at Bristol University. There was great rejoicing. Marge invited us all to a celebratory dinner at the Gairloch Hotel.

When Bids was with us, she was able to do some painting. At school she had done extremely well at art and loved it, but had since been so busy that she had let it lapse. However, she had taken it up again as a relaxation and had attended evening art classes in Taunton. She had a real gift for painting, and while we were walking or climbing, she was happy to settle down in some picturesque spot and sketch. She did some lovely watercolours. Much later, when she retired, painting became a major interest and her work won wide appreciation. She became President of the Somerset Society of Artists and exhibited each year.

Bids' job was very demanding, but she greatly enjoyed working with Rae Hodge whom she got to know very well. When Rae's wife died, we were not surprised when she told us she was going to marry him. The circumstances were rather sad because Rae had recently had a minor stroke and the outlook was not good, but they were very fond of each other and Rae's three sons missed their mother greatly, knew Bids well and liked her very much. The wedding was a quiet one in Stoke St Mary, a village a few miles from Taunton where Rae had his home. Tragically, Rae died from another stroke a few months later.

We were all so sad for Bids. She had loyally looked after Mother and Dad during the years when she would probably have married, and since then had never met the right person until Rae came along. It was very hard that she had had to wait until comparatively late in life and that her married life had been so short. She would have loved to have had children of her own and would have made a splendid mother, but it was not to be. Instead, she happily spent most of her working life helping other people's children, including our own. She had done much for our boys and was very fond of them, as they were of her.

Chapter Ten

The BBC and all that

I much enjoyed my association with the BBC over a period of some thirty years or so, during which I was privileged to take part in over 200 radio and television programmes. In this chapter I will trace some of the remarkable developments that occurred over this period by referring to a selection of programmes which stand out in my memory.

My introduction to radio was almost certainly a consequence of the publicity caused by the publication of my book and the interest it had aroused locally. So when the programme 'Down your way' came to Taunton in 1952, I was invited to take part; no doubt the thought occurred to somebody that the inclusion of an eccentric schoolmaster who watched badgers at night as a pastime might make a change from the usual. Richard Dimbleby was anchor-man for this series, and as this was my first broadcast, I was intrigued to discover how these programmes were produced. Richard quickly put me at my ease and explained what would happen, but there was no proper rehearsal. After being interviewed about badgers, I was asked to choose a favourite piece of music, and if I remember rightly, I chose part of the 'Dance Macabre' by Saint Saens. The interview seemed to happen very quickly; perhaps that was just as well.

Shortly afterwards, I was asked by the Bridgwater Naturalists' Society to make a display at the Bridgwater Fair to demonstrate that on balance, badgers do more good than harm and should therefore be left alone. Desmond Hawkins came from the BBC to cover the Fair and we concocted a plan to record the public's reaction to our badger propaganda. The idea was for a microphone to be concealed under the exhibit and conversations recorded when people were talking to me about badgers. The idea was promising, but in the event the remarks were not sufficiently interesting or provocative to broadcast. However, the incident was of significance to me as it was the start of a long friendship with Desmond. His contribution to natural history broadcasting cannot be overestimated as he was not only an excellent programme producer, but he founded the BBC Natural History Unit at Bristol, later becoming its Head.

A lot of interest in badgers was shown by the media and after a trial run on Children's Hour with 'Uncle Mac', in 1953 I was invited to take part in one of the early Naturalist programmes with Maxwell Knight in the chair and Desmond Hawkins producing. The subject, of course, was badgers. I remember the feeling of excitement as we listened to the call of the curlew which preceded each 'Naturalist' programme. By today's standards these programmes tended to be rather stilted as they were scripted throughout, although you tried to make it sound as sponta-neous as possible. It was rather like taking part in a play-reading! On this occasion, Eric Simms also contributed, and played his tape of the badger fight I witnessed at Camberley while filming.

Later that year I did a programme on 'The Behaviour of Badgers' on the radio channel known as The Third Programme, which allowed more time for serious subjects. I found it quite an ordeal as I had to read a script without interruption for 25 minutes. This seemed a very long time to concentrate, but it appeared to have been worthwhile as it was also translated into Italian and broadcast on The University of the Air. I found these programmes fun to do; they made a nice contrast to school teaching. I also met some very interesting people.

It was during this period, when housemaster at Foxcombe, that I became much more involved with the BBC - mainly in radio. I took part in other Naturalist programmes such as 'The Weather and Wildlife', and 'How to Study Mammals' - an opportunity to advertise the newly-formed Mammal Society. An interesting one called 'Guilty or Not Guilty' was a discussion between Ralph Wightman and myself on the good and harm various mammals do to man's interests; Ralph took the farmer's point of view and I the naturalist's. This was my first meeting with Ralph and I much enjoyed his sense of humour and expertise as a broad-caster.

Television took off rapidly after the war, but although by 1954 it was theoretically possible to transmit in colour, this did not come until later. Meanwhile natural history programmes - even in black and white - became popular, particularly when Peter Scott was the key figure in presenting films. At first these were mainly concerned with his own particular interest in wildfowl, using film taken during expeditions to Iceland, Greenland, South America, and from the Wildfowl Trust at Slimbridge. Although shot in colour and used by Peter when lecturing to raise money for the Wildfowl Trust, on TV the films had to be shown in

black and white. These programmes were monthly and usually transmitted after the news on Saturday nights. It was not long before new
films on different subjects were needed for the series and the BBC looked
for other film-makers to supply material. Humphrey Hewer and I were
thrilled to fill the November 1954 slot, show our badger film and discuss
with Peter on screen how it had been made.

Neither of us had had any previous experience of television and we
were both intrigued and somewhat apprehensive. The BBC had cut our
film down to 15 minutes, the remaining 10 being devoted to a discussion
with Peter. Desmond Hawkins was producer and the programme went
out live from the Lime Grove studios in London.

We arrived early in the morning and had the day to rehearse procedure. At first we knew nothing about the form the programme would
take except for the showing of the film; that evolved as the day
proceeded. Peter Scott joined us after returning from Scotland on the
night train having been given no more information of the content of the
programme than we had, but that did not seem to matter. We told him
the story of how the film had been made and the problems involved, and
he jotted down a series of questions he could use in the discussion
period. During rehearsal, Desmond had arranged us around a small
table against a background resembling a living room. Humphrey and I
were facing camera and Peter was on the end of the table in profile. I
remember with amusement, Peter seeing himself on the monitor when
we were rehearsing, and realising that he did not look his best in that
position because he had put on a lot of weight in the wrong place. He
stopped in mid-flow and suggested to Desmond over the microphone he
should change places with one of us. Quick as lightning came the reply,
"Sit up man and it won't show!" The rehearsal continued.

During our lunch break, Humphrey and I went outside the studio to
get some fresh air as it had been extremely hot in the studio due to the
intense lights they had to use. To our astonishment, there was a violent
sword duel going on between two men! We found they were rehearsing
a scene for 'The Three Musketeers'!

By evening the programme had taken shape, timing was about right,
and we roughly knew what each was supposed to say and do.
Humphrey was mainly involved with the filming side and was to show
his blimped camera, and I was concerned with the badgers' behaviour
and off-the-cuff commentary on the film. At that time, sound was not
dubbed on to film, and the whole programme was transmitted live. As
zero hour approached we were all sweating under the intense lights and
powder was liberally applied to parts of our anatomy which might

shine. It was all rather un-nerving, but once it started I had so much to think about that the tension lessened. In the event, some of the discussion turned out rather differently from rehearsal as we thought of other interesting tit-bits to add; this gave the programme more informality. We were all very relieved when it was over and nothing catastrophic had occurred. I am sure this applied particularly to Desmond, who had to be ready for any eventuality, but it had been a lot of fun for us and a most interesting experience.

The following year the famous 'Look' series started which immediately captured large audiences and excellent reviews. It got off to a wonderful start with a programme on woodpeckers, filmed by a German, Heinz Sielmann. Although it lasted only 18 minutes it was quite the most ingenious and professionally shot film to be televised so far on a natural history subject. For the first time he managed to show the adult feeding its young, deep in its nesting hole in a tree, by cutting a window behind the nest through which the camera could function. By 1957 nature programmes had become a regular and popular feature with David Attenborough showing his 'Zoo Quest' series and Tony Soper, Christopher Parsons, Winwood Reade and others becoming more involved in programme production both on radio and television. It was that year that most of this work became centred on Bristol and the BBC Natural History Unit was formed under Desmond Hawkins. It has never looked back, and has achieved a magnificent, world-wide reputation for wildlife and conservation programmes.

I did no further TV programmes until 1958 when two potential film stars arrived at Foxcombe. This happened late one afternoon on a cold, damp February day when I received an interesting phone call. It was from Mr Farrant, a parent of one of the boys. He had heard shrill pipings coming from a drain on the Somerset levels and thought the animals concerned might be otter cubs. Knowing I had previously brought up young badgers, he wondered if I was interested. This was very exciting, as for years I had wanted to find out more about otters and little was known of their early development. Now was my chance. Mr Farrant thought the cubs had lost their mother, perhaps through a road accident, and were probably starving; he offered to collect them for me. He was 20 miles away, and obviously they had to be fetched as soon as possible, but my car was in dock. However, my good friend, P.G. Smith volunteered and went off immediately to collect them.

The two cubs arrived in a box curled up together in some hay. It was impossible to resist their charm. It looked as if their eyes had just opened, so it was likely they were about 6 weeks old. They were very hungry. I was not exactly equipped for bottle feeding, but as a makeshift measure I gently squirted milk into their mouths from a pipette; it seemed to go down the right way. The cubs needed to be kept warm, so a hot-water bottle, covered in sacking, was put under hay in a wooden box, which was to be their home until the weather got warmer. Betty, with her better grasp of the implications, somewhat reluctantly agreed that the box should be left by the boiler in the kitchen. Late that night when I wearily went to bed, the problems of foster-mothering began to dawn on me, and at 6 o'clock the next morning, when I fed them again, the reality of the situation was reinforced. Four feeds a day was the routine for the next few weeks, and any mother blessed with twins knows the time it takes to cope adequately. Life was not topsy-turvy yet, but it might well become so, and the significance of this prompted me to call the female Topsy and the male Turvy.

I had found with badger cubs, that the proprietary puppy food, lactol, was better than cow's milk which was too low in fat. The cubs took this quite well from the sort of bottle used for raising lambs. Betty had searched all over Taunton before she found a teat of the right size.

Having rid the cubs of a number of large ticks and given them regular feeds for a few days, they settled down well. After their evening feed they became very lively and played together on the kitchen floor. I tried giving them small pieces of fish as well as lactol, and gradually they took to solids; they always preferred meat to fish and liver was their favourite. I had to feed them one at a time, so the otter-in-waiting played around my feet. This was the time when their eyesight was first developing and my feet became the objects which moved within their sight range, just as their mother would have done in the wild. In consequence, my feet became imprinted on their minds as a substitute for their mother. This had interesting results, as throughout their life they were irresistibly drawn to people's feet and playfully bit and wrestled with them. This was not always appreciated as their teeth became very sharp.

They got very messy when feeding from the bottle and could not clean themselves, so they had to be washed in a shallow bath of warm water, rolled in a towel to dry and placed near a heater to finish the process. One evening I carried them up to my study with the mistaken intention of doing some work. They took this new opportunity to indulge their inquisitive natures to the full and spent a wonderful half hour exploring. Their taste for literature was a surprise and I had to rescue some precious volumes from their attentions when they pulled them out from the book case. But it was when they got into the cupboard that the fun really began as all my photographic gear became the focus of attention.

Author with the 2 otter cubs, Topsy and Turvy, 1958

Having extracted the cubs with some difficulty from this marvellous collection of new toys, Turvy found the door ajar and slipped through. The landing outside led to a series of small dormitories and the boys happened to be going to bed. As they crowded round their unexpected visitors, the two cubs found the large number of bare feet within striking distance irresistible. It was some time before boys and otters could be put to bed.

The cubs created much interest at the school and there was a continual flow of visitors to our kitchen to see them feed. On one never-to-be-forgotten occasion we packed in twenty-eight boys for a practical lesson on 'The art of being a foster-mother'. As the news travelled more widely, callers became more frequent, and before long Betty was holding otter tea-parties almost every day of the week.

I had not taken up cinephotography at that time, but I was determined to get a good record of their up-bringing if I could. Fortunately, a friend was only too delighted to oblige and an excellent film of their behaviour was obtained. We also achieved good sound recordings of their vocalisations.

I couldn't get suitable baby-sitters when I had to go away, so the otters had to come too. Their first trip was to Harry Hurrell's home in Devon. H.G., as he was known to his friends, was an excellent naturalist and good at handling animals. He had never seen otter cubs before and was thrilled to see Topsy and Turvy. The cubs were bedded down while we went to a lecture in Plymouth and the next day H.G. filmed them being fed.

Sadly, when we returned to Taunton, Topsy became listless and went off her food and I became very worried. The vet gave her antibiotics but her condition continued to deteriorate and she died the next day. She was then about 9 weeks old. The cause of death was a mystery as Turvy was in splendid form and we had given both cubs exactly the same treatment. However, to my astonishment, the post mortem revealed that she had died of a perforated duodenal ulcer. I found out later that an otter cub at the London Zoo had also died of the same condition. It was very surprising that an animal not yet weaned should suffer in this way.

Turvy didn't mind travel and in the course of his career clocked up 700 miles! I took him to the Mammal Society's conference at Reading University where he created a lot of interest. However, Turvy didn't appreciate all the attention he received from those who were in the car park when we arrived, and took the first opportunity to hide away under a car. It was some time before he was caught. Maxwell Knight had brought up many kinds of wild animal and was intensely interested. He kindly looked after Turvy while I was at the conference, as his home was not far away.

Later in the month I was due to take a biology camp at Salcombe and I saw no way of taking him too, so I asked H.G. if he would oblige. He leapt at the chance, and I was greatly relieved as he was the ideal person to look after him; he even had a swimming pool in his garden. Turvy was quickly at home, and while I was there we started to teach him how to swim. He hated the large expanse of water at first, so we gradually got him used to getting wet in a swampy area and then in a small stream. When I had to leave, H.G.'s daughter Elaine took over the training and Turvey was soon enjoying the delights of the swimming pool.

I brought him back to Foxcombe for the summer term; the weather being warmer, he was able to use a large hutch and a wired run in the garden which gave him space for exercise. The boys were very keen to help, and in particular, Robert Speed and Keith Plumbe regularly gave him his food and looked after him . Every day some of the boys took him for walks and played with him in the garden. They also dammed part of the small stream which ran through the school grounds to give him a pool to swim in. This was greatly appreciated by Turvy. He spent much time searching under water for food and occasionally came up with a frog or newt.

In hot weather I gave him a large zinc bath of water in which to play and all manner of toys for his amusement, his favourite being a rubber ring. He soon learnt to put his head through it, wriggle his body like a snake and push and pull with his feet until somehow he passed right through it. Then he would do it all over again.

In July a measure of fame came to Ṭurvy with his first appearance on television. I had told Winwood Reade about Turvy, and when she had come over to Foxcombe and seen his antics, she was very keen to show him to a wider audience on her children's programme, 'Out of Doors'. She arranged for a new hutch and run to be constructed, but Turvy was not impressed; it took a week before it smelt sufficiently of otter to be accepted as a reasonable substitute for his old one. It was planned to treat the programme as a live outside broadcast on the lawn outside the BBC studios. Winwood was more confident than I was that he would behave well in front of the cameras, but I hoped fervently for the best.

On the eve of the show I took him to Bristol in the shooting brake along with the new hutch, zinc bath, the large log he used to play on and some of his favourite toys. On arrival, everything was set up on the lawn in readiness for the next day.

Keith and Betty brought Robert Speed the next morning. There was a short rehearsal so that the camera-men could plan for various eventualities and the possible exits to the main road outside the BBC were manned to prevent a disaster if he tried to escape. His favourite liver had been specially ordered for the occasion and Turvy was kept fairly hungry to increase the chances of a good performance.

The afternoon was fine and sunny and the moment arrived when shots were taken of Turvy in his hutch and the cue given for Robert to call Turvy from the hutch. To everybody's relief he came out at once, and as

Filming Turvy on the lawn of the BBC Bristol, 1958

soon as the scent of liver reached him he forgot all and gave a perfect performance. He begged for his food, chased Robert round the log, climbed into his bath, played with the rubber ring and acted as if he had been on television all his life. He certainly deserved his plate of liver!

As end of term approached a big decision had to be made. Turvy was now quite a large animal and I could not give him the conditions and attention he needed. H.G. was only too happy to have him, so regretfully I let him go, knowing that I could visit him from time to time to see his further progress.

We visited him seven weeks later. He had grown well, was eating two pounds of fish or meat a day and was a marvellous swimmer. H.G. had even taught him to dive off the spring board into the swimming pool from a height of 6 feet.

Soon after the autumn term had started, I had a phone call from H.G. saying he had just acquired another orphaned otter cub from somebody who was trying to rear it, but found it too demanding. It was a female and so was inevitably called Topsy the Second. She was much wilder and probably about twelve weeks old. H.G. asked if I would take her on for a few weeks, and Robert Speed was delighted to take responsibility. She never became as tame as Turvy and often had to be handled with leather gloves, but she thrived and quickly got used to water. She too made a successful TV appearance and was allotted a dressing room all to herself which she immediately claimed as her own by sprainting in the middle of the floor!

After the broadcast in Bristol she was taken straight back to H.G. who had made another hutch and run next to Turvy's, so they could get used to each other before being allowed to be together. I shall never forget visiting H.G. six months later. I was delighted when Turvy recognised me and at once started to play with my shoe as he had done so often when a cub. Topsy was nearly fully grown and weighed 11 pounds, just four lighter than Turvy. Their acrobatics in the pool as they played together were marvellous to watch, sleek bodies twisting and turning in an aquatic wrestling match which seemed to make the water boil. I looked at them with amazement. Was Turvy the same animal as that furry bundle I had fed on my lap with a pipette more than two years before? It was almost unbelievable.

Both cubs eventually went back to the wild, Topsy going first by digging under the wire of her enclosure and Turvy a few months later. It had been a great privilege to help bring them up, and as a bonus I had learnt much about the ways of otters. A much more detailed account was published by Heinemann the next year in my book, 'Topsy and

Turvy, my two otters.' H.G. also made a film of the otters when he and Elaine were looking after them at Moorgate; this was shown on television by the BBC.

In 1961 I did a number of TV programmes for schools. I felt much more at home with these, as when I looked into the cold, impersonal glass eye of the camera, I was able to imagine that I was in class and seeing a row of faces in front of me. Eric Simms was the producer, and the first I did for him was on badgers - a nice easy one for me to start with. Later I was asked to do a weekly series of four programmes on the wildlife of a town garden. The filming had been expertly shot by Geoffrey Mulligan in between expeditions with David Attenborough on his 'Quest' series to the Pacific and Madagascar. My job was to present the programmes and comment on the film material in an educational context.

It was during the same year that Eric Ashby became famous for his film 'The Unknown Forest'. This contained wonderful shots of badgers, foxes, deer and other wildlife of the New Forest. He had been able to obtain excellent material of badgers in daylight, using a secluded sett where the badgers often emerged early enough to give him sufficient light for filming. It met with immediate success although the commentary by Johnny Morris - excellent in many ways - was unsuitable for this type of film. The programme ran for 45 minutes and had taken Eric four years to shoot! I had been in touch with Eric since he wrote to me after our own badger film had been shown, and now his success with badgers cemented our friendship which has persisted ever since. Eric is a splendid naturalist and an excellent cameraman; after his success with 'The Unknown Forest' he collected much more material. It was decided to use this in a programme exclusively on badgers for the 'Look' series. Eric was a very shy man and shunned publicity, so when his film was ready for transmission in 1966, after Peter Scott had introduced the subject I did the commentary. To make the programme more comprehensive, Christopher Parsons, who was producing it, asked me to do a further piece, shot on location outside a large sett in the Mendips. This enabled me to bring in aspects of reproduction and how badgers had become urbanised in some areas.

The programme was planned for a November date and everybody was looking forward to watching it, but to our disappointment it was postponed at the last moment because it was precisely at that time that the first satellite link with the United States was demonstrated and our programme had to be shown on another night.

The next programme devoted entirely to badgers was not until 1977 when new and highly sophisticated techniques made it possible to film in the dark using infra-red. 'Badger Watch' went out live and aimed to show viewers exactly what was happening at a large badger sett in Gloucestershire. Five programmes on consecutive nights were shown late in the evening. I was particularly pleased to be in on the planning and act as one of the commentators along with Chris Cheeseman and Phil Drabble. The former had been doing research on these same badgers for some time, so his know-how was invaluable.

The whole operation was very complicated and involved about 40 people. As much of the work was carried out during 'unsocial hours', it was mandatory that everyone had a hot meal in the evening. This was brought over each evening from South Wales! The greatest difficulty was avoiding any disturbance to the badgers when setting everything up. This was done a week before transmission and involved the use of an infra-red camera fixed in a tree overlooking the sett. This could be remotely controlled from a vehicle rather like a large caravan 300 metres away. The cameraman, sound recordist, producer and commentators were all in this vehicle together.

The cameraman had a monitor in which he could see what the camera was recording, and by means of something like a joystick he could move the camera in any direction he wished and zoom in on anything he wanted to show in close-up. As the sett had ten entrances, the badgers had plenty of scope for coming out at unexpected places, so tiny microphones were attached to the roof just inside each of the main entrances to catch any sounds made by a badger in that tunnel. Wires from each of the microphones ran back to the sound recordist in the vehicle. Each entrance was numbered, and the sound recordist sat with his headphones waiting for the sound of a badger in one of the tunnels. But the cameraman needed to anticipate which one, so as soon as a sound was heard, the sound recordist switched off the lines one by one until the noise was cut off: then over the intercom he would say for example, 'coming out of No.5'. The cameraman would then pan to entrance 5 and be ready with the camera running to film the animal emerge.

It was of course a gamble whether anything would be happening when the programme was scheduled, so extra recordings were made earlier in the evening to fill in if that were necessary.

There was an air of suppressed excitement in the vehicle when the time approached for transmission. We all looked eagerly at the monitor. Fortunately, each of the five programmes had its highlights, and viewers for the first time were able to share the badger-watcher's thrills just as they occurred. The programmes captured the imagination of the public and as the week progressed, more and more stayed up to see what the badgers were doing.

Strangely enough, on the first night it was a young owl which stole the show. Quite unexpectedly it emerged from its nest hole in the trunk of a large tree within the sett area and fluttered to the ground. It could not fly properly, but attempted time and again to get back to safety flapping its wings and using its claws to try and clamber up the trunk. The question in everybody's mind was whether it would succeed before the badgers discovered it. The broadcast ended with the question still unanswered and the BBC switchboard was jammed with callers asking what happened. Fortunately all was well.

By the end of the week viewers had witnessed many characteristics of badger behaviour and everybody concerned with production had pulled off a major technical achievement. So much interest had been aroused that the material obtained was made into a single programme which was shown at a more convenient time of day.

Radio programmes on natural history subjects also developed considerably over the period when I was participating and as more people became interested in natural history broadcasts the programmes became more diverse and imaginative.

On the whole, I much preferred radio to television as I felt more at ease, and preparing scripts was much easier for me than speaking off the cuff. However, this was soon to change as radio programmes were becoming too stereotyped by being fully scripted and we were expected to prepare material, but speak from notes. This was a great improvement as it sounded much more natural and there was a chance to add things that came to mind on the spur of the moment.

There was plenty of scope for this, when in 1956, Winwood Reade bravely did a programme live, late on midsummer night on location in a wood in Dyrham Park, Gloucestershire. It was called, 'Waiting in the Dark'. Brian Vesey-FitzGerald was leaning on a gate at the edge of the wood with one microphone, and I was up a tree near a badger sett with another. Winwood controlled the programme from the tree I was in, and could communicate with Brian and also be in touch with London. We were expected to comment on anything we saw, and if nothing particular was happening, the programme was briefly returned to the studio in London for light music! Unfortunately, there had been so much disturbance during the preparation for the programme that the likelihood of badgers emerging was not great, but we hoped for the best. In the event, more happened during the rehearsal the night before than on the day we were broadcasting, and on the night we heard more than we saw, but we whispered into the microphone anything we thought might be of interest. The Observer aptly summed it up with more kindness than I expected, when it reported, 'This was the nightingale business all over again. Practically nothing happened, but everybody was pleasant, and the atmosphere was so good that it would not be kind to complain'.

On another occasion when doing a 'Naturalist' programme there was an item included on badger-watching. To make it more realistic we included a commentary made during an actual watch. Under most circumstances the badgers would have taken fright if they even heard a whisper, but a friend in Leicestershire, John Whall, had got the badgers at one sett used to the human voice and even to music as he always took his radio with him to pass the time before they emerged! We talked quietly to each other as we waited, and sure enough the badgers appeared and we were able to record a description of what was happening which could be inserted into the studio programme.

In 1959 I was particularly pleased to be asked to take part in the cele-bratory 150th edition of 'The Naturalist' with the title, 'Why be a Naturalist?', as this was one of the last programmes in which Julian Huxley took part. It was on this occasion that Ludwig Koch humourously referred to the only bird to be found on the moon as the Greater Crater Bird, a name he found almost impossible to make clear with his strong German accent.

Ludwig Koch had made a great name for himself with his sound recordings of birds. He had a priceless collection of the calls of most British species and was a real pioneer in that field. He used to cut his own wax discs on which the recordings were made. One day he rang me up and asked if he could come down to Taunton to record sounds of badgers; he thought it would be interesting to record some mammal sounds for a change. I told him badgers were not very vocal, but of course I would help if I could.

He thought it was going to be quite a simple matter and that all he had to do was to put a microphone near the sett, run out a long lead to the recorder and wait for something to happen. We had invited him to an early evening meal to leave plenty of time to get his apparatus up, but he was in no hurry to get going and I became worried that he would make a disturbance around the sett entrance and the badgers would not emerge, let alone make interesting vocalisations. When we eventually arrived at the site, it was not long before I expected emergence; Ludwig was so used to sight being the important factor when dealing with birds, that he could not be convinced of the importance of scent. However, I was able to persuade him not to trample around the entrance and we retired some 50 yards where he set up his recorder with a fresh disc and connected up the extension wire from the microphone.

He sat down and put on his headphones and patiently waited. One of the curses of sound recording, then as now, was interference from wind, aircraft or cars, but this time he was pleased. It was all very quiet. Emergence time came and went; still not a sound, so after waiting another hour and still hearing nothing we regretfully decided to pack up. On reeling in the wire he found the connection between the lead and the extension had been loose! No wonder everything had been so quiet. Poor Ludwig! He was quite shattered. It certainly hadn't been his day.

Occasionally I was asked to do different kinds of programmes such as book reviews. One book I remember particularly was 'An Otter in the House' by Dorothy Wisbeski as I could enter into her hilarious descriptions of an otter's mischievousness from personal experience.

I also had the privilege of joining Elspeth Huxley in interviewing Armand Denis on a programme called 'Frankly Speaking'. Armand and his wife, Michaela, had made great names for themselves for their series of early safari programmes in Africa. He had lived a very adventurous life in the wilds of Asia, Africa, Australasia and South America and had just written his autobiography. The object of the programme was to ask searching questions to bring out the character of the person concerned. I had not done an interview before and was somewhat apprehensive; in the event the problem was not asking the right questions, but stopping Armand from going on indefinitely. He loved talking and did so in a very amusing manner.

One of the radio programmes I enjoyed most was 'Country Questions'. It was started in 1946 to answer questions on a wide range of country matters, but mainly agriculture, horticulture and natural history. The three panellists were Ralph Wightman, Eric Hobbis and Maxwell Knight. I was very pleased to be asked to join the panel in the late fifties to alternate with Maxwell Knight. It was a monthly programme which went out on Sundays after the news in the lunch hour. We were given the questions about a week in advance, which was just as well as Max or I had to cover the whole range of natural history! Some of the questions were a real challenge and a few were unanswerable, so those of greatest interest were selected. We arrived on the Sunday morning ready for a rehearsal before lunch. Usually we were the only people to have lunch on a Sunday and the canteen was opened specially for us. However, Trades Union rules soon put a stop to that. The programme went out live, with Jack Longland as question master and Bill Coysh as producer.

Eric was always the first to arrive as it was a tradition that he always made a flower arrangement in the studio which was appropriate for the time of year; the flowers came from plants in his own garden. The arrangements were always beautifully done and it was a shame it was not a TV programme so that they could be seen rather than just described. However, it was a good talking point and an easy introduction to the programme for Jack Longland who was able to bring us all in quickly with our comments. Eric was an expert horticulturist who worked at Long Ashton Research Station.

Ralph Wightman was a most colourful character, his broad Dorset accent adding considerably to his broadcasting charisma. He had a wide knowledge of farming and country lore and could talk interestingly on many subjects. He was a popular broadcaster, and as a member of the team, I valued his contributions immensely. If I found myself stuck for a word, or got into difficulties, Ralph would chip in with some comment or suggestion which would give me time to collect my thoughts. He was a great ally.

After one of these programmes I had a letter from a Hilda Neal who wrote to ask if I was related to the Reverend Frederick Neal? She turned out to be a cousin of my father and invited me to call at her home when I was in London. She was an interesting lady who had run a secretarial school, but had long since retired. She was able to tell me quite a lot about other members of the Neal family I knew little about, and Bill and I used to call and see her every now and then until her death. She was our last link with that generation of Neals and it was with great interest that we listened to her anecdotes, related with vividness and charm.

I always enjoyed the bi-monthly trips to Bristol for 'Country Questions'. For a few hours I left all thoughts of school behind, and returned refreshed. The A 38 had very little traffic early on a Sunday morning and as I drove, I used to rehearse aloud to myself the main points I wanted to make when answering some of the questions. In the event, it usually turned out rather differently from what was anticipated, as Jack Longland often interjected questions which you were unprepared for, and which kept you on your toes and gave a genuine freshness to the programme. Usually, one of us led off with the main answer and the others commented appropriately.

One Sunday morning when Max was due to be on the programme, Bill Coysh, the producer, rang me up to say Max had been taken ill and would I stand in? I had not seen the questions and rehearsal was in a couple of hours time. He allayed some of my fears by saying he would select some questions he thought I could cope with without too many problems and read out several on the phone for me to think about on my journey to Bristol. The rehearsal was not as bad as it might have been, and when we went on the air, Bill seemed to be happy about it.

On another occasion it was the producer who was ill, so the studio manager took over the timing and we decided amongst ourselves what questions we would answer and the order of procedure. Thankfully, it went off without a hitch. Live programmes were always fun as you never quite knew whether all would go according to plan. In the middle of one programme I got frightful cramp in one leg and was in agony. Fortunately, it came on when somebody else was speaking, but I had to stand up as quietly as possible because of the microphone, walk around the room and do exercises. It soon went off and I was able to creep back to my place before it was my turn. The others soon realised that it was nothing more serious than cramp and carried on as usual.

To mark the 150th edition of 'Country Questions', the BBC decided to televise a couple of programmes as an experiment. Each of us was given a subject best answered with the help of visual material, and each asked to guess the nature of a mystery object and what it was used for. It was something nobody was likely to have seen before and had been borrowed from a museum. The programme was interesting to do, but I do not think any of us felt as relaxed as on radio and after two programmes we reverted to sound once more. Vincent Waite took over as question master from Jack Longland and the series went on for another seven years before the format was changed to allow experts from other fields to take part. This gave the public a rest from hearing the same old voices, although we continued to take part occasionally.

The new programme was called 'Country Parliament', and as listeners sent in questions, they were categorised to some extent so that when enough had been collected on a particular subject, such as birds, mammals, marine life, fungi, pests or farming practice, an appropriate person was invited to take part. The series was produced by John Sparks. However, it was not long before interest in wildlife programmes increased still further and a more flexible format was needed. The new series which went out weekly was then called, 'The Living World'. This had a long and successful run with Derek Jones as question-master and Dilys Breese as producer.

To bring diversity to these programmes, one week there would be questions and answers as before, the next would be more of a magazine programme with a number of topical items, the following week a more general subject would be discussed in greater depth, and the fourth would be a nature trail when Derek Jones was accompanied by a natu-ralist to some area he knew well and discuss anything interesting they saw during the trip.

I took part in two of these nature trails, the first taking place one December when we went to a favourite spot of mine in the Blackdown Hills, called Priors Park Wood. I had studied this area in some detail with boys from the school. It was an interesting locality as the geology changed as you climbed up the valley and this was reflected in the type of flora. You started with clay which supported oak woodland; then the soil changed to clay with limestone, with ash dominating the tree layer; higher up there was a boggy area dominated by alder and ferns, and near the top you came to the greensand and churt where bracken took over. There was even a little heather in places where the soil was acidic.

December at first sight was not an ideal month for seeing the fauna, but there was plenty of evidence of the activities of some species. Animal tracks were abundant, particularly those of roe, and one of their rutting rings was still visible although it had probably been last used the previous July. You could also see the damage they caused to young trees by eating the leading shoots or scarring them with their antlers. A fast-flowing stream ran down the valley from the boggy area above the clay and this revealed typical aquatic animals clinging to the undersides of the larger stones in the stream bed, such as caddis, mayfly larvae, leeches and a species of flatworm which was a relict of the Ice-Age. There was a large badger sett dug in the greensand near the top of the valley and all the usual signs of occupation were there for the finding. This type of programme is always interesting to do as you never quite know what will turn up on the day.

The other nature trail was to Steepholm Island in the Bristol Channel - about midway between England and Wales. I used to take my sixth-formers over for the day most years as it provided an excellent example of an ecosystem where the factors influencing the fauna and flora were fairly obvious. Being an island, it showed the effect of isolation; its calcareous nature and previous habitation by man influenced the composition of the flora, and there were clear indications of the effects of strong winds, salt spray and the thousands of gulls which nested there.

The cliffs are high and in places inaccessible, so we started the trail by going round the island in the boat. From this view-point we were fortunate to see the local peregrine fly from its nest site and get near to the small colony of shags on their ledges.

It is not always easy to land as there is only one proper beach, and if the wind is rough and in the wrong quarter you have a problem. On this occasion we had to land on some rocks on the more sheltered side of the island and clamber to the top with all the equipment. The rocks were very slippery, I was careless and fell flat on my back hitting my head on the rock. For a few moments I felt quite dazed. Dilys Breese, who was producing the programme, witnessed the event with mixed feelings, one being concern for me, the other, that perhaps this would be the end of her programme. I have a feeling the latter was uppermost in her mind! However, I was not badly hurt and the programme went ahead as planned which was just as well as it was scheduled to be broadcast during Nature Week which was only a few days away.

There was plenty to talk about on this programme as about 6,000 pairs of herring gulls were nesting and the young chicks were all over the place. There was a clear distinction between the choice of nest sites by herring gulls, the much smaller number of lesser black-backed and the few greater black-backed. It was the lesser black-backed that were more aggressive when we approached their nests, repeatedly dive bombing us.

The effect of the guano greatly influenced the flora, and where nests were concentrated, only alexanders, nettles and elders could cope satisfactorily with the extra nitrogen. The alexanders had been brought over by the monks in mediaeval times as well as the species for which the island is famous - the wild peony, *Paeonia officinalis*, which is found nowhere else in Britain; it is of Mediterranean origin. Another introduction was the wild leek, *Allium ampeloprasum*.

We all enjoyed our day as there had been so much of interest to see and discuss. When we had to leave we were relieved to find that the boatman could pick us up from the beach as the wind was no longer a problem.

Another innovation for radio was to broadcast before live audiences where the questions came from those present. A few were known in advance, but others were handed in as the audience arrived and quickly sorted according to the expertise of the panel. The idea was to give the audience an hour's entertainment, and the whole discussion was recorded. From this only half an hour was broadcast the following Sunday, so if anybody made a mess of their answer it could be edited out. That was merciful! I took part in several of these and found them fun to do, particularly the one held at Fyne Court, the Headquarters of the Somerset Trust for Nature Conservation where I was on my home ground.

I always enjoyed taking part in programmes, not least because I met so many interesting people and made such good friends. The Natural History Unit in Bristol always appeared to me to employ such congenial and enthusiastic staff and their expertise was phenomenal. I greatly appreciated my visits to the Unit.

Chapter Eleven

The life cycle of the badger

Having been encouraged at my M.Sc. interview to continue my research into the reproductive cycle of the badger, I took every opportunity to get more data. One of my main objectives was to correlate my field observations of badger behaviour at different times of the year with stages in the life cycle, deduced from the state of the reproductive system in any badger carcasses I could collect.

More field observations were needed on times of mating and sexual behaviour. This was too time-consuming for me to carry out on a regular basis. However, Keith and Roger were extremely keen to help and offered to watch as much as possible, especially in the early months of the year when data were scarce. I was also corresponding with a number of dedicated badger-watchers who were pleased to send me any records of mating they had noted.

From these various sources and from my previous observations, it soon became evident that mating could occur during any month of the year from February to October. (Many years later it was also witnessed during the remaining winter months.) Mating usually lasted a long time, sometimes up to an hour, at other times only a few minutes. I wondered why? It seemed obvious that long matings were more important but there might be some significance in the shorter matings too. It was puzzling. When the frequency of long-duration matings was plotted on a graph, there appeared to be three peak periods: one in February, another in May and a further smaller one in the autumn.

The explanations of these results could only be found by dissecting large numbers of badgers of different ages and during all months of the year. I looked for ways and means of getting hold of any bodies. Unfortunately for the badgers, but helpful to me, road casualties were not uncommon, and gradually the word got around that I was on the lookout for dead ones. Over the next few years people would give me a ring if they saw one by the roadside and I would go out as soon as possible to collect the body. Sometimes they arrived under unusual circumstances. On 11 March 1954 there was a ring at the door when we were having breakfast and there was a taximan who had heard I was collecting dead badgers. I confirmed that that was so. He said he had one in the taxi! Early that morning, he had run over one after taking a bend rather fast on his way to the station. It was a sow. In its stomach I found 203 large earthworms. A fortnight later the same man called again with another badger, this time a boar. He had knocked it over at the identical spot, taking the same man to catch the corresponding train! Clearly the two animals had come from the same sett and were returning at the same time using their habitual crossing place on the road. This animal's stomach contained 165 earthworms and 2 moles! Thus in various ways and over a long period I was able to collect a good sample of dead animals to work on.

On another occasion a zoologist who had been working in the Antarctic on penguins was lecturing to the school; we put him up for the night. While he was with us I had a call to say that a badger had been run over just outside this person's house only an hour ago. Fresh material is always more valuable, and as my friend was interested in my badger work, he came with me to pick it up. The body was still warm when we collected it. When I was making the dissection, a sudden thought struck him. He was a member of the Quadrupeds Club and very shortly was attending their dinner when each person had to provide a contribution obtained from the wild. He had heard that badger hams were edible and asked if I had eaten any? I said I had, and although a bit musky, when pickled in saltpetre were quite acceptable; so he asked if he could have a couple. When I took him to the station, the last thing he said to me was "You are sure those hams are all right?". I reassured him, saying that we knew the body was absolutely fresh and I had not suffered from having eaten badger hams. I thought no more about it until he rang me a few days later. He told me he had still felt uneasy about the hams, so that night had given a few small pieces to some rats in his laboratory. The next morning, the rats were dead! The only possible explanation I could think of was that the badger had eaten some bait containing strychnine, put down for foxes illegally, and staggered across the road before being run down. I learnt my lesson for all time and was enormously grateful for his hunch - just as he was!

It was always with some excitement that I made another badger dissection. Would it provide a further clue towards a better under-standing of the cycle or would it merely confirm what I already knew? It was rather like trying to solve a complex detective story from odd pieces of evidence collected over a long period. I enjoyed this sort of enquiry very much; for as long as I could remember I wanted to understand the reasons behind what I was observing concerning living things. I suppose most naturalists are curious creatures - at any rate in one sense of that word.

Each animal was weighed, measured, dissected and roughly put into its age group, by noting the size of the ridge on its skull and the condition of its teeth. Stomach contents were analysed and the reproductive system carefully removed. It was possible to tell from a superficial examination of the ovaries and uterus whether the badger was immature or adult, and if mature, whether it was nearing ovulation or had already produced eggs. In the latter case the *corpora lutea* - the glands which develop after ovulation - showed up as yellowish patches or bumps and could be counted. If corpora were present, it was likely that blastocysts would be there too, so I opened up the two horns of the uterus and searched for these transparent spheres less than 2mm in diameter, which if fresh, looked like air bubbles.

Blastocysts develop from fertilized eggs, and are hollow spheres of cells which remain unattached within the uterus, hardly growing at all for several months. I wanted to find out how early in the year they appeared. Fischer had not found them before July, yet we knew matings occurred before that. I wanted to find out how early in the year the blastocysts appeared and discover when they implanted in this country compared with Fischer's data for Germany. This would indicate the duration of the period of delayed implantation and also how it varied from one animal to another. In addition, there was the far more difficult question of why implantation occurred when it did.

When I made a dissection, the whole reproductive system was removed and placed in a fixative and representative portions were prepared for sectioning with a microtome - an instrument rather like a sophisticated bacon-cutter which cut extremely thin sections of the material which had been embedded in wax.

We had a microtome in the laboratory but the process of preparing the material - embedding it in wax of the right melting point, cutting the sections and staining them - was very time-consuming and you needed a lot of experience to get perfect results. I had done quite a lot at university and in school to provide specimens for classwork, but what I needed now were serial sections which showed progressive changes in the object as you sectioned it from one end to the other. I wished I had a technician who could do this; instead I had to do what I could with my limited skills when time was available. However, I gradually collected some very interesting slides illustrating different stages in the cycle.

I soon found I had two main problems: I needed specialist interpretation of the material, my own knowledge being inadequate, and I had too much material to handle with insufficient time and ability to do all that was needed. I was fortunate in my friends. Dr Leo Harrison Matthews was a reproductive mammalogist in addition to being a first-class zoologist, and when he saw my material, suggested I should get in touch with Professor Amoroso (inevitably nick-named Amo) who was Professor of Physiology at the Royal Veterinary College, London. I hoped he could spare the time and be sufficiently interested to help as he was in the forefront of reproductive physiological research. It would be wonderful to get his help.

I was delighted when Amo agreed to see me and examine my material. We met at his laboratory in London and he was very helpful and most intrigued by what I was able to show him. I demonstrated how I dissected a badger, and he asked me to take some photographs of the reproductive system *in situ*. While I was doing this, he had to go to another part of the building, saying he would return in a few minutes. It was a Saturday afternoon. I took the photos and awaited his return, but no Amo appeared. After an hour, I became somewhat alarmed as there was nobody else about and I could not imagine what had happened. I hoped he was not sufficiently absent-minded to have gone home and left me to it! However, he did at last turn up. He had got stuck in the lift and only escaped when the caretaker heard the alarm and took the necessary steps. He was not very pleased. However, he was very encouraging about my work and indicated that he thought he could help. He took me home to his flat for the night and we discussed things in detail. I was very pleased when he said he would get all my material sectioned in his department if I would bring it up to the Veterinary College.

Unfortunately, he made little progress; he was a very busy man and obviously my material was way down on his list of priorities. When he went abroad for a long spell, I realised that I was getting nowhere, so in desperation I asked his assistant to retrieve all my precious material. This he was able to do before Amo returned from America! Leo was distressed that I had been treated so badly and suggested another friend of his who might help. This was Richard J.Harrison, Professor of Anatomy at the London Hospital Medical School. He had been working on the reproductive cycle of seals and was delighted to hear about some of the intriguing problems the badger cycle was throwing up.

Richard was a wonderful help. He not only had the expert knowledge I lacked, but was willing to put his technician on to sectioning all my material. It was great to be able to collaborate in this way, and he became as excited as I was as the story gradually unfolded. However, we knew we would not get to the bottom of this complex cycle until we had much more material, especially at certain times of the year, so I redoubled my efforts to collect as many carcasses as I could. I made my own assessment of each animal dissected and sent the relevant material to him for sectioning. Periodically, I would go up to London and we would have sessions looking critically at the sections and planning further investigations.

My sixth-formers became very intrigued with what I was doing and I used to discuss some of the problems with them. Occasionally, I would use one of the badgers as a demonstration to more junior forms. It was exciting for them to see a dissection of something bigger than a rat. If anybody did not wish to see what was going on he was not forced to watch as some can be sensitive to such things, but I found it was a good opportunity to show how wonderfully all the organs were arranged inside the body of a large mammal, and one not all that different from their own. Most boys were very glad of the experience of seeing a dissection.

It was quite a problem disposing of all the bodies after dissection. When the central heating boiler was in action they could be incinerated, but at other times they had to be buried behind the science block by the boiler-man. I never quite knew what he thought of it all. This collection of skeletons, if discovered by future archaeologists, would certainly raise some intriguing questions!

From the sections of ovaries we were making, it became clear that most female badgers had an oestrus soon after the birth of their cubs and that young sows had their first oestrus about the same time, when about a year old. These animals would account for the February peak in long-duration matings. However, we found that many yearlings did not become mature until later in the year, which could account for some of the later matings. The research also showed that some sows had corpora but no blastocysts were present, suggesting that mating had taken place, but the eggs had not been fertilized. It was likely in these cases that they would have another oestrus after lactation had finished as this was so in some other species. These, along with those yearlings which were late in maturing, might provide the explanation for the May matings. We also had evidence that a few did not become mature until the autumn - a possible explanation for matings seen then. But we needed more material to test these hypotheses.

As more and more badgers were examined we realised that the cycle was even more complex than we had imagined. Some of the sows showed obvious signs of coming into oestrus and yet they already had healthy blastocysts within their uteri, so they had already mated successfully and yet were coming into heat again! No species exhibiting delayed implanation had previously shown such a phenomenon. We were very intrigued and excited. But how could we prove it?

We were lucky. In October, I dissected a sow which from superficial examination appeared to have just ovulated, and yet it contained several healthy blastocysts. I thought it must just have mated, and confirmed this by taking a vaginal smear which showed the presence of sperms. I sent the material to Richard and waited impatiently for the results.

I was staying with Marge when he rang me up to tell me he had some good news and could he come down and discuss it? My sister had a microscope and we looked at the sections. At last we had got proof of what we had suspected. The ovaries showed two sets of corpora, some old from the first mating, some new ones just forming - perhaps two days old - confirming the recent mating. That meant that ovulation had just taken place and the eggs should therefore be somewhere in the tube which leads from the ovary to the uterus. So the tube was serially sectioned, and there they were! So we had proof at last that badgers can have a secondary oestrus during the period of delay involving ovulation and the formation of new corpora. However, in this case the eggs were not fertilized and no further blastocysts would have developed. This explained our findings that the number of corpora increased from an average of 4.2 up to July, to 6.2 for the later part of the year. It also might explain some of the matings which had been observed in the wild later in the year, including short-duration ones. Very recently it has been shown that some eggs may be fertilized during a secondary oestrus and hence extra blastocysts can be added to those already there.

While this research was going on, John Sankey, who was in charge of the Field Studies Centre at Juniper Hall, Dorking, and a keen badger-watching friend of many years' standing, was keeping a group of badgers in captivity and trying to breed them. When I first met John, he had a tame sow called Sally which would accompany him in the car wherever he went and guard it in his absence. The car was never stolen!

John was happy to collaborate and provided us with details of matings which occurred on four successive years. When the sow was on heat, she copulated on a number of occasions over a period of five days, so he had a good indication of the length of oestrus. Unfortunately, cubs were only produced on one occasion but much was learnt from those badgers he looked after so well.

Richard had an animal house at the top of the London Hospital Medical School and kept some badgers there to try and find out more about conditions necessary for the implantation of the blastocysts, a problem we were very interested to solve if possible. On one occasion when I was there, one of these badgers escaped on to the roof. For one awful moment I had a frightening vision of it clambering over the parapet and hurtling down on to the Whitechapel Road far below. Fortunately this did not happen and it was quickly recaptured.

It became clear to us that implantation usually occurred in December or very early January in south-west England and was triggered off by hormonal stimuli which caused the lining of the uterus to become receptive. In sections of the uterus you could easily see the changes in structure of the lining cells under hormonal influence. But the big question was what factors were involved in bringing about this hormonal change in the first place?

Most researchers considered a climatic factor such as day-length responsible, but from what I knew of badger behaviour I could not see how this could be. Day-length was known to influence the time of implantation in some species; this had also been proved in badgers kept in captivity under experimental light conditions by a French worker, Dr Canivenc, but I felt this was most unlikely to occur in the wild for several reasons. In early winter - the period leading up to implantation - badgers were completely nocturnal and their emergence time quite unpredictable, so how did they receive the change in day-length stimulus? In addition, implantation often occurred before the shortest day, sometimes afterwards; furthermore it took place earlier in more southern latitudes where day-length changes were less extreme. I also knew of examples where two sows living in the same sett had had cubs five weeks apart and yet had lived under exactly the same climatic conditions, so I felt that the hormonal influence had to be triggered off by an internal factor which differed from badger to badger.

Field evidence showed that badgers were least active around implantation time and I thought this might be significant. We had evidence that during the long period of delay when the blastocysts were in the uteri, steroidal hormones were secreted only in small amounts, insufficient to bring about implantation. My hypothesis, developed over the next few years, was that during this time these hormones, being soluble in fat, gradually accumulate in the body fat, just as the insecticide, DDT is known to do. This continues throughout the period of delay until the sow goes into a state of semi-dormancy around mid-November and starts to live off its stored fat. Then, as the fat is broken down, the hormones are released into the blood stream in sufficient quantity to bring about implantation. This hypothesis would explain why sows living in the same locality or in different latitudes may vary in implantation times. This mechanism could also apply to other species such as bears which also have a period of delay with implantation taking place during their winter dormancy when living off their stored fat. I hope that one day somebody will do the necessary research to prove or disprove this hypothesis as I have had neither the time nor the opportunity to do it myself. Evidence that appears to support this view is that very recently it has been shown that sows which are in better condition and heavier by autumn (have more fat?) are more likely to breed.

The advantage of delayed implantation in badgers is that whatever the time of mating, implantation occurs at roughly the same period of the year and the cubs are born at the best possible time for their survival. Early February (which is usual) may not seem ideal, but the cubs are kept warm, thanks to the central heating system provided by the mother and the insulating properties of the bedding in which they lie. Also, because of the long period of lactation - at least three months - the cubs are sufficiently large by the time they are weaned to make full use of the good food supply which in a normal year is abundant about that time. This allows them plenty of time to grow and put on fat before the rigours of winter make feeding more difficult. Thus delayed implantation is a useful adaptation for their survival.

We wrote up our research for the Transactions of the Zoological Society of London, and I submitted it as a thesis to London University for a doctorate. I was awarded my Ph.D. in 1960. I certainly could not have done this without Richard's enthusiastic help and encouragement. It had been another rewarding partnership for me as it combined my experience of badgers and their behaviour in the wild with Richard's expertise in reproductive anatomy and physiology. Neither line of enquiry on its own would have got us as far. It was also a marvellous help to have such excellent assistance from his chief technician. My good fortune to work with Richard was underlined when he later became Professor of Anatomy at Cambridge where he continued his work on seals, and in recognition of his contributions to science was elected a Fellow of the Royal Society.

The publication of the research stimulated a lot of interest as a number of scientists in various parts of the world were working on delayed implantation. Richard and I were invited to attend meetings and conferences and I met a lot of interesting researchers in consequence. One symposium was rather special as it was arranged by the CIBA

Foundation for the promotion of international co-operation in medical and chemical research. The aim was to bring together small groups of people who were working on the same subject for intimate discussion. Travel and hospitality were funded. About 20 of us gathered to discuss implantation and Richard and I were asked to give a paper. He wanted me to present this, but I did so with some diffidence as I was the only one present who was not a professional researcher. However, it was a stimulating experience and the main bonus for me was to hear what others were doing and discuss the problems with like-minded people.

I continued to collect material during the 1960s which confirmed our findings and some of this proved of interest in other ways. At this time there was much anxiety over the effects of insecticides such as dieldrin on wildlife, one being a possible cause of reproductive failure in animals at the end of their food chain. I was now paying more attention to male badgers, and when the testes of some of these were sectioned, there were signs of abnormalities in tissues involved in sperm production. Cause and effect were not established but there was strong evidence that ingestion of the pesticide was the cause. The appearance of the histology was very similar to that found in other animals known to have died from this poisoning and the material we had was obtained at a time when these effects were being demonstrated in other species. Richard and I were fairly certain, but only experimentation would prove it, and this we did not pursue.

I had greatly enjoyed doing the research. It had brought me in close contact with scientists working on similar problems and given me the opportunity to have a foot in university life while still doing my main job at school. It had also given me greater insight into research techniques and I shall always be grateful for the knowledge gained and friendships made. However, circumstances dictated that the next ten years at Taunton School before I retired would be tough and bring greater responsibilities and there would be little time for further research, but I should at least be able to keep up with progress by attending symposia, analysing research papers and through correspondence. Retirement might bring further opportunities. Meanwhile my other enthusiasms had to be left for the holidays. Thankfully, one of the great advantages (and necessities) of the teaching profession was that holidays were long, and these I hoped to exploit to the full.

Chapter Twelve

Photography and Expeditions

I had been very keen on photography, always doing my own processing. I never had a proper darkroom, but could quickly adapt the bathroom for the purpose. All three sons helped at various times and were proficient in all the main techniques. I always enjoyed making enlargements of my best pictures, and thanks to a friend, who exhibited regularly and had taught me various techniques, I had badger pictures accepted soon after the war by the Royal Photographic Society for their annual exhibition. I was particularly pleased to go to the opening in London and meet other natural history photographers, including Eric Hosking and Walter Higham. Strangely enough they had only two eyes between them. I never heard how Walter lost one of his, but Eric lost an eye to the talons of an owl when photographing near the nest. However, the disability did not affect the excellence of Eric's bird photography for which he became world famous. The year I was there, the exhibition was opened by Lady Buchan, wife of Sir John Buchan, the novelist I admired so much as a boy for his adventure stories. All our family were photo-graphically-minded as Betty also took excellent photos and compiled a fine record of family activities over the years.

In 1959 I bought a 16mm Bolex camera for filming. When Topsy and Turvy were small I had to depend on others to do the filming and this prompted me to take the plunge and try my hand at cine work. Filming in 16mm was an expensive luxury, but I hoped I would be able to get the BBC to accept some of my material if it were good enough. However, what I wanted to do most was to produce films for schools, as I knew from my own experience how valuable they were for teaching purposes; very few were available which were ecologically orientated, so that was the line I wished to pursue.

I started on Woodland Ecology as this was something I had studied in some depth. Having written a small book about it based on Thurlbear Wood, I intended to do most of the filming there. My idea was to show the flora throughout the year and its adaptations to seasonal changes then give examples of how typical species of animals exploit the food available.

I started with the prevernal aspect: the trees bare of leaves and the ground flora beginning to blossom under good light conditions. Then, the leaves of the oaks and hazels unfurling, cutting off some light, bluebells and other typical plants taking over from the wood anemones, primroses and dog's mercury. At the end of May, when shade was considerable, how most flowering plants were over apart from a few later species found bordering the rides where there was still sufficient light. Also, how woodland plants adapted to this darker phase by enlarging their leaf surface or climbing to the light while others died down altogether and became dormant until the following spring. As summer merged into autumn, how fruits were ripening and being dispersed in various ways, many by woodland birds and mammals. In late autumn, the leaves turning colour and falling, providing ample material for the saprophytic fungi and bacteria to recycle the organic matter, enriching the soil. In winter, the prominence of evergreens such as ivy and the disappearance of many herbaceous species below ground. Signs of the latter were shown by scraping away the carpet of dead leaves and digging to varying depths to find their rhizomes or tubers - food stores which made quick growth in the spring possible and allowed these species to exploit the early light phase.

When dealing with the fauna, I wanted to give some idea of the enormous diversity of species existing in an oak wood, the majority of which are never seen by the casual observer. This gave scope for demonstrating how to search for them and show where they hide away. As the film was intended for schools, I used boys wherever possible to demonstrate techniques. Andrew was glad to help; I filmed him using a beating tray, sweep net, and sieving leaf litter to discover the specialised fauna in that habitat. Another boy turned over dead tree trunks and stripped off their loose bark to expose the animals below and broke up some rotten wood to find the beetle larvae in the tunnels they had bored. I also included shots of the moth trap to show the great number of moths found in woodland at night.

A good friend, Ken Watkins, who had made some excellent nature films, helped with some tricky close-ups and provided me with a few extra sequences I needed of woodland birds. Finally I showed some of the more shy woodland mammals such as deer and foxes. For deer, I went down to the New Forest where Eric Ashby showed me places where they were often to be found soon after dawn when the forest was undisturbed. Fox material was more difficult to get without spending more time than I could afford, but I was lucky because one of the boys, Maurice Kirk, was bringing up an orphaned fox cub, and although its actions were quite unpredictable when loose in a wood, I was able to get useful shots of its general behaviour.

Gateways, educational film makers and distributors, were willing to process the material and advertise the films. A number were bought by education authorities for use in schools under their jurisdiction, and I was very pleased that some of the work I had done with my own sixth-formers at Thurlbear could be passed on to a wider audience in an audio-visual manner.

One project I found fun to do arose from a request from Douglas Fisher to help over a film on badgers he wanted to make for Granada Television. I knew of a large sett at Hatch Beauchamp near Taunton which was on a slope in a deciduous wood belonging to Mrs Hamilton Gault. She was pleased to co-operate. It meant rigging up a mains supply of electricity and building a high platform further down the slope below the sett to obtain good views of the many entrances. We got this prepared early in the year ready for the time when cubs were expected above ground.

One evening before filming started we invited Mrs Hamilton Gault to see some of her own badgers as she had never watched them before. Betty came too. Mrs Gault was a lot older than we were but very game. Climbing the long ladder to the platform was no mean feat for her. However, all was well, the badgers emerged, and we got views of several before they went off to forage. Climbing down again in the dark was more difficult, but Mrs Gault thoroughly enjoyed seeing her badgers properly for the first time.

The filming was only partially successful, but sufficient sequences were obtained to make a short film. Douglas badly wanted to get under-ground pictures as these had never been taken before. The difficulties were considerable, but he was able to use the smallest remotely-controlled television camera available; this worked on a closed-circuit infra-red system. The camera was attached to a vehicle rather like a roller skate which he hoped to guide down the tunnel as far as possible on the end of a long springy wire. It would then be left in position and we could watch for any badger on a monitor in the van parked well away from the sett. This experiment was done in 1964 - long before the present sophisticated electronics were developed.

He had more faith in the contraption than I had, but nobody had experimented in this way with such a device before and it was worth a try. After a long wait we did actually see a badger in the tunnel and Douglas got some film, but the sequence was poor and not long enough to be worth including in the film. It was disappointing, as we had hoped for some unique footage, but it had been amusing to make the attempt.

One of the places I used to visit with members of the school Natural History Society to study freshwater ecology was the Somerset Levels. The rhines (ditches) were rich in plants and animals, especially those which were alkaline due to run-off from the Poldon Hills. We used to keep some of the more interesting species in aquaria for further study; one animal which greatly intrigued me was the water spider.

These spiders are wonderfully adapted to underwater life although they are really terrestrial animals dependent on breathing atmospheric air. The abdomen is closely covered in hairs which prevent the body getting wet when it enters the water. It swims well, taking the vital air with it like a silvery envelope trapped by the body hairs. We watched it making a home for itself under the water. First a network of silk was formed under a leaf to act as a roof, then longer threads were drawn out from the silk glands and fastened like guy ropes to any supports. Eventually an inverted bell was formed which was filled with air which the spider brought from the surface, bubble by bubble. This bell with its air reservoir acted as its home and refuge

I decided to film the whole life history if I could. It was difficult to get the intense light necessary for close-ups as my light source gave out much heat and had to be close to the lens which I feared might be damaged. I had to protect the lens with pliable asbestos sheeting and only switch on when something was happening. I had already obtained a number of shots showing general behaviour but badly wanted sequences showing the filling of the bubble with air. The spider always seemed to do this when I was not there!

One morning, I had a free period from teaching and had everything set up to film the spider if it would oblige. Nothing happened by the time the class bell went for my next period. It was, of course, at that very moment that the spider started to go to the surface to collect air. I switched on the light and started to film, but the spider was in no hurry. At last she broke surface, collected a large bubble of air between her hind legs and swam down with it, manoeuvring into position before releasing it into the bell. This was repeated and I had the sequence I wanted. I was so engrossed looking down the eye-piece that I had forgotten all about my form. When the shots were safely recorded I took my eye away from the camera only to find my whole class watching; they had been there for some time without making a sound! It had been an interesting change from a formal lesson.

Eventually, I was able to portray all the spider's typical behaviour, including catching its prey under water, defending its bell against other spiders and reproducing. A special bell was made for breeding which was white and opaque. In close-up you could see the spider squirting liquid silk on to its surface to make it stronger, the silk hardening immediately. Other threads were then laid down so that the entrance became a narrow cone of silk which made the job of guarding the nest easier. A number of eggs were laid under the roof of the bell and the spider remained on guard until they hatched. It was a great day when a number of young spiders emerged, each enclosed in its silvery envelope of air. However, they were troublesome to film, being so small and active.

The making of this film gave me a lot of satisfaction; I learnt much about these remarkable spiders in the process and it provided schools with an ideal example of specialist adaptations of a terrestrial animal to an almost completely aquatic existence. Apart from its use by schools, extracts of the film were used as an item on the children's TV programme 'Animal Magic'. This series was produced by Douglas Thomas and made so popular by Johnny Morris with his delightful brand of humour. The artist, Keith Shackleton, also took part, drawing animals in the studio with remarkable speed and skill.

Another film I enjoyed making was 'Seashore Ecology'. This was largely based on Salcombe as I had done so much work there with the boys and this locality could not be bettered for ecological classwork. My idea was to show good examples of different types of shore, the effects of tides and wave action on the typical animals that lived there and their adaptations to these difficult conditions.

Andrew was now particularly keen on filming and had already decided that what he wanted to do was to take a degree in natural sciences to obtain the background knowledge, then a diploma in photography which included cine, and apply for a job in the BBC. Little did I think at that time that he would become a leading wildlife producer and eventually become Head of the Natural History Unit in Bristol. He helped with the sea-shore filming with much enthusiasm and we spent some time together at Salcombe getting some of the sequences needed. I also involved boys who came on biological camps with me, as it was appropriate that students should demonstrate various techniques for finding the animals and the precautions to be taken to avoid harming them or the habitat in the process.

The film took some time to complete as it had to be done in the holidays, when the tides were right and, hopefully, under good weather conditions. I also wanted to include plankton and the species which live below the shore line as they play an important part in the food web of shore animals when the tide covers them. This would involve using a boat from which plankton collecting and dredging could be done.

By this time, 1964, Keith had graduated at Cambridge, done his teaching practice at Winchester College under Bunny Dowdeswell and was teaching biology at Harrow County School. We decided that it would be fun to combine forces and run a biological expedition to Inverary in Argyll for boys in both our schools. Loch Fyne was ideal for our purpose, being an extensive arm of the sea with good facilities for shore work in different habitats. Furthermore, we had heard that there was a good possibility of hiring a boat which once served as a small trawler and now belonged to a local schoolmaster.

Boys from both schools were glad to go, and I was particularly pleased that one of my old students, Neil Croll, could come and help. He was studying biology at London University and had been with me on several previous expeditions when at school. I also had valuable co-operation from a former pupil from Rendcomb days, Dick Margetts, who was a fisheries research worker at Lowestoft. He offered to send a small dredge to Inverary which I could use on the boat. Betty of course came too and helped with the organisation.

We put up at Dalchenna for eight days. The weather at times was extremely cold for early April and shore collecting was quite a challenge for the less enthusiastic, but everybody stuck at it and the trip was a great success. I was amused when we collected on the shore for the first time and was explaining what we were going to do, to notice that one of the London boys was wearing winklepicker shoes. Nothing could have been less suitable as they were very long and thin with pointed toes. For reasons difficult for most of us to understand they were fashionable at that time. There was no need to comment as I knew that within the next few minutes the conditions we were about to work under would make the point for me.

We fitted up some sea aquaria for observing the live animals and made use of the controlled conditions to get close-ups of some species behaving naturally. Under shore conditions, for instance, you never get the chance to see barnacles 'fanning' as their hard shells are tightly closed when exposed to air; in aquaria you can see them behaving as they do when the tide covers them, wafting small particles of food into their mouths with specially adapted legs.

The trip down Loch Fyne had its excitements. The man who owned the

boat had never done dredging before, so everything was rather experimental. Fortunately there was a winch to haul in the dredge, but
bringing it back over the stern was no easy matter; there was no
protecting rail, the deck was very slippery after a few hauls, and the
dredge was heavy when full of material collected off the bottom.
However, nobody fell in, and when the contents were strewn over the
deck, everybody was eager to discover what had been caught. We were
disappointed at first as there was so much seaweed, but as we
progressed towards Ardrishaig and the more open sea we obtained
excellent samples of bottom-living animals.

Filming the operation was not easy due to the vibration caused by the
boat's engine, but we obtained sufficient for our purpose by hand-
holding the camera. We then let out a plankton net and towed it behind
the boat. The net is a cone of fine-meshed material ending in a metal
container; it can be towed for some time and sieves off the water, concentrating the catch. In this way we collected many crustaceans and larval
forms of other species, the larger of which were filmed in specially
prepared glass containers on our return.

By the end of our stay we had not only done a lot of useful seashore
ecology but had also fitted in a number of interesting trips inland to
watch deer and birds. It was all good experience of field work for those
who had never done anything like it before. On my return, I had the
interesting task of editing all the material and writing the commentary
ready for 'Gateways' to fine-edit and print the film.

By this time, Keith had also taken up filming, and had bought another
16mm Bolex. He too concentrated on educational films, doing an excellent one on pond life. He also did a number of short films to illustrate
methods of dissection which helped students with their practical work.
Having two cine cameras in the family proved to be of great value later
on.

Over the years a number of gifted pupils have passed through my
hands and become professional biologists, many of whom have kept in
touch. One of these, David Bygott, was on the Inverary expedition and
has remained a close friend. He came to Taunton School at the age of 11.
From the start he was outstanding. He obtained an entrance scholarship
largely because of his extraordinary powers of detailed observation,
originality, and basic knowledge of natural history; he was obviously
very bright in other subjects too. He did extremely well at school and
became the most brilliant naturalist I had the privilege of teaching. He
was also a very gifted artist and loved drawing cartoons at the back of
the class. One of my treasured possessions is a little book he gave me full

of extremely amusing cartoons illustrating the life and habits of badgers. Some of these I have used to illustrate this book. His field work was so outstanding that when he was in the sixth form I took him up to Oxford to meet Professor Tinbergen as I knew he would quickly assess his abilities and make useful suggestions. He was very impressed and invited him to take part in a field course he was running for undergraduates in order to get a better idea of his potential.

David obtained an Open Scholarship to Oxford, and after getting a first in zoology, did a doctorate on male chimpanzee behaviour under Jane Goodall in Tanzania. This gave him wonderful scope for developing his powers of observation and originality still further. He followed a troop for days on end until they accepted him, and his final triumph came when one animal trusted him sufficiently to come over to where he was sitting and rest his head on his lap. His artistic talent stood him in good stead when he drew portraits of all the main chimps being studied at Gombe for Jane Goodall's book 'In the shadow of man'; he also depicted their facial expressions exhibiting various emotions.

Later, David married Jeannette Hanby who also had a doctorate, having specialised in animal behaviour. They did four years of lion research together at the Serengeti Research Institute, writing up the story of the main pride they had studied in their book 'Lions Share' (Collins,1980). In 1990 they built their own house in a remote area not far from Lake Eyasi. David has become well known for his wildlife paintings, and has exhibited his pictures in Nairobi. He and Jeannette play an important part in wildlife conservation, and have written and illustrated a variety of books including Tanzanian National Park guides, extremely humourous books for tourists illustrated by animal cartoons, and educational literature for schools. They have now set up their own publishing business, and when time allows, lead safaris. They feel very much part of their local community and are much liked and respected.

We have been in close touch since David's earliest days at school, and over the years, he and Jeannette have become very much part of the family. In 1992 I was able to stay with them, enjoy their company and see for myself the beautiful home they have built. It was a wonderful experience to live in such an oasis of civilization surrounded by virgin scrub with a permanent stream running through their land with its accompanying strip of riverine forest which attracts a great variety of wildlife.

In 1966, Andrew completed his three years at Aberdeen University prior to doing his diploma course in photography in London. During his time at Aberdeen he had founded the University Exploration Society and organised undergraduate expeditions to Greece (1964) and Iran

(1965). The latter was to make a zoological, botanical and sociological study in the remote Kuh-rang area of Bakhtiari. Data and specimens were collected for the British Museum (Natural History) and the Royal Botanic Gardens at Kew. Andrew, who led the expedition, made a film contrasting aspects of life of the settled and nomadic elements within the Bakhtiari tribe. For this he borrowed Keith's Bolex and took out 1,500 metres of black and white film. For transport they purchased an ex-RAF radar Austin lorry with four-wheel drive and modified it for the considerable journey across Europe, through Turkey into Iran. The Duke of Edinburgh was one of those who gave the expedition generous financial support. The trip was a great success and Andrew brought back an excellent film.

The summer of 1966 was the last time it was likely that Andrew and I could do filming together, so an expedition was planned to the Coto Doñana in southern Spain. This had recently been bought with the help of the World Wildlife Fund (now the Worldwide Fund for Nature) as a nature reserve. Previously it had been a hunting area for the Spanish nobility and contained a large hunting lodge called the Palacio where visitors could stay. David Bygott came too, and Peter Tolson, a good friend and excellent ornithologist, completed the party. The objective was to make an ecological film of this wonderful wildlife area in summer. We planned to be away for a month, with three weeks in the reserve itself and a week for the long journey there and back by car. We took my Morris Traveller which just about accommodated the four of us and a mass of gear.

Most people visit the area in the spring when the birds are nesting and it's not too hot, but we could only do so in high summer. However, we thought it would be interesting to see and film how the fauna coped at that time of the year.

We left on the night boat from Southampton, arrived at Le Havre early the next morning and took three days going south through France and Spain. We had previously made all the necessary arrangements with Dr Valverde, who was in charge of the reserve. Having obtained the necessary permits, we were surprised, on reaching the reserve boundary, to find our way barred by a padlocked gate and barbed-wire fence and 'Prohibito' signs! However, this obstacle was soon overcome and we drove on to the Palacio. On arrival we were greeted by a group of staff and their families who were watching a young red stag being suckled by a goat. We were not expected, and only one spoke a little English. However, when we showed our papers, we were told that Dr Valverde was in Scotland, but that rooms would be found for us!

The Palacio was a remarkable building with what had been a small bull-ring attached. The buildings surrounded an open patio with date palms and geraniums; a family of peacocks, two turkeys and other less distinguished poultry frequently passed into it through the hall from outside. Wall geckos were abundant within the Palacio, and the stags' skulls which festooned some of the rooms became roosting places for bats, although most lived in the roof. During our stay we caught three species: pipistrelle, serotine and greater mouse-eared. The stags' antlers had been used as nesting sites for swallows which could fly freely through an open window.

We spent the first week exploring the reserve to see its potentials for filming. It was a fascinating and very varied area being part of the old delta of the Guadalquivir river. It had been formed by the action of opposing forces. Silt brought down by the river and dumped in the Atlantic had been piled up by the currents to form a ridge of sand dunes; the prevailing south-westerlies had blown much of the sand inland on top of the alluvium of the delta and blocked up all but one of the river exits to the sea. In the winter much of the area is flooded; in spring it starts to dry up and by high summer most of the area is very dry.

We found there were five main ecosystems present with their characteristic flora and fauna and these made a logical theme for our film. First there are the dunes and slacks near the Atlantic seaboard. Behind these is a region of stone pines planted to prevent the dunes from advancing inland. Then comes the main region of scrub where deep sand covers the alluvium, and scattered throughout this region is a series of lagoons where water remains throughout the summer. Being the only extensive areas of water left in August, they attract large numbers of waders, herons, ducks, spoonbills and other water birds. Finally there is the marismas, a vast flat area which is flooded in winter and dry in summer.

In the spring, when there is plenty of water covering the marismas, large numbers of duck nest on any patches of slightly higher ground; when it dries up, the young have to make a long journey to reach the water of the lagoons and many are lost to predators. When we arrived, hundreds of these young birds were on the march. Many were helped on their way by some ornithologists who were also staying at the Palacio.

We had two Bolex cameras, as Andrew had borrowed Keith's, and we all took stills. Peter helped in many ways, not least by identifying some of the more unfamiliar birds and studying their behaviour and ecology. David was in his element looking for interesting species to film - something he did with uncanny skill. We went out at night with a torch to set live-traps for small mammals and on one occasion, David pounced on a garden dormouse - prettily marked in grey, black and white, with a long bushy tail. It can bite painfully as Andrew discovered. David also went for night walks on his own and discovered many species which were more active at that time, including mole crickets, tree frogs, stick insects and mantids. Apart from rodents, one trap, to our surprise, yielded a small specimen of the ocellated lizard. To film water birds we put up hides which were best used early or late in the day as at other times they became unbearably hot.

The mobile dunes nearest to the sea supported no life at all, but the more stable ones, due to the pines and marram grass, showed a mosaic of tracks indicating the presence of rabbits, small rodents, Lataste's viper, toads, lizards, antlions and beetles. The tracks made interesting subjects to film as they told a good story, and it was not difficult to get close-ups of an antlion larva throwing sand at any ant which slipped into its conical pit trap. One lizard that braved the heat of the day was the fringe-toed. We caught one, and I filmed it burrowing swiftly into the loose sand. Andrew was behind me watching, and when the lizard had disappeared from view I heard him say "keep it running", so I did, and almost at once an eye appeared through the sand to look at us. It made the sequence memorable thanks to Andrew's growing authority as film maker and producer!

The slacks between the dunes gave scope for filming insects, as there were many flowers which attracted them. Species included butterflies such as bath whites, clouded yellows and blues, and humming bird hawk moths hovered in numbers at the viper's bugloss flowers. There was also a graceful large neuropteran fly *Neuroptera sinuata*, which has the hind wings elongated to form oar-like structures with conspicuous tips which serve to distract the attention of predatory birds away from the body.

In the scrub area we caught a large montpelier snake which Andrew picked up by the tail. Its fangs are at the back of its mouth so it seldom bites a human. We released it in a more open situation where we could catch it again and found it orientated itself by the sun and made straight for the pines. By repeating the process, its direction could be accurately determined and focusing became easier as it made its fast get-away. We also found Algerian racer lizards *Psammadromus algirus*, the round-bodied skunk *Chalcides bedriagai* and under some pines, specimens of that strange burrowing lizard *Blanus cinereus* which looks like an earth-worm except for its covering of tiny scales; it has vestigeal eyes and no legs. We were able to film one on lifting a dung pat. Scorpions were also commonly found under animal droppings. On one occasion, David was taking a close-up photograph of one when it darted for the shelter of his knee and stung him. The pain was excruciating at first; this soon gave way to numbness. He made light of it, and fortunately, he was soon able to walk and quickly recovered.

The insect life of the drier parts was scarce, although we photographed the magnificent brown and orange butterfly *Charaxes jassius*, when it settled after sailing swiftly round and round its territory. We were also able to film some spiders - a large one in its orb web catching and eating its prey, and the common small tarantulas which usually sit at the bottom of their burrows in the ground, each topped with a turret of sand and sticks. Tarantulas can be coaxed out, and then if you nearly fill the burrow with sand, when the spider returns it cannot retreat out of sight and you can film it looking out of its burrow. There was also an opportunity to film harvester ants returning with seeds and pieces of vegetation to their underground nest; this had to be done before breakfast as they become inactive when it starts to get hot.

In moister, low-lying areas the tree heather, up to 4 metres high, formed a dense scrub which provided cover for some of the larger animals such as wild boar, red and fallow deer. The latter fed by day at the edge of the marismas or by the lagoons and could be filmed more easily, but the red deer kept under cover by day and migrated nightly out into the marismas to feed. At dusk, we watched them break from cover and wind their way slowly to their feeding grounds - up to a hundred of them.

The wild boar came out in the late evening to root in the mud around the lagoons. The difficulty was filming them while there was still sufficient light. However, we found that some individuals came out earlier than others and we got some reasonable shots. Wild boar are real opportunists; we saw one dash into the water, catch a duck and eat it within less than a minute, feathers and all. We had no luck with lynx although we saw their tracks. Badgers were also around, making their setts in sandy soil where it was sufficiently firm for tunnelling due to reenforcing plant roots. Judging by their dung contents, they appeared to be living mainly on rabbits and beetles.

David noticed on one of the lagoons some small triangular heads which stayed above the water briefly and then disappeared. They belonged to Spanish terrapins *Clemys leprosa* which grew to about a foot in length. Two rather smelly examples were brought back in triumph by him and spent the night in the hand basin in his room ready for filming the next day. European pond tortoises *Emys orbicularis* were also filmed in a shallow pool, and one of the common non-venomous water snakes

Natrix maura as it came on land and slithered away into the vegetation.

Large carp were seen sunning themselves in the shallows. If disturbed, they quickly swam into deeper water, but occasionally they were caught by birds; we came across one which was being dismembered by magpies. As we were filming them, a splendid imperial eagle swooped down to get its share of the fish. We were fortunate to get shots of this rare bird, which is about the size of a golden eagle. Several other species of eagle were seen including the booted and short-toed; there were a number of other raptors identified, including that rare migrant from North Africa, the long-legged buzzard. One of the most interesting birds we were able to film was the red-necked nightjar which is so wonderfully camouflaged when sitting on the ground. On our approach, it left its well-grown chick and did the broken-wing trick to distract us. On getting closer, the chick stood up and opened its bill to display its bright red throat in a most menacing manner. We quickly let the mother return. In all, with Peter's help, we identified 103 bird species, more than we expected for the time of year.

The guardas, or reserve wardens, had so recently been acting as gamekeepers that they found the change to conservation duties rather bewildering; we found their attitude somewhat ambivalent at times. However, they were friendly, and trudging home one evening, wearily carrying my tripod and film camera, one stopped and offered me a lift on the back of his horse. He took the equipment and I hung on grimly, perched on the widest part of the horse's anatomy behind the saddle. Nothing could have been more uncomfortable - however, it was a kind gesture!

Unfortunately, Dr Valverde only got back for our last few days. He was a splendid naturalist, spoke good English, knew the reserve extremely well and showed us some interesting things we had not previously discovered. His presence had a remarkable effect on the guardas who even put on their uniforms and had a shave!

To end the film, we took shots of spoonbills and herons coming back to roost on some fine old cork oaks against the red sky of a lovely sunset.

We left with regret, soon after dawn. David's last act was to donate false eyebrows to the bronze statue of a lynx which welcomed visitors to the Palacio! We had taken a surprising amount of film for such a short time. It had paid off to have two cameras to vary the angle of shots in some instances and spread the load at other times; Andrew's expertise had undoubtedly improved the quality of the material shot. It had also been a great experience exploring one of Europe's most exciting reserves; how long it will remain so is very doubtful as human and pollution pressures are great. It was marvellous to see it in its prime with no restrictions. After the long journey back home, the next thing was to get the film processed and rough-edited. It was finally used as an educational film titled 'Adaptation to Environment'.

In this chapter, I am omitting my expeditions to Africa as these will be described in more detail later, but I must mention that in 1969 Betty and I were in Uganda together and were fortunate enough to be working at night in the Queen Elizabeth National Park. On one occasion I had the opportunity to take a flashlight photograph of hyaenas on a kill after they had seen off a male lion which was guarding it. It made a dramatic picture and won the Wildlife Photographer of the Year Award for 'Animals Magazine' now 'BBC Wildlife'. Fortunately for me the standard of photography was not so high then as now! David Shepherd presented me with the gold medal at a ceremony in London. The other part of the prize was a trip on the ship 'Lindblad Explorer', to the Forgotten Islands of the Indian Ocean. This was a wonderful prize, marred only by the fact that although I offered to pay, I was not permitted to take Betty with me as the ship was said to be full. That was sad.

It was impossible to take my cine camera but there was much scope for still photography. It was a particularly exciting trip as the 'Lindblad Explorer' was our hotel for a fortnight and we visited various islands of the Seychelles before sailing on to Desroches, Aldabra, the Comores and Zanzibar. Tourism had made no impact at that time as there was no sizeable airstrip on the Seychelles and getting there by boat was difficult, the islands being off the main shipping routes. Mahé, the largest island, was 1000 miles from the mainland.

Strangely enough, our party travelled on the same plane that Marge was on. She was going to Mahé to do a medical locum for a friend of her's who was going on holiday. She went from Mombasa by a very devious route in a small piper plane via the Comores and Madagascar. We agreed to meet on Mahé.

Our party had two days to spare before the 'Lindblad Explorer' left Mombasa, so I took a day trip by plane to the Serengeti which I greatly enjoyed. The next day, when having a drink outside the Thorntree cafe in Nairobi, I heard my name called. I looked up, and to my astonishment, there was my previous Head of House. His father was a geologist and the only Englishman at that time in the Kenyan Government. He was having coffee at a table nearby with his mother and brother, so I joined them. His mother invited me for an evening meal at their home outside Nairobi and later in the day I was picked up. I spent a delightful evening with the family, and was very touched when his mother told me that her son had combed the Nairobi shops to find a bottle of apple Schloer for me. It was surprising that he found any. He knew I didn't take alcohol and had often been given this drink by Betty when we had entertained the prefects of Wills East, and had remembered.

The first part of the cruise from Mombasa to Bird Island - one of the islands of the Seychelles - took three nights and two days. For much of the time many of the passengers were not seen in the dining room as the wind was blowing strongly and the considerable swell hit us sideways. I was fortunate, as my stomach operation in 1949 probably helped prevent sickness. The porthole in my cabin was near sea level, so one moment it was blotted out by water and the next there were views of the sea. This gave me the chance to watch flying fish at eye level leaping out of the water and gliding through the air. One night the wind reached gale force and I kept sliding from one side of my bunk to the other. The journey gave me a chance to get to know some of the tour organisers. Dr Lyall Watson led the expedition and gave talks; with him were Professor François Boulière and Dr Mireille Bertrand who were French mammalogists, and Keith Shackleton whom I already knew from 'Animal Magic' days at the BBC.

Bird Island was my first experience of a tropical coral island; it certainly lived up to expectations. It was incredibly hot and the light reflected from the coral sand quite blinding. François and I went straight away to the part of the island where sooty terns were nesting - over a million birds and young; the ground was covered with them. The chicks were about half-grown and collected together in groups of 50-100 wherever there was shade. There were greater noddy terns on the palms and fairy terns on the casuarinas. After much photography we retired to the shade and gratefully drank coconut milk. After returning to the ship and having a shower I went on my first fishing trip, trolling from a rubber zodiac at speed. There were four rods and several large fish were caught. Suddenly my rod was nearly knocked out of my hand and my arms were aching when eventually a 16kg jackfish was landed. Between us we brought back about 60kg of fish to augment the ship's menu.

The next morning we arrived at Mahé, and Marge walked up the gang plank. It was great to see her. When introduced, she was invited to spend the day with the party exploring the island and visiting special places famous for their delicious creole cooking. Late that evening François invited Mireille and me to accompany him on a visit to the house of an Indian conservationist who was an expert on the fauna. His rooms were full of priceless treasures he had collected - porcelain from China and India, jade masks, and carvings in wood, ivory and jade. They were everywhere: on shelves, in cupboards, on the chairs and settee; it was like the backrooms of a disorganised museum. Cabinets were full of shells he had collected - I believe there were over 400 species. His enthusiasm was unbounded and he wanted to show us everything, including remarkable carvings of ships, fish and other things he had made from polished shells. We eventually got away at 12.30 am. It had been quite a day!

The following morning we landed on Cousin, recently acquired as a nature reserve. The warden showed some of us around and we saw brush warblers which are found nowhere else in the world apart from neighbouring Cousine. Noddy and fairy terns were everywhere and the whole island smelt of bird droppings. It was difficult not to tread on lizards which congregated under nesting colonies and scavenged on fish brought back to the chicks and dropped. A few gorgeous white-tailed tropic birds were nesting, bridled terns were swooping around the top of the hill and there were many burrows of wedge-tailed shearwaters.

It was pouring with rain when we visited Praslin the next day, but it cleared later and we were able to explore the Vallée de Mai with its fascinating palm forest. The coco-de-mer palms are found nowhere else in the world apart from a few on a nearby island. The male trees are said to grow up to 30 metres and have strange, elongated, pollen-bearing structures; some of the female trees showed fruits in all stages of development - they may reach as much as 45kg in weight, and their seeds which are bilobed, 18kg or more. It was General Gordon who suggested the Valée de Mai must be the Garden of Eden and the coco-de-mer the Tree of Life. It was certainly a weird and wonderful place. However, we were unable to stay the night there and test out the legend that at certain times the male trees wandered about the forest looking for female partners. Perhaps it was as well, as the story goes on to say that anyone witnessing the courtship is invariably found dead! We saw bright green geckos on some of the huge fronds and large slugs which may play a part in the pollination of the palm. We also obtained views of the rare black parrot.

We travelled by night to Désroches which is an atoll. It represents the only part of the coral reef remaining above water level, the original central island having sunk. The island had about 40 inhabitants and is largely devoted to the growing of coconuts. We saw how they harvested the crop, cracked open the nuts, separated the milk, sun-dried the meat and extracted the oil from the resulting copra using a large wooden vessel with a central pestle of wood which crushed it, the oil being run off. The pestle was turned by four donkeys which moved monotonously in a wide circle controlled by a creole who kept replenishing the vessel.

A boat visits the island about once a month to remove the products.

We then sailed for a day and a night and anchored off Aldabra. This was a very exciting island, second only in importance to the Galapagos as an example of evolution through isolation. It has 60 square miles of land surface and consists of a ring of three islands with an extensive lagoon in the centre. We were looking forward to seeing the giant tortoises. To land we had to cross the reef in rubber zodiacs and all had to put on life-jackets as it was rough, but we did not ship too much water and our clothes dried quickly in the hot sun. We soon found a giant tortoise which was calculated to be 47 years old judging by the rings on the scales. We saw many more later but they kept to the shade in the intense heat. We also saw tracks of green turtles which had come ashore to lay their eggs in the sand. Raised coral on the shore had been eroded to form incredible mushroom-like shapes with razor-sharp edges which cut the skin if touched carelessly.

Two of us explored inland and found the indigenous euphorbia shrub, the juice of which is so poisonous that it causes blisters on the skin and can cause blindness if any reaches the eye. Aldabra sunbirds were hovering and sipping nectar from flowering shrubs and we saw the indigenous forms of the drongo and sacred ibis. Egrets, boobies, greater and lesser frigate birds and green reef herons were also seen.

In the afternoon we dressed for a soaking, and wearing life jackets, again crossed the reef and entered the central lagoon through a very narrow channel between the south and west islands. The lagoon is 20 miles long, and at every tide much of the water pours in and out through the few narrow channels to the sea at as much as 15 knots. It is safest to go through when the tide is slack as the channel sides are composed of sharp coral. Safely through, we explored the lagoon, edged by mangrove swamps. Our main objective was some islands where grey herons, red-footed boobies and greater frigate birds nested. Unfortunately when we got close, the rain came down in a deluge; we were completely soaked. The storm did not last long, but everyone was very cold and there was no sun to dry our clothes, so after a quick look round and a few photos of the dimorphic egrets - some white, some black - we started for the channel and the 'Lindblad'. Just at that moment the engine of our zodiac failed! Fortunately, one of the boats had not left for home so we were able to get some help. After a lot of tinkering, while we all shivered, the engine sprang to life and we got back to a much-needed hot shower and dry clothes.

The weather deteriorated, so the captain decided not to wait another day off Aldabra; instead, he offered to land us on Gloriosa, an uninhab-ited island 114 miles NW of Madagascar. It is $1^1/_2$ miles long and had not been visited by biologists for 64 years, when a list of flora and fauna had been compiled. Those of us who were biologists were allotted different animal groups for study and specimens were to be taken back to the British Museum for identification. I found myself responsible for land invertebrates.

We crossed the reef and shallow lagoon without difficulty and landed on the coral sand. We worked in pairs, and I went with François. We penetrated inland looking in every likely habitat for invertebrates. They were not common, but we succeeded in collecting a wide range of species including butterflies, moths, beetles, ants, two kinds of grasshopper, one just like coral when it settled, sandwasps, lacewings, termites and centipedes. But not a single land mollusc.

Suddenly we heard a noise and we both stopped. We could not believe our ears - it sounded like a tractor! Going further we found a track, and sure enough, there was a tractor coming towards us on this 'uninhab-ited' island. The driver was equally surprised to see us. He was French. François asked him what he was doing? He invited us to climb on the tractor and said he would show us. After a short, bumpy ride, we came upon a few huts, a radio mast and various instruments scattered about. It was a French weather station manned by a couple of scientists. They made daily weather forecasts for shipping, but François was told the real reason for being marooned on this tiny island was to keep tabs on the Russian navy! Having so little to do apart from their work, the two men had made some very interesting observations on the fauna, and had found that the island was a regular breeding place for green turtles. This was good news as they were becoming rare due to exploitation.

Back at the ship we had a discussion about our findings. The birds, in particular, turned out to be very interesting and three appeared to be indigenous sub-species: the Gloriosa fody (different from the Madagascan), a brush warbler unlike the unique one on Cousin, and a very small quail. Our findings were eventually written up.

We landed next morning at Moroni, the capital of the largest island of the Comores, famous for the finding of the first coelocanth - a fish thought to have become extinct many millions of years ago. Grand Comoro is dominated by Mount Karthala over 2,440 metres in height. Volcanic eruptions in various parts of the islands had been frequent, the most recent being within living memory. The sea coast looked strange as the rocks were made of black lava which was in stark contrast to the coral sand in between.

For me the visit was notable because of a trip to an old crater containing a lake. Trees clung precariously to its steep sides, and large numbers of flying foxes roosted there. These fruit bats *Pteropus rufus*, had a wing span of about three feet and looked like large birds when in flight. It was difficult to get near enough for good pictures without taking risks.

On our way back, we went to a village called Itsandra and witnessed a traditional Comoro dance. This is danced by the men only, the head-man leading, followed by the others in ritual order. They danced in a circle to the music of drums and singing, while all the women and children looked on. It was a most colourful spectacle with the villagers in their bright dresses. It gave me a splendid opportunity for photography as everybody's attention was fixed on the dancing and I could concentrate on the eager faces of the wide-eyed children without being observed.

Zanzibar was our last port of call. It was of particular interest as we were one of the first tourist boats to be welcomed there since the coup. We were met by a fleet of taxis, each one driven by a guide provided by the People's Republic. The guide spoke a little English and was anxious to know our impressions of Zanzibar almost before we had seen anything of it.

We were shown the museum with pride. I was intrigued by the reference library of the natural history section which our guide appeared loath to show us. This made me even more curious, so I had a look inside. It was crammed with communist literature, mainly copies of 'The Thoughts of Mao'! We saw the Anglican cathedral built on the site of the old slave market, Livingstone's old house and the colourful fruit market. It was fascinating to wander through the narrow streets of the old city which seemed to be unchanged from remote times. Having had no visitors for some years, the shopkeepers were delighted to do some trade. I was particularly interested in a ramshackle curio shop, owned by an Indian, which contained a great variety of craft-work brought over by dhow from India as well as from the African mainland. A tour of the countryside was too restricted for us to see much wildlife but it was interesting to see acres of cloves being grown, coconut plantations, cinnamon, coffee, yams, cassava and kapok.

Back on the 'Lindblad' for our last evening before the final leg of our trip back to Mombasa, I watched the sun go down. As the off-shore wind got up, all the dhows raised their sails and made their way out of the harbour against the backdrop of a magnificent African sunset. It was a grand finale to a wonderful trip.

Chapter Thirteen

My last years at Taunton School

In 1960, I was invited to become Second Master at Taunton School as deputy to John Leathem. I felt it a great honour to accept. I had been one of his first appointments and had enjoyed working with him as assistant master and housemaster. I always greatly respected his vision for the school, enlightened attitude, academic excellence and the way he encouraged his staff. It would be splendid to work with him more closely and take greater responsibility for running the school.

This appointment meant that I had to live within the main school campus, leave Foxcombe and become housemaster of a senior house, Wills East. This had between 40 and 50 boys between the ages of $14^1/_2$ and 19; no catering was involved as the boys had their meals centrally with other houses and I was expected to have lunches with them.

I knew that combining the post of Second Master with housemastering and Head of Science would be extremely demanding and that during term time there would be little chance of doing anything much outside the school. However, schoolmastering was more important to me than my other interests and I would have more influence on school policy without the ultimate responsibility of a headship. Perhaps, being the youngest in my family and much dominated as a child by my brother I was better suited to being number two than number one. We moved from Foxcombe to Wills East in late August.

There is always a Common Room meeting on the first morning of term; it felt strange taking the chair for the first time. I wondered how some of the older men would react to my appointment and hoped I could win the support and confidence of my colleagues from the start. A happy staff is the key to a successful school and I wanted to keep it that way. I knew from my predecessor what the post entailed, my priorities being to deputise for the headmaster when he was absent, act as liason between headmaster and staff and be responsible for the discipline and well-being of the school. I was also expected to organise major events in the school year, such as Commemoration, make staff duty lists, arrange supervision of classes when somebody was absent and work out invigilation for examinations.

I soon found that apart from the everyday duties which helped the school run smoothly, I needed to be sensitive to the stresses that were bound to occur in any community. This meant taking an interest in all that was going on and trying to keep a finger on the pulse for early signs of unrest and minor irritations before they blew up into major problems. This meant taking time to listen to staff, prefects and boys, and getting their co-operation whenever possible. Being a housemaster of a senior house was an enormous help as you soon got to know your own boys well, and if you had their confidence, they would discuss problems with you - useful indications of what was happening in the school as a whole. The opportunities were endless, but time was finite; choice of priorities was all important. I had no illusions about the difficulties of making a reasonable job of it without prejudicing my other responsibilities as housemaster and Head of Science. I was glad I had an excellent resident assistant in the House and a Science Department with very competent and responsible staff.

When we moved into Wills East, Keith had completed his third year at Cambridge and was about to do a teachers' training year prior to becoming a biology teacher. David was starting his second year at Bristol enjoying his engineering course, and Andrew was doing well at school, preparing for his O-levels.

With two boys away and I having so many duties during term time, family life became more restricted; this was very hard on Betty. She saw very little of me during the day, and as there was no catering to organise she had less responsibility with boys and staff. However, she made the very best of her opportunities as a hostess. The boys much appreciated her welcome and hospitality; prefects came in regularly to discuss house matters; she got to know new boys; helped to entertain parents and co-operated with other staff wives over school events. We were both glad that Andrew preferred to come home for lunch, so she saw a little more of him, but for the next few years it was not an easy time for either of us. Betty's tremendous support when things were tough, and her understanding of the realities of divided loyalties when school duties were particularly demanding was of inestimable benefit to me. Fortunately, we did have the holidays together, and these gave us a real break from the stresses of term time.

John Leathem, Jo, was a bachelor, and the school suffered from not having a hostess to help develop the social life of the school and foster the female element so helpful in such a monastic institution. However, he was a good headmaster to work with and a first class academic classicist. He set high standards, and during his time at Taunton, raised the status of the school considerably. With much help from the War Memorial and Centenary Fund he did a lot to bring buildings up to date, but his more ambitious plans for the further development of the school were limited by a very modest budget and a Council, who in my opinion, lacked vision and certainly ran no risks such as putting up fees to pay for greater improvements.

Jo understood people and had a gift for choosing the right staff and boys for key activities. One thing I appreciated particularly was his willingness to leave staff whom he trusted to get on with their jobs and use their initiative. What is more, if he agreed with their ideas, he would give them his full support. He was an outstanding speaker, had been President of the Union at Cambridge and his talks in chapel and on formal occasions were always thoughtful and polished. When I became his deputy, he had 6 years to run before retirement at 60; perhaps understandably, towards the end, he was more concerned with keeping the *status quo* than embarking on new initiatives. New to the post, I sometimes wished he would risk a clash and take a stronger line with a few staff whose influence was not helpful. However, he was a wise man and probably knew best.

Society was changing rapidly, boys were becoming more anti-authority; understanding, flexibility and firm leadership were required. This was difficult for a man nearing retirement. I felt the school would soon need a younger man who could critically assess old traditions, build on the splendid principles which Jo had helped to establish, retain what was of value and have the vision to adapt to a changing world with courage and wisdom. It would not be easy for his successor, but in the meantime we worked together very closely and with mutual understanding. He taught me much and I greatly respected his integrity.

Since coming to Taunton, I had given talks in chapel occasionally; in my new post I did rather more of this. Chapel was compulsory on Sundays, so there were two services in the morning; boarders from senior and junior houses together were too many for the relatively small chapel. One advantage was that the speaker did not have to cope with such a wide age range. The chaplain made all the arrangements for services and also a rota for staff who were interested to take the short chapel assemblies which took place each weekday before periods started. The headmaster and chaplain were both strong nonconformists according to school tradition, but the boys came from very varied backgrounds.

Chapter Thirteen

Giving talks in chapel was always a challenge. Boys are quick to criticise, easily bored and cannot stand being preached at. However, they respond to sincerity, ideas which are relevant to their own growing-up process and the society in which they are living. In these respects I always felt fortunate to be a biologist as I could call on interesting relationships within the natural world to illustrate religious and moral concepts and help them understand themselves. Parables always worked better than precepts. However, I knew only too well that unless they respected you for the way you lived you might as well save your breath. This was the real challenge. Your only hope was to make it clear that you failed like everybody else; the struggle to live a meaningful life and fill your niche within society was not easy for any of us. We were all in it together and the only real difference between us was the stage we had reached in the continuing growing-up process.

In 1962, the Headmaster created quite a stir in the national press by appointing Peter Thomas, a Nigerian, as Head Prefect. He was thought to be the first coloured boy to be honoured in that way. He was selected on merit and was both popular and a great success. I saw no signs of racial prejudice within the school.

Jo Leathem always encouraged staff to pursue interests outside the school and contribute to the larger community. My predecessor as Second Master, Freddie Dowell, had been a county councillor and had served as Mayor with Jo's blessing, and he himself was a Justice of the Peace. He could not have been more helpful over my out-of-school activities, taking the line that any broadcasting and lecturing were good both for the school and for me; I was grateful for his interest and encouragement. I saw to it that most of my engagements came during the holidays whenever possible.

In the early 1960s we had several very wet winters, and on one occasion the small stream which ran through fields north of the school became a torrent. Normally, the stream went through a culvert under the road and proceeded underground below the playing fields, eventually entering the River Tone. During the night the culvert became clogged with debris and the water poured over the road and flooded the field near Wills to a depth of about two feet. A few of us tried to clear the debris, but the night was dark, and the job dangerous, as near the culvert the water was very deep, so we had to leave it until morning. Waking early, an extraordinary sight met my eyes. The grounds were like a lake, and on making my rounds I found that the Science Block was surrounded by water. I was anxious because the heating boiler was below ground level and thought there might be an explosion, but the door was strong and the level of water inside only rose slowly. Fortunately, when it did reach the boiler, all it did was to put the fire out! With plenty of boy labour available, the debris blocking the culvert was soon cleared and the water gradually drained away. Later in the day, planks were used to help the boys reach the entrance of the Science Block for classes.

Taunton town suffered badly. The River Tone overflowed and the lower floors of many houses were flooded; damage was considerable. Many of the boys were organised by staff to help those whose lower rooms had been flooded - a major operation. The local paper had a picture of one of my sixth-formers canoeing down Station Road.

I enjoyed being housemaster of a senior house. It was both possible and desirable to leave more of the administration to the prefects who were a particularly good group. Some of the better ones had parents abroad and their wider experience seemed to give them greater maturity and initiative.

Wills East and West had been built fifty years before, thanks to the generosity of one of the Wills family. Betty and I thought we should mark the occasion in some way. We were very conscious that House facilities were poor in many respects, and a new extension to the building was high on the list of school priorities. Perhaps this could be a good time to exert a little gentle pressure? There was a member of the Wills family on Council, so we thought we would have a House party and invite him along. He would then get a first hand idea of what the House was like and what went on there. I knew him quite well, so I sounded him out. He was intrigued and delighted.

The House responded with enthusiasm and the menu was discussed with the prefects. However, the only cooking facilities were in our small kitchen, so it was decided to have fish and chips - more than fifty portions at special rates from a shop not far away. They could be delivered and kept hot in the kitchen. Betty took responsibility for the second course. Mr Wills duly arrived to an enthusiastic welcome by the boys; the meal was excellent, and afterwards there were speeches. Years afterwards, he reminded me of that evening which he had enjoyed so much - he had never felt so much part of the school before. It would be nice to conclude that as a result we got our extension. We did in the end but unfortunately had still to wait a few years. Notwithstanding, everybody enjoyed the party.

It was in Jo Leathem's last year that I received a pleasant bolt from the blue. It was a letter from the Zoological Society of London, saying that Council had nominated me for the Sir Stamford Raffles Award. I could hardly believe it; I wasn't even a member of the Society! The letter stated that 'the award was founded in 1961 and was presented each year to an amateur zoologist in recognition of distinguished contributions to zoology.'It was a wonderful surprise and I silently thanked the badgers for their co-operation.

The Duke of Edinburgh, who was President of the Zoological Society, made the presentation at the annual general meeting in April. The award was a Henry Moore bronze called 'Animal Form'. The sculptor had been persuaded by Lord Zuckerman, who was secretary of the Society, to make an appropriate sculpture and donate it to the Society for that purpose. Henry Moore allowed seven copies to be moulded. The Duke had presented one the previous year and appeared not to be greatly enamoured by modern sculpture, judging by his reference to it as 'that thing'. Rather naturally, I thought rather differently about it and couldn't believe my good fortune. I was sitting next to David Attenborough, who received the Silver Medal of the Society for his excellence as a communicator on zoological subjects. He laughingly offered to swap his medal for my bronze. At the reception afterwards Betty and I were presented to the Duke who questioned me closely about delayed implantation in badgers! I had previously been advised to insure the sculpture before travelling home with it. This I did, but nobody had thought about how it should be carried as it was very heavy and larger than I expected. The assistant secretary was helpful, wrapped it in newspapers and packed it in an old cardboard box - the only thing available. We tried to get a taxi, but none came, so I ended up carrying the parcel on my knee in a No.74 bus. We were relieved to get it back to Taunton safely.

The sculpture is fascinating because it suggests a number of different animals according to lighting and viewpoint. Andrew skilfully took a number of pictures of it to illustrate these likenesses.

The Zoological Society also made an award - The Prince Philip Prize - for an essay written on a zoological project by somebody still at school. I persuaded David Bygott to enter the next year. To our mutual delight, he won it - a small bronze head, also by Henry Moore - for 'Observations and experiments on a common house spider'. It concerned some ingenious experiments he devised to demonstrate how this species depends on the tautness of the web for prey recognition.

For many years I had attended the annual meetings of the Association of British Zoologists in London each January. These were occasions I valued as I met old friends and got to know other zoologists. Nellie Brown, from Chelsea days, persuaded me to join in the first place and used to attend regularly herself. There were always subjects of interest discussed, and I remember in particular a most amusing talk given by Miriam Rothschild, an expert on fleas among other things. She was a delightful character with a dry sense of humour and needle-sharp mind. Later, the Institute of Biology was formed and there was less need for the ABZ, so I became a member of the Institute. This grew rapidly and became the representative body for biologists in this country, later receiving the Royal Charter. In 1963, to my great surprise, the Secretary wrote to say that I had been nominated as a Fellow of the Institute, an honour I greatly appreciated. Many years later, Keith was also made a Fellow for his outstanding work as a school teacher of biology. This made me doubly pleased as we were the only father and son within the Institute to be awarded Fellowships.

Jo Leathem retired as headmaster in 1966 after 21 years. He had done much for the school in the difficult years after the war and raised its academic standards and reputation for being one of the best schools in the south-west. He was respected by staff and boys for his fairness and wisdom, two qualities he demonstrated as a Justice of the Peace. After retirement he devoted more time to this work and became Chairman of the Taunton Bench.

The Governors had appointed Dr John Rae to be the new headmaster. He had taught at Harrow, been master in charge of rugby football and had already made a name for himself as a writer and for his progressive ideas. He could not have been more different from Jo Leathem. He was 35, had a wife and 4 daughters and was full of radical ideas about how independent schools should change with the times. I had met him the previous year when he had been appointed, had liked him as a person and knew that we could work together.

My job was to familiarise him with school routine and traditions so that he could see what changes were necessary, and discuss issues with him. He was stimulating to work with as he was brimming with ideas, some of which struck familiar chords from my experiences at Rendcomb. I had longed to apply some radical ideas to Taunton, but had been up against traditions which had been too strong and had never been in a position to do much about them. Now, to my surprise, I had to play a restraining role, as John lacked experience and his impetuosity made him liable to make mistakes. It was not surprising that he upset some of the senior staff; he wanted to change things much too quickly; no teacher who is set in his ways wants a gale-force wind to blow him out of his familiar course. I could sympathise, because I too was due to retire in five years time! I found that one of my main jobs was to keep the peace within the Common Room and prevent too much polarisation between those who were for and against John's policies.

With the social revolution in the country gaining momentum and political opinion moving strongly towards comprehensive education, criticism of the public schools was mounting; there were also threats of their abolition if a Labour government returned to power. Our greatest safeguard was to demonstrate excellence. John shared some of the main criticisms levelled against the independent sector and was determined that Taunton would react in a constructive way. I was very much in agreement. The main criticisms of the average public school were their monastic life style, isolationism, and social divisiveness. There was some truth in all of them as far as Taunton was concerned, though far less so regarding the last as we had a very mixed entry, there were no signs of racism and most boys were proud of their school without showing much evidence of the 'us and them' attitude. In that respect it was probably a help that a third of the school were day boys. Jo Leathem had taken steps towards getting the school more involved in the life of the town, but this needed further development.

Breaking the monastic tradition had to be a long-term objective; there were no short cuts. John Rae's wife, Daphne, was the first to put the cat among the pigeons by coming to the chapel service on the first Sunday. This broke the all-male tradition, and I remember the surprise and shock amongst some members of staff when I escorted her to a seat beside the headmaster. A storm in a tea-cup - ridiculous in retrospect - but a signal to all of the Raes' future intentions of normalising the role of women in the school. At that time only the wives of housemasters played a significant part and furthermore, not all housemasters were married. Betty supported Daphne from the start in her efforts to involve wives of staff in the social life of the school, and gradually progress was made. There was also a growing liason with girls at our sister school, Weirfield, just down the road; dances were encouraged and there was more co-operation in music and drama. Four years later this policy was developed further when girls were admitted into the sixth-form, and during the next headmaster's reign, the school became fully co-educational.

The school also joined in town events and competitions and invitations were given to outsiders to attend organ recitals and other Sunday afternoon musical events. These and other opportunities to include the school in the social life of the town were a great step forward from the more isolated life the school had previously taken for granted.

Over the next year or so there were a number of staff changes; some felt uncomfortable under the new regime and found new posts; two were asked to leave. The school undoubtedly benefited from the changes but more sensitivity for the people concerned would have eased the situation and avoided some of the resentment and sense of insecurity it provoked among some of the staff.

An important appointment was that of the Revd Alec Knight as the new chaplain; like John, he was an Anglican. He was an old-boy of the school, so he knew it from the boys' stand-point - a great advantage. He had been one of my pupils, was young, sincere, full of ideas, and eager to play a part in all the coming changes, not only in the religious life of the school. He became a good ally, played a full part in school activities, became respected by the boys and soon was able to fulfil a significant pastoral role in collaboration with housemasters.

It was not long before Sunday evening services became voluntary; far fewer turned up, as was expected, but the atmosphere improved. With the blessing of the Bishop, combined communion services were arranged between Anglicans and Nonconformists, with wives of staff invited.

It was a difficult four years. The permissive society was reflected in the behaviour of the boys. Old values were out of fashion, anything smacking of authority was condemned as outmoded, long hair and sloppy manners were symbols of revolt, weaker members of staff had difficulties in keeping order and the papers were full of student unrest in the universities. This was a real challenge to all of us with authority - it was a time to reflect critically on what was important and should be fought for, what traditions were outmoded and should be changed. Drugs were a growing menace in society and we had to be very vigilant.

One incident which brought home to the headmaster and me what we were up against was a letter to the head prefect from the University Students' Union urging him to take any action possible within the school against authority and join in the national protest! Fortunately, the head boy was a most responsible person and the three of us were able to discuss the implications constructively and the letter was neither answered nor acted upon.

John made mistakes, as he would be the first to admit. As a headmaster for the first time, deep down he felt insecure. This made him feel he had to be seen to assert his authority which he did by taking autocratic decisions which were often controversial. Consultation with senior staff beforehand would have eased the situation. Early on, a few senior boys were expelled or suspended for a term for absenteeism, having disregarded a previous warning as to the dire consequences. This action probably had a beneficial effect on school discipline at a time of relative instability for both boys and staff, but it was considered too harsh a sentence by many and caused much bad feeling amongst senior boys, some staff and the parents involved.

I used to see John every morning after chapel before periods started. I much appreciated having his confidence; we discussed problems as they arose. However, a few decisions on policy he would merely inform me about; he had made up his mind, but usually he would at least give me a chance to discuss how best to pursue them. Occasionally there would be some crisis and he would come to a quick decision as to how to deal with it. Then he might ask for my opinion, and if the subject was serious I would often reply, 'Let's wait until tomorrow before we decide'. On the other hand there were some actions which we both knew had to be taken and I would urge him not to put it off but act at once.

He made the unpopular decision to abolish the Combined Cadet Force - some staff involved were understandably indignant as they had put much effort into running it. However, a number of other activities were organised in its place which gave scope for a greater variety of interests. The Duke of Edinburgh Award Scheme became more popular, nature conservation schemes were organised in conjunction with the Somerset Trust and more boys became involved in social services.

John also relaxed the rule that rugby and cricket should be played by everybody and instead gave much more choice. This went against tradition in a big way and angered many Old Boys who in his view put sport too high on the agenda of the school's achievements. This move made a lot of boys happy who greatly disliked being made to play certain games, but it was at the expense of weakening representative school teams as the best people were often good at several sports and had to make difficult decisions. Hockey had been given greater status by Jo Leathem and now tennis and athletics became options; squash and fencing also became popular.

The staff were inevitably divided about the wisdom of some of his ideas. In all communities there are vested interests which are threatened by radical change, some become hurt, some benefit. It is always difficult to weigh up the good that will result for the whole community against the suffering caused to a few individuals; I found myself in that difficult no-mans' land of divided loyalties between headmaster and staff. It usually came down to the primary question - if the policy was good for the school, did the end justify the means? If it did, how could personal relationships be improved? If not, were there better ways of doing it? In some respects it was a lonely position to be in. I had many friends among the staff, but knowing John's mind and many of his policies, and having to translate them into action without upset, sometimes gave me a feeling of isolation. However, I had much loyal support from colleagues who understood my position.

After a time John became more sure of himself; he realised he was alienating some staff and senior boys and did his best to mend bridges, spent more time with staff and gradually gained the respect of the majority of staff and boys.He became much more approachable.

One of John's great achievements was to bring real quality to the school environment. He had vision and was content with nothing less than the best. He obtained the backing of the School Council to employ a new architect and decide upon a five-year development plan backed up by a Re-development Appeal run by a professional fund-raiser. John and others put enormous energy into this with gratifying results. It culminated in the opening of the Sixth-form Clark Centre by Her Royal Highness The Princess Anne in the summer of 1970, which was John's last term.

This event required more preparation than I had imagined. Several meetings were arranged to plan in meticulous detail the order and timing of events. The planning committee included amongst others the Lord Lieutenant of Somerset, the Chief Constable, Lionel Evans (Chairman of the Governors), John and me. For some weeks John had been suffering acute spinal pain and had to lie flat on his back; I had to take a lot of responsibility. It was not at all certain until the last moment whether I would have to deputise on the auspicious occasion, but knowing John, I was certain he would make it whatever the circumstances, so I was not unduly worried. On the day he was fine.

Betty was asked to provide a retiring room at Wills East for the Princess, so the garden was spruced up, the house made spick and span and there were lovely flower arrangements. Betty was very annoyed with the detective, who, while we were away, inspected the premises, opened all the drawers and failed to shut them properly afterwards! There were similar precautions when we had lunch in the marquee; I found a detective crawling under the table where we were about to eat.

Everything went according to plan and the Princess seemed to enjoy herself. It was one of her first official engagements after leaving school. To the amusement of the boys, her chauffeur found the royal car had a soft tyre and the wheel had to be changed. Fortunately, the discovery was made after she had arrived so there was no delay. I never imagined this would happen to a Rolls Royce!

John left at the end of the term to become head of Westminster School. He had carried out some very necessary reforms at Taunton during his four-years spell, brought new vision and vigour into the community, and had succeeded in providing a firm foundation on which his successor could build. I was sorry he did not stay longer; we had got to know each other well and I had enjoyed his friendship and trust throughout a very difficult period of social and educational change. The new post he was offered was obviously too good to turn down and it was clear to all that he had a great future. For me, it meant easing another headmaster into the job.

I had one year before retirement when Norman Roberts arrived as the new headmaster. I had given up Wills East when John Rae left, having been a housemaster for 17 years. It was high time I gave up something! I always considered housemastering a privilege as well as a responsibility. Sometimes it had been a joyful experience, occasionally a sad and depressing one, but on the whole it was satisfying; it personified what education was all about. It gave me the chance to get to know a great variety of boys extremely well and gain a little more insight into the growing-up process.

Betty and I had lived in school property or rented accommodation from Rendcomb days, so it was essential that we bought a house within easy distance of the school. It was no financial joke buying a house for the first time just before retiring, but having known that this would have to be done eventually, I had saved a reasonable sum, but it was not enough for the type of house we wanted. However, Marge, with characteristic generosity, made up the deficit.

We were delighted with Mansell House. It was situated in Milverton, a charming village at the foot of the Brendon Hills, eight miles from Taunton. It was an old, stone-built house, Georgian in style, with a lovely garden surrounded by ancient red-sandstone walls. As soon as we saw the garden, we knew that it was what we wanted. We were very fortunate to buy just before the cost of houses rocketed. We moved early in the summer holidays and for my last year I commuted every day.

Norman Roberts had been headmaster of Sexey's School, Bruton; he and his wife, Bea, with their family settled down quickly. I found him an excellent headmaster to work with and from the start there was mutual understanding and trust which blossomed into a strong friendship. Having no longer a House, I was given an office in the Clark Centre where I could work and interview boys when not teaching.

A great deal happened during this year. Some day-girls were to be admitted into the sixth form the following September, and during the year it was learned that our sister school, Weirfield, which was privately owned, was to be sold. Taunton School successfully negotiated its purchase and plans were laid for complete integration for class work for boys and girls over the age of $13^1/_2$ by 1976. Many meetings took place to plan this. Younger girls were to remain separately taught at Weirfield and younger boys at Taunton Junior School which would be enlarged. The scheme was to make the change gradually, one year's entry at a time, starting with the lower sixth form. Girls who were boarders would still be accommodated at Weirfield until new buildings could be erected on the school campus in due course.

I was only involved with the planning, but I was very much in favour of the school becoming co-educational and would have liked to have taught mixed classes, especially in the sixth form. However, I retired just before the first batch of sixth-form girls arrived.

Meanwhile the Redevelopment Plan was going ahead. An all-weather hockey pitch was constructed and plans made for rebuilding the main dining room so that a cafeteria system could be introduced in September.

It was school policy for staff to retire at 60, although the headmaster, if he so wished, could invite you to stay on longer. Norman asked me to continue, but I declined for several reasons. The main one was that I had accumulated too many responsibilities within the school and my teaching was becoming less effective. Being deputy to a new headmaster took up a great deal of time, and with all the new developments in the pipe-line there would be still more planning to do. I knew I was cutting corners in order to fulfil my obligations, and disliked that intensely. Another reason was that Betty was now on her own in Milverton and we wanted to do more things together. I also needed a rest from routine and do things in my own time and at my own pace. However, education had been my vocation; it had taken pride of place over other enthusiasms and I had learnt a lot about teaching methods and particularly the growing-up process. I did not want retirement to be a complete break from education in its widest sense and looked forward to the opportunity that writing might bring to share with others some of the lessons I had learnt. I wanted time to write two books, a biology textbook for O-level and a new book on badgers to bring the subject up to date. I also hoped to develop my interests in travel, conservation and broadcasting. Retirement for me was a misnomer, more a change of occupation; there was so much of interest to do.

Just before the end of the summer term, Betty and I held a garden party at Mansell House and invited all the staff and their wives. We were pleased that it was a lovely sunny afternoon and the garden looked its best. It was a most enjoyable occasion and a means of saying 'thank you' for all the kindness we had received during our time at the school.

My last Commemoration was a memorable one for Betty and me, although like most goodbyes, it had its elements of sadness. I had been on the staff for 25 years, seen great changes for the better, and over the past 11 years had been privileged to be deputy to 3 headmasters with whom I had had close, friendly and constructive relationships. Life had been full and rewarding. Our three boys had completed their education at Taunton and had greatly benefited from their long association with the school; they had also been able to contribute in good measure in a variety of ways and had left with excellent qualifications. We could not have asked for more.

The President of the school, Lionel Evans, was retiring at the same time. We were both very surprised and honoured when the headmaster in his speech said that one of the day-boy houses had become too large and was to be divided into two: they were to be called Evans and Neal. It was bad luck that a few years later, when age of entry to the main school was raised from 11 to $13^1/_2$, Neal House disappeared in the process, but that was of little real consequence; it had been a nice gesture which I greatly appreciated.

Now it was time to move on. We looked forward to the future.

Badgers are colourblind so they can be watched with a red torch

Chapter Fourteen

A home of our own in Milverton

We spent 17 happy years in Milverton and made many friends there. The village, 8 miles from Taunton, was a good mix between those who had lived there most of their lives and others who had come there to retire. An unusual feature was the presence of so many houses of character, many stone-built in Georgian times when it was a thriving local centre of the wool trade. Much of the village was designated a conservation area including Mansell House; the raised cobbled pavements were an attractive feature. The village was strategically placed in Taunton Vale at the foot of the Brendon Hills - excellent sheep country, and incidentally, with a high badger density! There was a friendly feeling about the village; life was lived at a slower pace and there was time for a chat with people you met casually. Local news travelled fast! The village was large enough to support a number of societies and there was a lot going on which helped to provide a feeling of togetherness. We soon felt we belonged.

Mansell House in its present form dated back to the 1790s, but the cellars, which consisted of a number of rooms with cobbled floors, were older - 1607. One of the larger of these rooms served as the old kitchen and still contained the iron cooking range and bread oven. In the corridor outside was a fine row of bells, each with its distinctive note to summon the maids to the appropriate rooms. The ancient deeds gave us an interesting flavour of the house's history; on three occasions it had been a public house, first called 'The Roebuck', then,'The Glove', and finally, 'The Admiral Vernon'. When we arrived, there was much to be done to renovate and modernise it.

When I retired from teaching, I realised that I would still have to supplement my income as I was not eligible for a state pension for another 5 years, my teacher's pension was inadequate and the lump sum teachers receive on retirement had been swallowed up when we bought the house. However, what I wanted to do most was to write a biology textbook for O-level candidates which would reflect the needs of a fast-changing society. Keith was keen to be a co-author although it was obvious that I had more time than he had for doing the actual writing. It was a satisfying father and son partnership as we could combine our very different experiences of teaching the subject. He was Head of Science at Harrow County School, an excellent grammar school. By contrast, my experience had been within the independent sector. The generation difference was a help as he was more up-to-date while I had longer experience; we had similar objectives and two heads were better than one.

We were convinced that any secondary school course in biology should be educational in the widest sense and should provide future citizens with a better understanding of themselves and the world in which they lived. For this reason considerable emphasis was placed on human anatomy and physiology, and the application of biological principles to human affairs at all levels - personal, social and world-wide. We also wanted to give emphasis to such subjects as health, behaviour, ecology and conservation because of their great interest and relevance. This gave us the chance to introduce important social problems in a factual way in their appropriate biological context. For example, when dealing with the respiratory system it was possible to include facts about smoking, silicosis and asbestosis; when studying the nervous system, to bring in the effects of drugs, ranging from alcohol and marijuana to heroin and LSD, and when on the subject of human reproduction, to introduce birth control methods and sexually-transmitted diseases. In 1971 these subjects were seldom mentioned objectively in a school textbook in their rightful scientific context. There was no need to preach; the facts spoke for themselves and we hoped they would form the basis for class discussion.

It had been my experience that the project-orientated Nuffield approach was splendid for the bright boy, but was far less successful with the less talented. What we wanted to do was to integrate the traditional approach with the more exciting, experimental and enquiry aspects, bringing together the practical experiments and projects within the text.

We called the book 'Biology for Today'. Blandford Press invited us to write it in the first place and were enthusiastic to publish it. We were allowed to be in on the design and lay-out at all stages. This co-operation between publisher and authors was essential as the numerous illustrations had to be inserted at exactly the right places. We used colour as well as monochrome photographs and the diagrams were professionally done from our roughs by two artists, one having been previously taught by Keith.

It was published in two volumes as it was rather long, but with hindsight, this was a mistake. Later it was bound as one to make it more competitively priced. Nevertheless, it found favour in many schools and over 100,000 books were sold.

A publisher in Nigeria was interested in the book and wanted us to adapt it for West African schools. We agreed to do this, and I studied the textbooks which were already available and the relevant syllabuses. I found that much of the text could stand with only minor alterations; some sections had to be re-written using local species as examples and biological principles applied to very different social conditions. I could not do this without visiting the country, so the publisher invited me to come out for a fortnight when he would introduce me to biologists in education and show me around.

The visit had its problems. The Nigerian Commission in London was reluctant to give me a visa and only after several visits was the red-tape overcome. Then, when I arrived at Heathrow, the Nigerian Airways plane which shuttled between Lagos and London failed to arrive. We heard that water had got mixed with the petrol and it had never left Lagos! As an alternative I flew to Paris and caught a French Airways plane which arrived just before dawn the next day. I was to have been met at the airport and taken by car to Ibadan, but of course the driver had long since given up, having heard that the plane had been cancelled. Fortunately, our son, David, who was working for an engineering firm, Kiers International, had asked me to deliver some plans to an engineer in Lagos and had telexed my time of arrival. He heard what had happened, made enquiries about alternative routes, jumped to the right conclusions, and to my great relief was there to meet me.

Nigeria at that time was under military rule, troops were guarding the airport, and it was not easy to convince the officials at Lagos of my *bona fides* as I couldn't give them the home address of my host, the publisher - only his P.O.Box number! However, I was eventually able to satisfy them and they let me in. My engineer host took me to his home, I was given a welcome shower and breakfast and later taken to the airport again where he expected my car to be waiting for the arrival of the next day's plane. The car was there! Much relieved and thankful, I was driven at speed to Ibadan where I met the publisher.

I had an extremely interesting time going to various schools, meeting biologists and taking numerous photos to replace those in the book which were Britain-orientated. I visited the hospital to obtain medical details and the biological department of the University of Ibadan for other data; I got a real flavour of that part of the country. The time passed quickly.

Six months later the text had been amended, new diagrams and photos inserted and printing started. 15,000 copies were sent out and before long another 30,000 were ordered. Everything sounded splendid, but all was not well - money could not be sent out of the country without a government permit and this was not forthcoming. The publisher made all sorts of excuses, but naturally, Blandfords refused to send the second batch until some payment was made, so there was stalemate. The problem was never resolved. It was little compensation to us to hear that other publishers had suffered in the same manner. Eventually, some books were bound with the Blandford imprint and sold elsewhere, but there was no future in it. Keith and I just had to write it off, and I started my next book.

For a long time I had wanted to write one on badgers, but had not had the time. Surprisingly, my Collins monograph, first published in 1948, was still in print and in its fifth edition, but I had collected so much new material since and taken many more badger photographs that I now wanted to write something much more comprehensive and quite different in style. I hoped to incorporate data I had received through correspondence with other badger-watchers, new research from abroad, bring the reproductive story up to date and add other data arising from my own research and field observations since 1948.

I had accumulated a very large number of extracts from publications and personal correspondence about badgers which had to be sorted out according to subject matter. Winwood, who had now left the BBC, offered help and did a wonderful job, sorting through all this material collected over more than 20 years. I was very grateful; it brought order out of chaos and saved me much time. The book was published by Blandfords in 1977. It was good to see it in print at last.

I enjoy writing. Like teaching, it helps to impart ideas as well as knowledge; there is something very satisfying in sharing with others your experiences and conclusions; when it brings pleasure it is doubly rewarding. There is always something special about seeing the first copies of your book - something like seeing a new baby after a long and sometimes frustrating gestation. Then comes the excitement of seeing the reviews; satisfaction over the good ones, disappointments over others, frustration when it is only too clear that the reviewer has merely read the blurb. However, thoughtful criticism can be of great benefit when considered constructively and dispassionately. Only once, (in a later book), did a reviewer use the opportunity as an excuse to write a personal attack on me, hardly mentioning the book at all - he obviously had a large chip on his shoulder and disagreed to the point of hatred with what I hoped was my scientific objectivity over the badgers and tuberculosis question. That was sad, but the reviewer's motives were so blatantly obvious to any reader that it boomeranged on the writer, and at the same time brought me much support from unexpected quarters. Even the publisher of the review was castigated by the editor of another magazine for allowing it to be published. These things are hard to take, but they are a sharp reminder that if you go public you must expect a few brickbats. I sometimes wonder how politicians survive!

I kept in touch with publishing by editing a few mammal books for Blandfords, and when this ceased, became editor of the much more successful series published by Helm. This aimed at filling the niche between the popular and the academic and was intended for the keen layman and professional biologists who needed an up-to-date reference. During the late 1970s and early 1980s there was a great upsurge of interest in wildlife and a deepening concern for conservation. This had been greatly stimulated by the international influence of natural history television programmes. In parallel with this interest there had been a great expansion of knowledge and understanding as more and more field workers carried out painstaking studies of many species, analysing their intricate behaviour and relationships. Thus there was a real need for such a series which dealt with groups of mammals world-wide and brought to the public's notice the latest researches. I was in the useful position of knowing most of the British experts as I was then Chairman of the Mammal Society, so finding good authors was not too difficult. However, they were all busy people and the major difficulty was getting a script out of them on time. After publishing 12 volumes, the series was taken over by Black for a short period and then by Harcourt Brace Jovanovich. It still continues successfully under the Poyser imprint.

My Blandford book,'Badgers', went out of print and no reprint was forthcoming in spite of steady demand, so the copyright reverted to me. I took the opportunity to publish it in the Helm series, having revised it considerably in the light of all the new research that had been done by professional zoologists since 1976. Paradoxically, this research had been financed largely because of the possible link between badgers, cattle and bovine tuberculosis. However, much of it also threw further light on badger ecology, population dynamics and behaviour. The success of some of this work was due to the use of radio-telemetry and infra-red and light-intensifying binoculars. It made me think back to the time when the only aid for seeing in the dark was to eat more carrots! Now, my badger book is being comprehensively revised once more to incorporate the remarkable advances of the past 8 eight years; it will be published by Poyser , probably towards the end of 1995.

During our time at Milverton, much was happening within the family. Our three sons were in good jobs; Keith was Head of Biology at Manchester Grammar School, David was with Kiers International as a civil engineer, and Andrew, having moved from London where he had been producing educational films for the BBC, had joined the Natural History Unit in Bristol. All three were happily married.

In 1965, Keith married Ruth Candy, a biology teacher he had met at Cambridge as an undergraduate. She had been a great help with her suggestions when we were writing our textbook. In 1971, David married Rachel Hallowes, a nurse he had known when they were both doing voluntary work in India, and in 1972, Andrew married Ghyslaine Bourdais, who was French, and director of the English branch of Eurolanguage - an educational firm which arranged study-holidays in Britain for French students .

Betty and I were now on our own. While I was writing and doing conservation work, Betty was helping Ghyslaine in finding suitable homes in Somerset for French students and tutors to teach them. She much enjoyed this work as it gave her a degree of independence after spending so many years bringing up the family and helping with school affairs.

It gave great joy to Betty and me to see our family diversifying and enlarging. By the late 1970s we had acquired five grandchildren, two boys and a girl to Ruth and Keith (Peter, Margaret and Robert) and a boy and a girl to Rachel and David (Alastair and Hilary). It was fascinating to watch them developing their own particular interests and personalities in a more objective way than we had been able to do with our own three boys. Above all, it gave us profound thankfulness to see them grow up in happy homes and strengthening bonds between us all. As an extended family I could see the great rewards of togetherness, now a reality in 3 generations. How fortunate we were!

By the time the youngest grandchild was six, I had had the privilege of taking all 5 for their first badger watch. I had always loved the experience of being in a wood at night; the feeling of being very close to nature; all senses alerted ready for the unexpected; life stirring all around you in the stillness. It was an experience well worth passing on to another generation living in a world that was becoming more and more artificial. It was wonderful to feel their great joy at being out late and at night; the anticipation and suppressed excitement; that first glimpse of an enquiring snout; the romping of the cubs. Magic! Then the trip home full of excited comments and the triumphant shout on arrival 'We saw five badgers, a fox and six rabbits!'. Full circle? Yes, there is something very special about badgers!

To our delight, Bids came to live in Milverton in 1972, taking a flat a few hundred yards from us. We were able to see a lot of her; she settled down very happily and made many good friends in the village. With more time, she was able to continue with her painting, and exhibited regularly at the annual exhibitions of the Somerset Society of Artists. In 1976 she joined Betty and me on a tour to Israel which she greatly enjoyed. However, it was not long afterwards that she began to feel unwell and cancer was diagnosed. It turned out to be inoperable, and in spite of bouts of radiotherapy and excellent treatment in Bristol, she gradually went downhill; by the end of 1977 she became confined to her bed and was clearly near the end. It was a very sad time for us all, but it was good that Betty and I were so near. She was completely serene and never complained; her faith and depth of spirituality were remarkable - a reflection of a life lived for others.

When she died in January 1978 a ray of sunshine had gone from our lives and we all felt her loss greatly - she had been so special to all of us. Her memorial service in Milverton church was a wonderful thanksgiving for a busy life of great quality; she was much loved by many.

Meanwhile, Bill had gone from strength to strength. His collection of antique firearms had become the most important in private hands anywhere, and he was recognised as one of the world's leading authorities on the subject. He had also produced a series of scholarly books, several in conjunction with David Back and illustrated with his own superb photographs; they became definitive works in that field.

His house at Warminster became the mecca for enthusiastic gun-collectors from many parts of the world; he was always happy to show them his priceless collection. However, he understood only too well how vulnerable it was to professional criminals even though he took all the precautions he could. In 1976 he decided to settle in the Channel Islands where protection was easier, finding an ideal house on Guernsey with a building attached which could house his collection safely. I visited him on a number of occasions and we regularly kept in touch by phone. Although we were so different, family ties were strong and as we got older we became much closer. As the elder son, he took his responsibilities seriously and showed the greatest interest in all his near relatives. He was very proud of his Keith ancestry and lived out with sincere conviction the Keith motto, 'Truth will Conquer'. He remained in Guernsey until his death in 1990 at the age of 84, his wife, Jane, having died the previous year.

Bill received many honours, the most notable being his election on three separate occasions as Master of the Worshipful Company of Gunmakers. One year, he invited me to their nomination dinner, held in the Hall of the Worshipful Company of Carpenters in Throgmorton Avenue. It was a glittering occasion with much pomp and ceremony; I felt very honoured to be the guest of the Master who was obviously so respected by all present. My neighbour at dinner was the Marquis of Bath who, two years later, invited Bill to use Longleat House for the wedding reception, following the marriage of Bill and Jane's daughter, Diana, to Julian Berry - another magnificent and memorable occasion.

Marge was forced by age regulations to retire from the National Health Service, but continued for a number of years as a private consultant. Medicine was her life; it was a very sad day when she felt it was wise to give up altogether. By this time her husband was suffering from depression and was not at all well. Much as she would have wished to travel - her other great love - this became impossible as she would not leave Brooke; then her own health deteriorated. All her life she had been a dynamic personality, immersed in the work she loved. Enforced inactivity, as she would describe it, was a hard cross to bear, but she looked after Brooke with great loyalty until he died at the age of 93. Now (1993) at 92, she is bedridden and nearly blind, but her mind is active and she continually listens to Radio 4; she discusses world politics with remarkable clarity and objectivity. She is thankful to have lived through such an interesting century of change.

Apart from writing, travelling and photography I was becoming more involved in nature conservation and allied matters. It was in 1964 that a small group of us met in the committee room of the Somerset Archaeological and Natural History Society in Taunton Castle and agreed to form the Somerset Trust for Nature Conservation; each put a pound note on the table to start it off and officers were elected. Somewhat reluctantly, as I was much involved in other projects, I had agreed to become chairman on condition that Peter Tolson became honorary secretary. He was a dynamic personality with wide contacts within the county and an intimate knowledge of agricultural interests - he had been secretary of the Somerset branch of the National Farmers Union. His first brief was to approach key people in the county who represented organisations with important links with the countryside and invite them to serve on our council. Agriculture, forestry, the planning department of the county council, university biology departments, natural history societies and the legal profession were all represented. We also liased closely with the Nature Conservancy Council, the Countryside Commission and the National Trust. Lord Waldegrave enthusiastically agreed to be president; his influence was invaluable. He was well known and greatly respected in the county, had an estate on the Mendips, was a former alderman of the county council, the government spokesman on matters pertaining to agriculture and in full charge of forestry in the country. We were fortunate to have such an eminent working president.

With such a large county to cover and only part-time members to run the Trust, we knew our efforts would be very limited until we could afford professional, full-time staff. To start with we decided to divide the county into four regions, each with its own committees to deal with local conservation problems, and elect a scientific committee which could be called upon by any region to give expert advice. We were fortunate to have a formidable array of scientific talent within the county drawn from Bristol University, the BBC and two major natural history societies. We then had to go public in a big way to attract many more members, bring in extra helpers and increase our income for expansion. As I knew them well, I was able to persuade David Attenborough and Bruce Campbell to be our star speakers at the inaugural meeting in Taunton and the BBC lent us an outstanding film with a conservation theme. We soon had our first 1,000 members.

It was not long before we were able to appoint a full-time conservation officer and someone to take charge of everyday administration. The County Council kindly gave us office accommodation at Cannington Farm Institute until we could obtain our own headquarters. This became a reality when we negotiated with the National Trust for the lease of Fyne Court, Broomfield, a property situated in lovely country on the Quantocks. The main building had been destroyed by fire around the turn of the century, but the old library, music room, stables and other buildings remained, along with 24 acres of beautiful grounds. At one time, Fyne Court had belonged to Andrew Crosse, a contemporary of Faraday. Crosse was famous for his experiments with electricity. He strung long lines of copper wire around the estate, using it to concentrate atmospheric electricity to charge enormous batteries. One post which helped carry the wire is still attached to a beech tree in the grounds.

The National Trust was willing to renovate the buildings if we provided the money for their internal furnishings and conversions and the grounds restored to a standard worthy of a National Trust property.

This meant raising something like £20,000. The country was in recession, money was tight, grants difficult to obtain and the timing unfortunate as we had to compete with a large appeal recently launched in the county for the restoration of Wells Cathedral. Some members of Council were fearful of committing the Trust to such a large project, but a few of us felt very strongly that such an opportunity was unlikely to occur again, that we should be bold and take the risk. It was decided to go ahead.

With hindsight, our faith in the future was handsomely rewarded. Although getting all the money we needed proved very difficult, we got off to a good start with grants of £5,000 from both the Carnegie Trust and the Countryside Commission and made a public appeal for the remaining £10,000. It was a struggle, but with much volunteer labour and great enthusiasm the conversion was completed. There was an office block for staff, an excellent interpretation centre illustrating the main geological features of the Quantocks along with a series of delightful pictures painted by a local artist depicting the basic ecology of the main habitats found there. In this way the centre became the focal point for visitors to the Quantocks as well as the Trust. A shop was designed to sell Trust goods and was manned by volunteers at the week-ends. The music room was turned into a fine lecture hall which could be used for Trust events and also hired out for concerts, wedding receptions and other purposes; it had a small kitchen attached which served teas for visitors. All these things helped to provide more income for the Trust. The grounds were tidied up by gangs of volunteers and the pond, which Keith and Roger had used years before to study the breeding habits of frogs and toads, was made to hold water again. Much effort went into the improvement of the grounds; an arboretum was established with help from the County Council and nature trails were constructed.

There was a delightful old house in Broomfield belonging to the Fyne Court Estate which was ideal as a warden's house. We needed somebody to look after our headquarters, supervise and help develop the grounds and contribute much needed practical expertise and ideas. David Stewart filled the job admirably and later combined the post with the wardenship of the Quantock Hills under the County Council.

Fyne Court was officially opened amidst great rejoicing three years after signing the agreement. Sir Peter Scott performed the opening ceremony in May 1977 before a distinguished gathering of Somerset personalities including Lord and Lady Waldegrave, the Bishop of Bath and Wells and his wife, Lady Bickersteth, and representatives of many county organisations. The Trust was now truly on the map and was in a position to take off as a major influence for nature conservation in the county.

Having been one of the later county trusts to be formed, we had considerable experience to draw upon. Our policy was to map out all the major wildlife areas of importance in the county, provide factual evidence about each and notify the planning department of their locality and importance for consideration when dealing with applications for planning permission. We wanted to achieve a public image of a society which aimed to protect the countryside and its wildlife from avoidable damage, to fight hard for what was important, but not be unnecessarily negative over minor matters. In this way we hoped to build up trust and a reputation for fairness, so that when we did oppose a proposition our views were seriously taken into account. My conviction right from the beginning was that the success of the Trust would depend on team building, to harness the enthusiasm of naturalists, conservationists, scientists, farmers and professional people in relevant occupations, united with a common aim. It was a formula that could not fail. All praise to the many helpers who made it work.

At the Annual General Meeting the following year, which was held at

Opening of Fyne Court, 1977. From left: The Right Revd John Bickersteth, Bishop of Bath and Wells, The Rt Hon The Earl Waldegrave KG GCVO, Lady Bickersteth, Lady Scott, Betty Neal, Sir Peter Scott, the author

Fyne Court, I resigned from the chair after 14 years; I felt it was time for a change. However, I did not want to withdraw any help I could give at this critical stage in the development of the Trust but I wanted to help in a less demanding capacity and hand over the reins to somebody with new ideas and plenty of energy, so I agreed to continue as chairman of the Fyne Court committee and a member of Council. I was delighted when Dr Chris Smith agreed to take over; he had done sterling work for the Trust in the north of the county for many years. He retired from a senior post in industry at the age of 50 in order to work full-time for the Trust and remained chairman until 1993, guiding the Trust's affairs with great success. Today, the Somerset Trust is now one of the leading Wildlife Trusts in the country with an annual income of nearly half a million and assets of two million. There are now 64 Trust nature reserves and the staff has grown to 18. Chris played a major role in this success story. Now Dr Jeremy Cherfas has taken over as chairman with enthusiasm and considerable expertise. I look back with great thankfulness to those early, faltering beginnings based on enthusiasm, hard work, hope, faith and charity.

Before I stood down as chairman, I was delighted to receive a letter from the Prime Minister's office saying that my name had been put forward for an MBE in the New Year's honours list for services to nature conservation in Somerset. Thousands of people have received such honours, but when it happens to you it becomes something very special. The investiture was in July 1976. Keith drove Betty and me to Buckingham Palace; it was an extraordinary experience driving through the gates of the Palace with the great throng of people outside watching the arrivals. Ascending the red-carpeted stairs, Keith and Betty were directed to the large hall where the investiture was to take place, while I, with other recipients, went to the Queen's picture gallery where we were briefed about the ceremony. It was an extremely hot afternoon; there seemed to be little ventilation, and morning dress was not designed for such high temperatures!

What impressed me most, when my turn came, was the way the Queen made you feel that you were not just one more to be invested, but that she was interested and well enough versed to ask relevant questions about the conservation work I had been doing - a feeling no doubt shared by the many others who were treated in the same gracious and personal manner. I felt very proud to receive recognition not just for myself, but for the many other members of the Trust who had done so much. On our return to Keith's home, I was brought down to earth when our small grandchildren obviously showed more interest in my top-hat than the account of the day's proceedings!

Today, one of the more satisfactory features of nature conservation in Britain is that it is accepted as necessary by a wide spectrum of the population. At one time conservationists were often looked upon as a cranky minority. They cut little ice with industrialists. There also seemed hardly any common ground between conservationists and many farmers and field-sports groups.

Some bridge-building was started in 1965, when a symposium was arranged by the Council for Nature on 'The place of predatory mammals in the British countryside'. It was a remarkable occasion because it brought together representatives of eighteen organisations with such diverse interests: conservationists, landowners, gamekeepers, members of field-sports societies, farmers and foresters. I was invited to give one of the talks, as an MP had recently introduced a bill to legalise gassing of badger setts - a subject very relevant to many present. I was strongly against the bill and argued that the case for protecting the badger was strong, but should include a clause for humane action in the event of unusual instances of specific damage. However, gassing was not the answer, it was indiscriminate, and if made legal, would open the door to much abuse by gamekeepers and landowners. Little did I realise then how prophetic the warning was.

As a consequence of this meeting, a working party was set up to write a booklet,'Predatory Mammals in Britain', which was a factual account of the characteristics of each species, the good and harm they may do, the best and most humane methods of control when necessary - emphasising that prevention of damage was better than destruction of the animals - and any legal matters involved. It marked an important co-operative initiative. The committee met regularly at the House of Commons under the chairmanship of Marcus Kimball MP with the Home Office, Ministry of Agriculture and Forestry Commission represented as assessors.

The booklet was published in 1966 and was brought up to date at intervals to include new information and legislation. However, when this matter was concluded it was agreed that the committee could be reconvened if other relevant matters arose. Thus, when pressure was mounting for the legal protection of the badger, I wrote to Marcus Kimball asking him to recall members to discuss the various proposals being put forward. Being a private member's bill it was essential to ascertain the attitude of the Home Office and get a consensus of views from interested parties, otherwise it could easily be thrown out in the Commons by the hunting lobby - hence the importance of getting

Marcus Kimball's support as he had much influence in the Field Sports Society.

Public opinion was greatly in favour of legislation to protect the badger. Articles appeared in the press from people such as Ruth Murray, Jane Ratcliffe and Arthur Killingly outlining the persecution that was going on and the great increase in badger digging. The Womens' Institute wrote to me about the wording of a resolution they hoped to pass at their Annual Meeting at the Albert Hall, and Jane Ratcliffe, who was a member, did much to get it passed. This resolution was sent to the Home Office. However, the official attitude, prompted by the Nature Conservancy, was that protection was unnecessary as badgers were not endangered. This was true, but it took no account of the increase in persecution and the cruelty involved. I wrote Baroness Young at the Home Office voicing my concern about the official line which was clearly out of date. She replied, asking for hard evidence of the widespread nature of the persecution. Ruth Murray had collected a lot of evidence, but for reasons best known to herself was unwilling to forward it to the Home Office. However, enough had been collected from other sources and I was granted an interview with Baroness Young. My two badger-expert friends in the Mammal Society, Dr Richard Paget and Derek Warren, came along too. It was an interesting experience for all of us; we were graciously received and had a constructive time giving her the evidence she needed. She was very positive about it.

I was also invited to speak at the Commons to the inter-party conservation group about the pros and cons of legislation and give what facts I could of the status of the badger in the country and the pressures they were undergoing through persecution, snaring, gassing and road deaths. Lord Craigton kindly acted as my host, showed me around the Lords and gave me tea which included seed cake - the one thing I disliked from childhood days!

It was remarkable that two badger bills were proposed almost simultaneously, one by Lord Arran in the Lords (his wife kept pet badgers), and Richard Paget's friend, a Yorkshire Labour MP, Mr Peter Hardy, in the Commons (he was a keen badger-watcher). I had lengthy correspondence with both of them about their respective bills. Arran's was a very comprehensive protectionist one, but for practical purposes came in for considerable criticism; it was also very badly drafted. Hardy's Bill was much more limited in scope and dealt with badger digging mainly from the tresspass angle.

When I reported back to the Badger Group of the Mammal Society, Lord Cranbrook (our president at that time) was at the meeting and offered help. He was keenly interested in badgers, had had experience of legislation over seals and knew Lord Arran. He was very helpful. We discussed the clauses together and made a number of amendments which would make Lord Arran's bill much more acceptable; these were successfully incorporated into the bill at the committee stage. Peter Hardy kindly withdrew his Bill and agreed to pilot Lord Arran's through the Commons. It could have been wrecked by an objector, but Marcus Kimble had told me privately that he was happy about it and would not dissent on behalf of the Field Sports Society. It was passed on 25 July 1973.

Many other people and organisations played important parts in getting the Act on to the statute book; it was very much a co-operative effort. My part was largely played backstage by stirring up public opinion, providing data and trying to improve relationships between opposing factions. I strongly believe that more can be achieved by fostering trust, showing understanding of other viewpoints and working with people, than using uncompromising tactics which immediately put any opposition on the defensive.

The Act was far from ideal but an important step had been taken. In 1981 it was amended through the Wildlife and Countryside Act, and other loopholes closed by further amendments in 1985. Finally, protection of badger setts was achieved in 1991. Thus at last badgers are now fully protected. However the greatest problem has always been effective implementation of the law. Fortunately, public opinion in favour of the badger has been growing all the time, badger protection societies have been formed in many parts of the country to safeguard them locally, and magistrates are becoming tougher over convictions. It is a constant battle but much progress has been made.

The other mammal which was attracting grave concern was the otter. A considerable and rather sudden decline in their numbers was apparent from otter hunting statistics. Having been interested in otters for many years and helped bring up Topsy and Turvy, I was glad to assist in their conservation if I could. The matter was discussed by the Mammals Committee which met at the Commons and the Mammal Society carried out a survey run by Paul Chanin to get more data on the otter's status. To pursue the matter further the Joint Otter Group (JOG) of which I was a member was set up in 1976. Consequently, further surveys were carried out in England, Wales and Scotland using similar techniques of counting spraints (droppings) along standard lengths of waterways often in the vicinity of bridges (otters like to use ledges under these for sprainting). These surveys confirmed the considerable decline of the otter in England and Wales, with numbers in Scotland keeping up well, particularly in the west, in coastal regions, the Western Isles and Shetland. After data had been analysed and dead otters tested for toxic residues, it was concluded that pollution of rivers by dieldrin and aldrin had been the most likely cause of the sudden decline, with increasing loss of suitable riverside vegetation, an important subsidiary factor. There was little evidence that hunting had been responsible, but its persistence when numbers had already fallen had probably been detrimental.

There was much pressure for protective legislation. The Nature Conservancy Council considered that as a short-term measure the otter should be given full protection in England and Wales by means of an amendment to the Wild Creatures Act of 1975. This was accomplished in 1978. The hunts pre-empted the passing of the amendment by a voluntary ban on hunting, switching in some parts of the country to mink. It was hoped that in the longer term a more comprehensive Wildlife Bill would be drawn up to include many species of plants and animals. These would be placed in various categories which attracted different degrees of protection, and combine in one act much of the previous legislation concerning separate species. This became law in 1981 as the Wildlife and Countryside Act. As a consequence the otter was given complete protection, also in Scotland.

Legal protection was a useful step, but otters were already extinct in many parts of England and very scarce in other areas; they needed all the help they could get even to maintain numbers. Much was done by voluntary bodies to improve the environment for otters. There was close liason with water authorities and riparian landowners; otter havens were set up in key places where they could lie up or breed, and educational schemes promoted. The Hon. Vincent Weir, with great vision, personal commitment and generosity played a considerable part in these initiatives with grants from the Vincent Wildlife Trust. In addition, Philip Wayre formed the Otter Trust where otters were bred under controlled conditions. Many have now been successfully released where water quality and habitat requirements were suitable. By 1993 a slow, but significant improvement in otter populations had occurred in some areas.

It was good experience for me to have a spell on the Advisory Committee for England of the Nature Conservancy Council. This helped to give a national view of the conservation movement and put into context the work I was involved in with the Somerset Trust. In some ways I was disappointed, as so much time was spent in assessing, acquiring or negotiating agreements over nature reserves or preparing consultation documents on nature conservation in relation to agriculture and forestry. Of course these subjects were of great importance, but not matters on which I had particular expertise. I certainly learnt a lot, but felt my contribution to the debates was not of great value - I was happier with the practical side of conservation than the administrative. However, I found the visits to special sites particularly interesting as I then saw the problems at first hand, spoke with those who were trying to cope with them and felt better equipped to help formulate long-term strategies. At that time the main issues were the Norfolk Broads, the New Forest, the Somerset Wetlands and the development of certain national parks where visitor pressure was increasing.

I felt much more at home when working with the Mammal Society. It was a great honour to be elected chairman for six years from 1974. I took it on knowing that the new honorary secretary, Professor Michael Delany, was very experienced and his guidance would be invaluable. It is usually the secretary who does most of the work! My job was also made easier by having a council with so much expertise and enthusiasm.

This was an interesting period in the development of the society; we were becoming more widely known, and knowledge of British mammals within its ranks was second to none. At this time the conservation movement was also gathering momentum and one of our major functions was to provide scientific data for others to use. Much of this was done through country-wide surveys of individual species; I have already mentioned badgers and otters in this connection, but there were many others. Individuals within the society were keen and active conservationists but the society itself kept strictly to scientific parameters. Thus a reputation was built up for objective reliability, not as a pressure group. This helped considerably when legislation was being considered. In later years the society's remit was widened to support actively the conservation of mammals.

When I had finished my stint as chairman, I stepped into Dr Southern's shoes as president. At the annual dinner, it was very gratifying to receive the society medal from him, as 6 years previously my first and very pleasant duty as chairman had been to present one to him! It was interesting to think back to the time of the formation of the society and compare what people knew then about British mammals with what was known 26 years later. The advances had been incredible, thanks in large measure to the dedicated fieldwork and researches of members of the society. The presentation was a proud moment for me; I felt I was with friends as well as colleagues.

It was in 1971 that a sinister cloud appeared over the world of badgers. I had a phone call from a Ministry veterinary surgeon asking if I had heard of badgers suffering from bovine tuberculosis. I thought for a moment and remembered hearing about two cases from zoos, but nothing regarding wild badgers. He said he had found a case in Gloucestershire! That was the start of a long saga which continues to this day.

A little later, when I returned from a three-months spell in Africa I was dismayed to find TB had become a political issue, the press had made the most of it, and even a programme of 'The Archers' had mentioned it, giving the impression that badgers in general were a danger to the farmer, so the whole country heard about it and farmers became worried before many facts had been established. Many took it into their own hands to destroy badgers on their land and there was soon a strong farming lobby calling for Ministry action.

For some years, cattle breakdowns in the south-west had occurred more frequently than elsewhere and a wildlife source of infection was suspected. A particularly bad area was the Cotswold escarpment; it was here that the first tubercular badger had been discovered.

I was invited to attend a gathering of Ministry veterinary surgeons from the south-west at a symposium held in Torquay. The chief veterinary officer brought up to date the Ministry's evidence and I was asked to give a talk about the behaviour and ecology of badgers within that context. A discussion followed about the possible connection between badgers and tuberculosis. Clearly much research and experimental work needed to be done to clarify the situation.

The problem as I saw it was the desire for quick action on the one hand and on the other, the paucity of research on which appropriate action could be based. The veterinary view was the standard one when a species was thought to transmit a disease: destroy the carrier. I thought of the awful consequences of that policy when it had been applied to sleeping sickness and nagana in Africa when so many of the large mammals which hosted the causal trypanosomes had been destroyed to little avail. Was this to be another tragic story? Much depended on how widespread the disease was in badgers. Nobody knew. Over the next few years it became clear that there were pockets of infection in Gloucestershire, Cornwall and parts of Wiltshire, Devon and Dorset. In a majority of cases infected badgers were discovered nearby. On this evidence, the Ministry decided to kill all badgers in places where cattle breakdowns occurred if it were proved by sampling that there were infected badgers in the neighbourhood.

At this time, gassing was illegal and snaring, as normally carried out, very cruel. A field trial was set up using the most humane method of snaring available, but there was an outcry led by Ruth Murray who took the Minister to court on grounds of cruelty. She lost her case, but much bad feeling against the Ministry resulted. Live trapping was the method used for several years, but gassing was thought to be the most humane method as it had been used successfully for rabbits. An amendment was introduced to the Wildlife Act of 1975 to enable the Ministry to use this method under license.

One of the conditions imposed by the government was the formation of a Consultative Panel to keep under review the evidence related to TB in badgers and the operations of the Ministry in its attempts to eradicate the disease in badgers. I was invited to be a member, and recall the irony of the Chairman's statement that 'the appointment would be for 3 years, but it was to be hoped that the problem would not prove to be so intractable that my help would be needed for so long!' I served for 15 years and the problem still remains!

Panel membership included representatives of a wide range of organisations including conservation, animal welfare and scientific bodies. All agreed reluctantly that the position was serious and some action had to be taken. I was fortunate that I represented no society and had no vested interest except wanting the best for the badger. By our first meeting, more data had been collected, the correlation between cattle breakdowns and infected badgers was strong and rather crude experiments had shown that in captivity infected badgers were capable of passing on the disease to cattle when confined together for some months.

Public interest was considerable and there was much press coverage. Following the first meeting I was asked to represent the Panel in a short debate on Independent Television with Lord Arran, following the news. I was amused that we were kept in different rooms until we were led into the studio. The programme was not very helpful as scientific evidence and emotion became inextricably mixed.

The whole TB saga for me was a distressful one. On the one hand I wanted to do the best I could for badgers; on the other I valued my integrity as a scientist and had to weigh the evidence, be objective and try to be constructive. What I hoped for from the Panel was a genuine attempt to find the truth and act on it. What I found was much prejudice, political pressures and early on a grossly naive understanding of the complexity of the situation. The veterinary side looked upon it as a straight-forward disease problem which could be solved by drastic culling of badgers; many farmers in the counties affected saw the badger as a threat to their livelihood; responsible conservationists hated to see badgers killed and did their best to limit the damage without affecting the efficiency of the campaign, and public attitudes, much influenced by emotive reporting, became polarised; the lunatic fringe was vocal in its condemnation of the Ministry and anybody who sought to face facts and try to hold a balanced view. As always, the public debate on such an emotive matter produced more heat than light. This was not surprising; gassing was a very emotive subject and people generally were very fond of badgers.

When lecturing, the first question asked was usually about TB. I always tried to give the evidence objectively so that others could judge for themselves, but it was evident that in some instances I was up against closed minds - sentimentalists who were not interested in the truth, only their own prejudices. A few key figures became particularly nasty and having access to the press wrote letters full of fallacies and half-truths which misled the public and unfortunately polarised the debate. Most of the inuendo and invective I ignored, but when the Mammal Society was also brought into it, a reply was called for, so a letter was sent to the Daily Telegraph signed by the president, chairman and secretary. This refuted the allegations and provided the facts. One lady, who was looked upon as an expert on the badger in her area, was particularly vocal in her opposition; she claimed her investigations showed that badgers never even had TB and there was no possibility of a connection between badgers and the disease in cattle. She was invited on two occasions to come to a Panel meeting to present her case, but each time she refused at the last minute. She was also asked to be one of 3 speakers on Independent Television to debate the question; I was told on arrival at the studio that she had decided not to take part after all!

The TB problem generated a great deal of research including a splendid field study at Woodchester Park which continues to this day. This provided much needed information about badger behaviour, population dynamics, the way TB is spread amongst badgers and recently, the interactions between cattle and badgers - a subject researched earlier by Paul Benham at Reading University. These studies should help farmers take sensible precautions to lessen the likelihood of cross infection in problem areas. Dr Chris Cheeseman has led this research from the start. It was most interesting, early on, going out with him and tracking badgers with radio collars and viewing their behaviour through infra-red binoculars.

The gassing programme continued until 1982 except for a short moratorium while Lord Zuckerman was preparing his report. Experiments to discover what concentrations of gas were necessary to kill badgers effectively showed that the reaction of badgers to cyanide gas was different from that of rabbits and cast doubt on the humaneness of the method. Consequently, the Rt Hon Peter Walker MP, who was then Minister of Agriculture, decided to stop all gassing, coming to a Panel meeting to explain his decision. This was greatly welcomed. Live trapping followed by shooting, took its place. This meant, in contrast to gassing, that the carcasses could be examined and the numbers infected assessed. This new technique was accompanied by a clean-ring strategy. This meant removing all social groups of badgers around an outbreak and continuing outwards until sampling showed no infection in the badger population. I strongly disagreed with this as the disease was far too widespread for such a strategy and much unnecessary culling was bound to take place. However, it was practiced for several years. When Professor Dunnett and his independent team assessed the policy, it was discontinued and action was confined to the immediate neighbourhood of the breakdown.

One scheme that looked promising was the formation of an oral vaccine which would give some immunity to badgers against TB. It could be fed with bait to badgers in affected areas over a series of years. Dr John Stanford developed such a vaccine at the Middlesex Hospital. However, it only gave partial protection and the Ministry did not allow field trials in England. Instead, they preferred to put much money and effort into producing a live-test which could be used in the field. It is comparable in effect to the tuberculin test in cattle. This was accomplished, but unfortunately, field trials showed that a high proportion of infected badgers were not detected and it has done nothing to advance a more satisfactory strategy. Even if it had been successful, I was never convinced of its usefulness for disease control, only as a research tool which might reduce the number of healthy badgers destroyed.

For some years I was a member of the Mini-panel - a subcommittee of the main Panel. This was a small group which met in Bristol. It looked in great detail at every new cattle breakdown which occurred in parishes where there had been no trouble during the previous six years. Large-scale maps were produced by field workers, on which all badger setts, signs of activity and social group territories were marked. The disease history of neighbouring areas was also taken into account. Decisions on whether or not to take action were only taken after careful assessment of these data. I was very glad to have worked on this committee as knowledge of badger behaviour helped considerably in reaching decisions.

After many years of culling badgers, the situation is little better than it was in 1975. Sadly, the Ministry has never agreed to the setting up of control areas so that the effect of policies could be assessed, so there will always be arguments. However, there is no doubt whatever that bovine tuberculosis is endemic in the badger population and there is strong circumstantial evidence that badgers do infect cattle under some circumstances, but to what degree they are a danger has not yet been established - probably far less than previously thought by veterinarians.

I had to resign from the Consultative Panel in 1990 due to ill health, but continue to take an interest in the problem. In 1992, like many other scientists, I felt the time had come to stop all action against badgers for a period of at least 5 years and carefully assess the effect of this policy. If TB did flare up (which seemed unlikely from evidence obtained at Woodchester Park) action could be resumed. If there was no detectable change, the moratorium should be continued; badgers would then have some respite at last and an extremely costly operation would come to an end. Nevertheless, all agreed that it was imperative that research should continue and farmers take recommended precautions to minimise the risks. Sadly, there was a rise in numbers of herds infected and this strategy was turned down by the Ministry as too risky. Instead, a compromise strategy was adopted which satisfies nobody in terms of a solution to the problem. However, it does include research into a vaccine for TB in badgers and improved diagnostic tests to detect the disease in both cattle and badgers. These provisions could be helpful, but they will take many years to perfect. Meanwhile, badgers will continue to be culled with little chance of much improvement in the short term. One thing is certain and must be faced; the disease is most unlikely to be completely eradicated from the badger population

For 55 years badgers have given me much pleasure. At times this has been tempered by sadness due to the disease problem and the persecution they have suffered. However, during that same period I have seen their popularity increase to an extraordinary degree. It is astonishing that so many people from all walks of life and of all ages spend hours often under uncomfortable conditions waiting for that magic moment when a black-and-white face appears at the sett entrance and the cubs come out to play. Whatever the reasons for this, there is no doubt that badger-watching has brought interest and relaxation to many thousands of people - long may it continue!

Chapter Fifteen

Africa

It was probably when I was about nine and read 'Gorilla Hunters' by R.M.Ballantyne that I first had a longing to go to Africa. It fired my imagination, gave me visions of jungle, strange and exciting animals, above all, adventure. I must have read the book half a dozen times. Looking at it now it seems probable that the author had never even been to Africa, but he knew how to write stories for small boys. My father told me about David Livingstone and his journeys, and occasionally a missionary from the Congo would speak at my father's church and tell of his work there. I began to have thoughts of becoming a medical missionary; if so, it would be to the Congo. When I first learnt geography, it was Africa I wanted to learn most about.

Later, and at university, thoughts of Africa faded, but after I had graduated and was looking desperately for a job during the slump, the thought of emigrating to Kenya as a teacher did enter my head. However, I got the post at Rendcomb and that was that. Much later, when at Taunton, my headmaster suggested I should apply for the headship of one of the Nairobi schools, but with a young family and good prospects where I was, it seemed inadvisable; I did not apply.

In 1961 my great friend and colleague P.G.Smith made a trip to East Africa bringing back some elephant dung in a matchbox and regaling me with stories; this stimulated my interest once more. The following year my chance came. Stephen Curry, whom I had taught at Rendcomb, was in Britain and came to visit us. He invited Betty and me to spend the summer holidays with him in Kenya. He was an entomologist in the Forestry Department based near Nairobi and was planning a safari in August to various national parks in Kenya and Tanzania with his wife, Barbara and their four children. It was the perfect way to celebrate our Silver Wedding! As an afterthought, Stephen mentioned that he would like to climb Kilimanjaro - would I join him? Knowing nothing of what this would entail I happily agreed.

I find it fascinating to look back on that first visit to East Africa in 1962 before Kenya became independent and consider the profound changes I have witnessed during the course of more than twenty subsequent visits. I am so grateful to have seen something of the area before tourism and a population explosion took their toll.

It was our first long flight; very exciting. We flew in a Britannia -'the whispering giant'- a wonderfully quiet turbo-prop plane. I took my Bolex camera and heavy tripod to film as much as possible of the fauna. We were met by Stephen and Barbara and taken by car to their home at Kikuyu, north-west of Nairobi. Everything was so different: sights, smells, sounds, trees, flowers, birds and of course the people. We were astonished to see long lines of Kikuyu women wending their way home, bent under the weight of huge bundles of firewood kept in place by a leather strap around their foreheads, often with the husband following behind carrying nothing!

It was not long after Mau Mau and there was still an African employed to guard the house at night; he carried a spear. Stephen and Barbara were wonderful hosts and showed us a great deal. We visited the Forestry Department at Muguga where I was fascinated to see the night's catch in the moth-trap Stephen was running; all the moths were different from those we had in England and yet their relationships were often obvious. We were taken over the Veterinary Department nearby and shown something of the research being done on the resistance of various cattle breeds and hybrids to drought using identical twin calves, one of each pair acting as a control. We were also invited to see something unusual in a staff bedroom. Under the bed was a cardboard box secured by string; it was carefully opened. We were met with spitting and snarling from two balls of fur - small leopard cubs! Not quite what we had expected. The mother had been killed and they were being reared on the bottle; gloves had to be used!

Nairobi National Park was next door to the airport. Barbara took us there several times; it was most exciting, it being our first chance to see the larger animals. It was a thrill to find our first pride of lion and film them on a kill. Few cars were about except at week-ends, and in places I was able to film outside the car using a tripod. We even had a picnic by the lake. The Park had been developed after years of effort by Mervyn Cowie whom I had met in London when on a lecture tour. When I rang him up, he was pleased to arrange a meeting. He gave us a guided tour in his vintage Buick car - brass fittings, leather upholstery and a rhino pennant on the bonnet. We felt very honoured.

At week-ends Stephen was free to take us further afield. We visited

Lake Naivasha, one part covered with a mass of blue water-lilies. It was a paradise for water-birds: pied and malachite kingfishers, lily-trotters, crakes, spoonbills, sacred and hadada ibises, goliath and grey herons, egrets, many waders and a huge flock of pelicans which Stephen told us had come from Lake Nakuru; the number of species was bewildering.

I spotted a hippo grazing on land and stalked it until near enough to film, but at the expense of learning how thorny the African terrain was when crawling on my tummy. Today, this wild area is part of the garden of the Lake Naivasha Hotel! A recent rise in water-level had isolated a number of trees; now these stand dead and bereft of bark, festooned with cormorant nests. Not far from the lake was an area of scrub where game was plentiful; today it is a huge expanse of carnations grown for export to the capitals of Europe.

We also climbed Mount Longonot (good training for Kilimanjaro) and admired the wonderful symmetry of its crater. Its floor was full of vegetation, but jets of steam could be seen issuing from vents in its steep sides. From the summit we had marvellous views of the Rift Valley, mile upon mile of reddish, parched scrub several thousand metres below us; a few dirt roads ran like lines on a map across it.

On another occasion we walked the long trail through Hell's Gate until we reached the hot springs where boiling mud and sulphurous steam erupted in a spectacular manner. Today the area is turned into a geothermal plant to supply energy; visitors are denied access.

We made a trip with Stephen on one of his entomological excursions into the forestry reserves of the Kikuyu Escarpment, wonderful country with a host of bright butterflies including many swallowtails; lovely birds such as turacos; black and white colobus monkeys leaping from branch to branch. There were many interesting trees and flowers including a red orchid a metre high which we later had identified in the Coryndon Museum. We came back with the Land-rover loaded with tree specimens showing wood-boring insect damage.

When Stephen had his leave we started our safari. Somehow we all piled into his large Peugeot car and followed the dirt road to Amboseli Game Park. Police checked our papers, stopping the car very effectively with a wooden beam studded with vicious spikes, stretched across the road. The Park was very dry; dust was a menace - it got into everything. Stephen was anxious to press on to Namanga on the border with Tanganyika (Tanzania) in good time to book into the Namanga River Hotel, so there was little time for photography and we missed the better areas. However, we saw gerenuk for the first time and watched these delicate, long-necked antelopes reaching up on their hind legs to pluck the tender leaves. We got close views of elephants and many other species but it was frustrating not to spend more time there - how I longed to do some filming! Having driven right through the Park we arrived at the hotel - very impressive with its bamboo-thatched roof, cool, white-walled lounge and welcoming staff wearing smart fezes and white kanzus with wide belts.

Early next morning we crossed the border, taking the Arusha road as far as the base of Mount Meru before turning off towards Lake Manyara. We stopped briefly at the village of Mto Wa Mbo at the foot of the escarpment. Maasai and their donkeys were much in evidence and a wonderful flamboyant tree in full bloom dominated the centre of the village. Slowly we climbed the steep escarpment to reach the Lake Manyara Hotel, a small newly-constructed building perched high on the edge of the escarpment overlooking the lake and the national park. Today it is huge by comparison. Visitors could use a telescope to view the animals far below. We were longing to go down there, but only had time for a quick visit. However, it was a wonderful experience to see so many animals, especially elephants and a huge herd of buffalo which I wanted to film. As we slowly approached, I followed on foot using the car as a shield, ready to hop in quickly if necessary. It was thrilling to be quite near a herd of several hundred of these huge beasts.

Next day we started early in a Land-Rover owned by the Lake Manyara Hotel to get to the Ngorongoro Crater before closing time for the descent (there was a strict time-table for going up and down as there were no passing places). We arrived with five minutes to spare. Carefully we made our way down the boulder-strewn track which snaked its way with a series of hair-pin bends down the side of the crater wall. It seemed a miracle that the vehicle could make it. It has since been improved and a second track constructed.

We had a splendid day - the most impressive collection of mammals and birds we had ever seen. Within the 100 square miles of the crater floor the habitats are so diverse: savannah, woodland, swamp, fresh-water and a soda lake - all with their characteristic fauna. However, we had hoped to see black rhinos and more lions as the Crater was famous for them, but the ranger could find none. We found out later that this was due to a plague of blood-sucking Stomyx flies. They breed in wet mud impregnated with dung, and from November 1961 until May 1962 the weather had been consistently wet and they had bred in astronomical numbers. Some of the antelopes had appeared black with flies and were literally sucked to death, and lions and rhinos were driven to distraction, some of the former climbing trees up to 13m to avoid them.

However, the majority had either died or left the Crater for many months, so we missed them.

The next day we made the long journey from Manyara through Arusha and Moshi to the Marangu Hotel in the foothills of Kilimanjaro. Climbing expeditions were organised from here and Stephen had booked for the two of us some time previously. While we attempted the climb, Betty, Barbara and the children were to spend the time at the coast. As we said 'goodbye', I thought how sensible they were; it was beginning to dawn on me what I was in for. We arrived on the Thursday, the plan being to do some training climbs on Friday and Saturday, rest on Sunday and start the climb on Monday. It would take 3 days to get up and two down - something over sixty miles in all if you took the most direct route.

Kilimanjaro is the highest mountain in Africa, thrown up by 3 eruptions. The first was Shira to the west, now greatly eroded; Mawenzi erupted next and stands high and rugged to the east, and this is connected by a saddle to the most recent upthrust, Kibo, 5,895m (19,340') at its highest point. This still retains its crater, now surrounded by perpetual ice and snow. By 1962, small parties regularly made the attempt, but two of the three huts *en route* were fairly primitive. Optimists described the climb as 'just a long walk, uphill most of the way'. No climbing skill was needed, the difficulty being the altitude and the consequent shortage of oxygen. I was comforted to be told that being on the wrong side of 50 was no problem if I took it slowly - many much older had made it successfully.

We were told that our companions would be two couples and an art student - seven was rather a large party for which three guides and fourteen porters would be needed.

Monday morning arrived at last, sunny and warm. We collected and checked our things: warm clothes, balaclavas, scarves, anoraks, fur-lined mittens, snow goggles and any personal things we needed to take. All these were placed in a sleeping bag and put into a large kit-bag to be carried on the head of one of the porters. Others took boxes of provisions, paraffin lamps and other necessities. We were each given a staff and I carried my camera. Finally, we received some comforting advice: if we had a blackout it was wise to give up; if we merely felt awful with sickness and headache we could go ahead if we wished; and to cap it all, we were told that the cost of bringing you back on a stretcher was £4 between any two huts! I hesitate to think what it would be today.

The Marangu hotel was at 1,500m. Our first day's objective was to reach Bismarck hut (now called Mandera) at 2,600m. We had plenty of time to get there so we took it slowly, pausing to observe anything of interest and take photographs. We first passed through well-populated Chagga country where most of the huts were hidden among banana trees. The land was very fertile and crops such as coffee, ginger and sweet potatoes were grown in abundance. Instead of taking their cattle to the pasture the women brought back grass to their huts where the cattle were housed. In this way the dung was not wasted and could be used for their crops.

Eventually the huts became fewer and we saw the line of the forest ahead. This was the montane rain forest and marked the boundary of what is now the Kilimanjaro National Park. We followed the dirt road through the forest for a short while. A stream of safari ants were crossing at one point - a broad ribbon of dark brown against the red mud of the road. I revelled in the variety of butterflies flying in the morning sunshine. However, a narrow forest track roughly parallel to the road looked most inviting, so we took it, hoping to see a greater variety of wildlife. A troop of blue monkeys, disturbed by our approach, disappeared at high speed; later we saw black-and-white colobus doing their aerobatics high in the canopy. There were not many flowers where the shade was deeper, but by a small stream we were delighted to find the scarlet and yellow balsam which is a species unique to this mountain; the pink balsam was common. Stephen identified the more striking trees for us.

We reached some open moorland by Bismarck hut by mid-afternoon, so we had time to explore before the porters arrived. Here there were gladioli, red-hot pokers, many pink orchids and a host of other flowers.

The evening became very cold, but our chief guide soon produced a roaring fire and a splendid hot meal eaten by the light of a single paraffin lamp. It was early bed for all, but I had no sleep that night, my mind was too active and I was unaccustomed to the altitude. When the sun rose we looked down on a continuous sea of cloud just below us, but we were in full sun. Washing under a stand-pipe (we were less enthusiastic about such civilised behaviour later), I was interested to see fresh footprints of a leopard in the mud nearby.

It was still cold when we started off. First, there was a stiff climb along a muddy, slippery path through the remainder of the rain forest; our staves were very useful. There were *Podocarpus* (a type of conifer), wild olives, rose wood, giant heathers 10m high, tree-like *Hypericums* and many others. Some were festooned with drifts of hanging sage-green lichens - like Masefield's mermaids 'with long green weeds for hair'.

The forest stopped abruptly; we were out in the sun once more. What a magnificent sight! There in the distance was Kilimanjaro in all its glory with snow-capped Kibo and the more rugged Mawenzi brilliant against the deep blue sky. We realised the climb was just beginning; it would take another two days to reach the last hut before the final ascent. We hoped to reach Peter's (Horombo) hut that night. The morning's walk was a slow, steady climb through heathland with scattered bushes and bright with flowers - several species of everlasting flowers, papery to the touch, a few *Protea* with immense globular flowers, yellow daisies and many others.

It was in a more sheltered area that we saw our first giant groundsels. It was unbelievable that these 'trees', some 5m high, were related to the rather miserable weeds we pull out of our gardens. The younger plants have their stems covered with a mass of dead leaves which protect them against frost; as they grow in height the lower leaves fall off exposing the main trunk to give them a top-heavy appearance. Giant lobelias were also present with their tall spiked inflorescences, but their flowers were over so we saw no sunbirds which sip nectar from them when in bloom.

It was late afternoon when we reached Peter's hut, a small, corrugated-iron erection with four double-bunk beds on two sides, an old iron stove in the corner, a table and two benches. Hardly 3-star accommodation, but we were glad to have shelter and a chance to sit down. A guide raked the old ashes on to the floor and got a fire going from wood brought from the last hut. We knew there would be a heavy frost that night.

Some hot soup and the warm fire made us feel more comfortable, but we soon discovered that very little of the smoke was finding its way up the tin pipe which should have acted as a chimney. Our eyes started to smart and it became a moot point whether we should open the door to let the smoke out and the cold in, or keep it closed and suffer accordingly. We rather unwisely decided to keep warm.

I went to bed, but not to sleep. I had a splitting headache due to the altitude; there was too little ventilation and it was uncomfortably hot. My heart was bumping along at a faster rate than usual, and I could tell from the tossing and turning of the man in the bunk above that he could not sleep either. He, poor man, was nearest the fire and the ceiling, and it was no surprise when I saw two legs dangle over the side as he tried to reach the floor. I guided his feet on to the edge of my bunk, but there was a slithering crash as he landed in a faint on the floor with his head in the ashes by the fire. I scrambled out of my sleeping bag - a sudden exertion which made me feel queer - and lifted his head out of the ashes I was relieved to find cold. I called for help to drag him away. Once the door was opened, the frosty air acted like a douche of cold water and he quickly came round, but was violently sick and felt ill for some time. The one compensation was the breath-taking beauty of the night. The full moon shone brightly out of a star-spangled sky brilliantly lighting up the snows of Kibo.

The morning was sunny and clear. While waiting to start, we saw several striped grass-mice near the hut, alpine chats and a white-necked raven. A small stream nearby was the last place where we could get water - all needed for drinking and cooking had to be carried on the head of a porter. A 4 gallon tin was filled, but to our dismay, it leaked! This could have been serious, but one of the party supplied chewing-gum, another some sticking plaster and 4 gallons of water survived the journey!

The morning's climb was planned to take us to the foot of Mawenzi at about 4,000m; then we had to cross the Saddle between the peaks and up another 300m to Kibo hut. The climb was tough and slow. Whenever it got steeper we had to pause to regain our breath. Taking photographs was a wonderful excuse for me to make frequent stops.

It was very cold when we reached the foot of Mawenzi - not so high as Kibo but much more difficult to climb. I was glad our objective was Kibo. Another steep incline and the Saddle lay before us; it was a desolate spot. With a strong wind the fine pumice can blow across it like a sandstorm, but we were lucky. There was a little stunted vegetation to start with, then nothing. We saw Kibo hut shining in the distance when the sun was reflected on the corrugated iron, but after hours of weary trudging we seemed little nearer. I rested at short intervals on my staff. I knew now what a vital piece of equipment it was. I found myself taking less interest in what was going on but was brought up with a jerk when I saw a line of large footprints cross the path. Apparently, eland occasion-ally cross the Saddle from one feeding ground to another.

The relatively flat desolate Saddle came to an end at last; we were at the foot of Kibo with only another short climb to the hut, but it was steep and took a long time. We struggled up grimly keeping our thoughts to ourselves. 40 paces at a time was all I could manage but we made it at last - all but one who was very sick and had to be supported on both sides by two guides. She recovered to some extent after a rest, but there was no question of her completing the climb.

It was now 5 o'clock; swirling mist cut off any view of the mountain above us; there was no vegetation, more like a moonscape. The hut was tiny; missing planks from some of the bunks and the absence of a door on the 'sentry box' (which acted as a toilet), bore witness to the desperate need for fuel of previous climbers. Fortunately we had brought just enough to make a fire.

The plan was to have a meal as soon as possible, get as much sleep as we could until midnight and then prepare for the final assault. The early start was essential as we had not only to make the ascent, but walk all the way down to the middle hut (Peter's) by evening. We were also told that if there was moisture in the pumice it would freeze and footholds would be easier. In the event it was cold enough to freeze anything, but not enough moisture to bind it! We made our last preparations. I put in a new film and essential things in pockets where I could get at them easily. The paraffin lamp was put out and I tried to sleep. What a hope! Again I had a splitting headache and my heart was pumping at a steady 100 beats per minute. I felt depressed about the whole project. Why had I been such a fool to say "yes" to Stephen? Stories of people losing control of their senses when on the last lap became exaggerated in my mind as I turned restlessly from side to side. I was very glad when one of our guides said it was after midnight and time to get ready.

We found preparations took about an hour; bending down to lace up my boots was an exhausting business and we had to put on all the warm clothes we possessed. At last we were ready; anorak, balaclava, fur mittens and the rest, with snow goggles in a pocket ready for the morning.

Outside the hut the keen frosty air bit into you in spite of all you had on. It was a bright moonlight night, so the lanterns carried by the guides were only used for signalling to each other. The head guide led the way with the 2 toughest members of the party; 3 of us found we could go the same pace and a second guide came with us; the third took up the rear with the sixth climber.

I felt very much better as soon as I got going. We went very slowly, 60 paces at a time, but when it got steeper we had to force ourselves to do 30. It was intensely cold - many degrees below zero Celsius - but we could not go faster to keep warm. In spite of fur mittens my hands were numb with cold when I rested on my staff. I lost all sense of time; all I could do was concentrate on getting a few steps higher. About half way up we saw our first few patches of snow, and there at last was the cave where we had been told we could rest. We sat down thankfully and the guide produced a thermos flask of hot lemon and water. Wonderful! Then the final lap began.

My new-found strength soon ebbed away as the slope got steeper. We were at the worst of the scree and had to zig-zag as best we could; the pumice was like clinker raked out of a boiler and very loose. I would fix my eye on some wretched boulder a few metres ahead and will myself to reach it, but on arrival I was breathing as if coming out of an anaesthetic. It was difficult not to go to sleep leaning on my staff. Then came the dawn; first a line of red, soon a few little clouds near the horizon caught the glow, the ridge of red broadened and then we saw the rim of the sun. It appeared to rise very quickly; the scene was transformed with light and colour everywhere. Mawenzi looked majestic with a ring of cloud like a halo near its summit. Down below was a solid bank of cloud at about 3,000m. Above us were the snows of Kibo peak.

I felt more optimistic. The ridge of the crater seemed encouragingly near and it would soon be warmer. I took a photograph and struggled to my feet, vowing I would not sit down again until I reached the top. Half an hour later we reached continuous snow; a hundred or so more metres to go. I saw two figures at the top; so two of us had made it! It was tempting to try and increase the pace, but the guide knew better and kept saying in Swahili "pole, pole"(slowly, slowly). The last 100m to Gillman's Point took an hour, but at last three more of us were there.

I sat down thankfully, and as I became more rested I began to appreciate the beauty of the scene. I was looking into an immense crater; the rim was steep and rugged, stretching in an immense arc into the

Party at Gilman's Point, Kilimanjaro, 1952

distance. There were fantastic cliffs of ice and strange snow formations. I took more photographs. Then the 5 of us duly signed the book at the top, kept in a metal container.

We thought we had earned a longer rest, but the guide was already anxious for us to leave - we had a long, long way to go to Peter's hut! We met the sixth member of the party still struggling. He made it in the end with dogged determination. We reached Kibo hut by 12 o'clock, avidly consumed a tin of peaches, the only food left for us by the porters who had gone on ahead, then on and on, crunch, crunch, crunch on the pumice of the Saddle - the journey seemed endless; we walked like automatons. On arrival at Peter's hut we had the first decent meal for some time; we were famished. Another party had arrived who had not booked, so some of us put our sleeping bags on the floor. Then sleep, real sleep.

On our last day we had to get back to the Marangu Hotel and were at Bismarck hut by mid-day. Here, each who had made the top, was ceremoniously given a garland of everlasting flowers to wear as a hat-band.

We had only done what hundreds of others had done before us, but for each it was a very special experience - particularly in retrospect! The snows of Kilimanjaro are as vivid to me today as when I was privileged to stand on them 30 years ago.

Betty, Barbara and the family met us next day; they had had an interesting time at the coast. The Currys returned home, but we went on to Mombasa to spend a few days at a beach cottage north of Kalifi owned by Mr Pradhan. His son had been a member of my House at Taunton School and had warmly invited us to meet his parents. Stephen took us to Voi where we boarded the train from Nairobi at 3.45am. The huge engine was most impressive with two searchlights to illuminate the track and a cowcatcher in front in case game strayed on to the line. We were met by two of Mr Pradhan's sons and taken to their house in Mombasa for a wonderful meal with the family. We went on by car north to the cottage, crossing Kalifi Creek by the old ferry which was man- handled by the crew pulling on chains, chanting as they hauled.

The coral reef and lagoon was my first experience of the Indian Ocean - fantastic! It was a splendid few days - recovering from the climb, bathing in the warm sea, reading and exploring. However, when the tide was out we spent most of the time filming the fauna of the coral pools. Never had I seen such wonderful marine animals: sea snakes, many kinds of sea cucumber including one like a rope over a metre long, large tiger cowries, shoals of tiny, brilliantly-coloured fish, strikingly beautiful starfish, long-spined sea urchins, hermit crabs and a host of others. I also

Arriving at 'TreeTops' for filming, Kenya, 1962

filmed the ghost crabs scavenging on the tide-line, digging burrows, defending their territories and conveying messages to others with a semaphore-like action of their curious claws. Our brief visit to this wonderful area ended far too soon!

Back on the night train to Nairobi we were whisked off for a night at 'Tree Tops'. In 1962 this was an adventure of the highest order. The small, oddly-built hotel, incorporating a huge tree and overlooking the water-hole, had to be approached in single file with a white hunter, rifle at the ready, leading the way. I was able to set up my tripod and film until the light faded. It was magical to see the buffalo herds emerge silently from the forest to drink, warthog families, dainty bushbuck, colobus monkeys in the surrounding trees and a multitude of birds. After dark, with the help of the 'artificial moon', we saw our first black rhino - a male, then a female with calf. There was much huffing and mock charging. After a ceremonial dinner we watched entranced until we wearily retired to bed at 1 am.

Stephen's leave was now over, but we had a little time left to see more of the country. We had been warmly invited to visit two farms in Kenya and stay for a night or so; this gave us a different and most interesting aspect of the country. On one farm near Nakuru, owned by the

Hopcrafts, our hostess took Betty to the farm clinic which was held each morning for the workers and their families, while I was given a tour of the farm. It was a thriving, happy community. Later, we were taken to Lake Nakuru where we saw thousands of flamingoes. To see them take flight, the sun picking out the pink of their wings, was breathtakingly beautiful. John Hopcraft was an ardent conservationist, later becoming executive director of the wildlife sanctuary around the lake when the World Wildlife Fund gave generous aid for Nakuru National Park to be extended.

Before we left Britain, Rennie Bere, who had been in charge of the two major national parks in Uganda, had urged us to visit Queen Elizabeth Park during our trip. He had recently retired and I had got to know him well through the Mammal Society. His successor, Dick Laws, invited us to spend a few days at his home there.

We said grateful goodbyes to the Currys - they had been wonderful hosts - and flew from Nairobi in an ancient Dakota to Entebbe. Here we transferred to a bus belonging to the Mweya Safari Lodge - the hotel for visitors to the Park. The Laws' house was very near.

We only had two full days and the afternoon of our arrival, but we made the best of the time. Arrangements had been made for us to go out in the launch later that first afternoon. It was a magnificent introduction to the Park. Cruising slowly along the Kazinga Channel we followed the shoreline, getting very close to some of the animals. A huge bull elephant feeding at the water's edge was so close I could hardly get it all in the frame of my camera using a standard lens. Hippos were abundant, some with very small young. I was able to film a 5ft monitor lizard hauling a large catfish up the bank. The fish was so big the monitor had to straddle it in order to inch it up the slope. However, it was the birds that were in such abundance: cormorants, pelicans, storks, egrets, herons, ibises, gulls, kingfishers, lilytrotters, plovers and many waders. It was a photographer's paradise, although the vibrations caused by the motor meant that cameras had to be hand-held. That night, coming back from a meal at the Lodge, we remembered Rennie Bere's warning, "Keep a sharp look out for elephants; they visit the dustbins around the houses and can be dangerous."

For the next two days we hired a Land-Rover driven by a ranger. This was my great opportunity to do some filming as we could spend as long as we liked at any location. The ranger took us to all the main places of interest in the northern part of the Park; it was a great experience. Elephants were abundant, large herds of Uganda kob were feeding on the red oat grass, and there were so many hippo that any land near water was heavily over-grazed and badly eroded. This had caused the great herds of buffalo to move inland where grass was available. There were several lion prides in the area; we heard their roars during the night. Bushbuck were common and we came across several packs of banded mongoose snaking their way in single file through the grass. It was not difficult to finish off our stock of cine film.

This visit to Queen Elizabeth Park was the highlight of our game-viewing. It was a most beautiful area with the Ruwenzori Range just visible to the north-west, bushy savannah all around us, a region to the north pock-marked with small volcanic craters and the freshwater of Lake Edward and the Kazinga Channel contrasting strongly with the various soda lakes in the crater region. We knew there was also a great area we had not had time to visit which included the mysterious Maramagambo Forest and the southern Ishasha Plains with their great herds of topi, and lions which rested by day in trees. Another time perhaps!

On returning to Entebbe we accepted a kind invitation to stay the night with Professor Beadle at Makerere College, Kampala. He was an authority on the lakes of East Africa, their ecology, and the evolution of fish species isolated over vast periods of time in their waters. That evening, he invited some of his post-graduate students for a seminar and I much enjoyed hearing about the research going on and their obvious enthusiasm for the work. Then, after a marvellous six weeks, we flew home from Entebbe, with an enforced stop at Nice because the plane had insufficient fuel due to headwinds. It had been a wonderful experience for both of us; Africa had undoubtedly cast its spell; we had become badly addicted!

It was a great day when all the reels of cine film were processed. I took a rough-edited sample to the BBC and Jeffery Boswall thought he could use it in the series, 'Let's Imagine' - in this programme - 'Going on Safari'. The only bother was finding connecting shots - I had concentrated too much on the animals! However, Jeffery solved the problem. We dressed up in safari clothes, took our old car on to Clifton Downs, Bristol, and Jeffery took a number of shots of us, for instance looking through binoculars, from a low angle so that the British vegetation did not show! When the programme was transmitted, I was in London and popped into a television shop in Tottenham Court Road where the manager kindly turned on a display set for my benefit. I also did a radio programme on my climb of Kilimanjaro.

Some years later I got in touch with Keith Eltringham, the new Director of the Nuffield Unit of Tropical Animal Ecology (NUTAE) which had its headquarters in Queen Elizabeth National Park. I told him about my interest in returning to Uganda one day and asked if there were honey badgers in the Park; he was aware of my work on badgers here. The upshot was a letter inviting me to come out for a few months to do a preliminary research project on any species of medium-sized mammal I could get a line on. He said honey badgers were rare, but genets, civets and several species of mongoose were frequently seen. He did not mind which species I worked on, as he said anything I could find out about their ecology and behaviour was likely to be valuable as at that time only the larger carnivores had been studied in any detail. What a marvellous chance for a field zoologist to study a little-known mammal. This was a tremendous thrill! However the invitation was for 1969 and I was extremely busy at school.

I showed the invitation to my headmaster, John Rae, who consulted the School Council. I was over the moon when I heard I could take a sabbatical for the Easter term; so with the Christmas and Easter holidays included I could go for four months. Betty of course would come too. I successfully applied to the Royal Society for a grant, so the last hurdle was cleared. I was enormously grateful to everybody who had made it all possible.

This was going to be a trip of a lifetime. We were both very excited when the ancient Dakota touched down on the grass airstrip at Kasese. Keith Eltringham was there to help man- handle the cases into his Land-Rover and off we went to Mweya where the Park Headquarters and NUTAE laboratories were situated. Our house had previously been used by the Chief Warden and had been built for H.M.Queen Elizabeth, the Queen Mother, when she visited the Park in 1969; the Park had been named after her. We felt very honoured. There was still a canopy over the bed which served a useful purpose, as the thatch above contained a most varied fauna which periodically lost its footing!

Our first task was to get to know the northern part of the Park intimately and find out as much as possible of its ecology. Keith showed us the main areas and gave us a lesson on driving techniques in difficult terrain, what to do if you got a wheel stuck in a warthog-hole for example, and above all, what you must or must not do when driving at night. Most of the smaller carnivores were nocturnal so Betty and I were given a permit to be out at night - normally strictly forbidden.

To help identify the animals we used a spotlight run off the car battery to pick up eye reflections. We soon learnt to identify species by these before getting near enough to see other details. The main points of difference were their colour, relative size, distance apart, height from the ground, whether you saw one at a time or always two and the pattern made by the eyes when the animal moved, either keeping horizontal or gently moving up and down. The ones we were most interested in were golden, near to the ground, close together and rather large; these belonged to the smaller carnivores. If the eyes reflected red, were small and well off the ground you approached with caution - hippos when frightened can charge a vehicle. Likewise, eyes far-apart at first-storey height would be those of an elephant, and if on the track, should be given right of way.

By this means we saw many species, including civets, genets, servals, white-tailed and marsh mongooses, but most encounters were brief, and although we marked each spot where one was seen, and searched by day in the vicinity for dens, we only made limited progress. We had hoped to use radio-telemetry (which was then in its infancy as a research tool) to follow some of these animals, but the apparatus never arrived. However, that may have been a good thing as our time was very limited and we soon got a good line on a diurnal species, the banded mongoose, which gave us fewer problems.

The Park Engineer had seen several bandeds enter a termite mound, and observations showed that this was where they were living; we could concentrate our watching there. For the next three months we observed several packs of these fascinating mongooses and were able to discover the basic facts of their life history and behaviour. The story of this research and the adventures we had while carrying it out, is recounted in my book, 'Uganda Quest'.

Our son, Andrew joined us for a few weeks in February; by using two vehicles it gave us a chance to make observations on mongooses in two localities simultaneously. We preferred to watch from a distance using binoculars as the animals were easily disturbed and we wanted to record their natural behaviour, but towards the end of our stay I used a bush near a den as a hide. This was very productive, but had its hazards when elephants approached too near.

We found that packs of up to 32 bandeds occupied a single termite mound for periods in excess of two months when breeding and undis-turbed, but moved home much more frequently at other times. At night the whole pack occupied the enlarged middle chamber of the mound all huddled together. They were strictly diurnal, leaving the den about an hour after dawn, the time of return being more variable but usually during the hour before dark. They hunted as a pack - probably a diurnal adaptation, there being safety in numbers. If caught in the open by a potential predator such as an eagle, they bunched together, heads

Pack of banded mongooses, Queen Elizabeth Park, Uganda, 1969

pointing upwards, pink mouths wide open and very menacing. Food consisted mainly of small items such as dung beetles and giant milli-pedes. To find enough they often had to travel long distances, often following the trails of elephant and buffalo, exploiting the rich fauna in their dung. They were strictly territorial, demonstrating possession of a den by frequent scent-marking and using a communal defecating area nearby.

We discovered that their reproductive behaviour was particularly fasci-nating. Mating was seen on several occasions and litters appeared to be synchronised, as at one den, a batch of 8 kittens of the same size were suckled by three mothers, the young sucking from any mother according to opportunity. When the pack went off foraging, an adult always remained behind to act as a baby-sitter. We were surprised their social life was so sophisticated.

When Andrew was with us we made a number of trips to other parts of the region. During a three-day public holiday we went south via the Impenetrable Forest to Kisoro nestling at the base of Muhavura - 4,128m (13,540'), one of the Virunga volcanoes. We stayed at the famous Travellers' Rest run by a German who had been there many years. We hoped to climb Muhavura the next day, hiring Zachariah, an experienced guide, to accompany us. However, it was an extremely tough climb, the track being very steep with no let up; it seemed to go straight up the cone-shaped mountain. We passed through an interesting montane forest zone where the giant *Hypericums* with their large yellow flowers were in full bloom, ferns were plentiful and some of the trees were festooned with lichens. Then we reached the bamboo zone which led to more forest with giant heathers. These gradually became more bushy before we came to the alpine moorland where everlasting flowers were abundant. Only Andrew reached the summit; Betty and I called it a day at about 3,350m. However, the climb was very rewarding as we had wonderful views of the whole area and discovered some most interesting insects and plants.

On another occasion we visited a remarkable cave containing some 50,000 Rousette fruit bats; it was in the depths of the Maramagambo Forest. We would never have found it without the help of a ranger and his two friends - armed with rifle and spears because they said "it was a bad place", possibly because there were buffalo about which might be awkward. We had to walk some distance, first through thick grass higher than our heads, then through dense forest. The going was difficult and it was stiflingly hot. We realised we were nearly there when we heard a high-pitched hissing sound and smelt a strange pungent odour. The forest opened out and there was the cave at last. The roof and walls were crammed with bats which peeled off in their thousands when we entered and whirled around our heads, some settling on the bushes outside. One bat in particular caught our attention - an albino. Inside, the smell was almost overpowering and the floor slippery with droppings.

On returning to England I wrote up our researches on the banded mongoose in the East African Wildlife Journal. Jon Rood, who had been working in the Serengeti, read the paper and as a consequence, decided to continue our work on the same packs at Mweya. This was the beginning of a long-term project for Jon which proved very rewarding. We kept in touch, and in 1971 he suggested Betty and I came out again to help him. By this time I had retired and gladly accepted the chance to spend another three months co-operating with him and his wife, Hazel.

Jon had been able to capture most of the animals in one pack near Mweya and mark them with a dye; this enabled us to identify individuals in the field; they were also sexed and weighed. This was a great step forward. It was not long before Jon found that baby-sitters could be of either sex but were usually males!. This was a surprise. We watched extraordinary interactions between neighbouring packs at the boundary of their territories, and as one pack was marked, could interpret more easily what was going on. By working together, more packs could be monitored, and several times, watching in shifts, we were able to follow the activities of a pack throughout the whole day. On one occasion, I saw a pack change dens when five kittens were just old enough to travel, but they soon got tired and the nearest adult responded by picking one up in its mouth, carrying it for a few hundred metres before giving it another run.

I had brought out a BBC tape recorder with a parabolic reflector and spent some time recording the range of sounds made by the bandeds under different conditions. It was possible to distinguish between ten different vocalisations, ranging from the constant low contact calls which kept them together when travelling, to intense, high-pitched screeching churs when interacting with a mongoose from another pack. One day I put the microphone into the mound before the pack returned, using a long lead. They appeared somewhat surprised to find this strange object but this did not spoil the interest of the long recording which followed.

We were very glad to have had the chance to co-operate with Jon and contribute in a small way towards greater understanding of this fascinating species. Jon continued studying both banded, and later, dwarf mongooses for many years, mainly in the Serengeti. He became a leading authority on the two species.

Apart from our work on mongooses, we had many more adventures during our time at Mweya. We took the opportunity to visit the Maramagambo several times and climb in Ruwenzori. In the latter, at about 2,744m (9,000ft), where montane forest was merging into the bamboo zone, I happened to catch sight of something moist, shining and pinkish-brown amongst the thick ground-vegetation. On closer inspection I saw it was segmented and another portion was visible about 9" inches away. Realising it was probably a giant earthworm, I gripped it simultaneously at both visible points and pulled it out. It was 16" long when fully contracted and as thick as my middle finger. An expert at the British Museum later identified it by means of photographs and habitat almost certainly as *Diogaster itoliensis*. This species lives in damp humus below the ground vegetation and does not burrow. If attacked by a predator it is said to contract suddenly and spray its attacker through its dorsal pores with jets of fluid which birds find obnoxious.

We spent a memorable week-end in the Kibale Forest, near Fort Portal, at the invitation of Dr Tom Struhsaker who was doing primate research there. We stayed in a grass hut with openings for windows and doors and a gaping hole in the thatch which let the rain in. The forest is famous for its monkeys; we watched a troop of twelve black mangabeys feeding, saw black-and-white, and red colobus monkeys, blue monkeys and redtails. We obtained useful recordings of their vocalisations as they moved through the trees and fed on various fruits. We also took the recorder out at night and taped two wood owls duetting as they flew through the forest with a background of crickets, cicadas and tree-frogs. I played the tape back to make sure it was good and found to my horror, that at one point where I had swung the parabolic reflector to follow the birds, I had picked up music! Apparently a forester was using a radio in his hut in some distant part of the forest. We thought we had been quite alone.

Some weeks later we were in Fort Portal again; we had heard that an old Taunton colleague of mine, Bill Snee, was working there for the British Council. We did not know his address, but assuming he probably shopped at the supermarket, we enquired of the Indian manager. He was most helpful, dialled a number and gave me the phone - there was Bill at the other end! We visited his house and in the course of conversation mentioned our visit to the Kibale Forest. He knew it well as an excellent place for butterflies - his special interest. I told him we had counted 30 species along 200m of track ourselves. "Did you enjoy your trip?" he asked, and on hearing our account, continued,"Did you see any bodies?" Apparently, during Idi Amin's recent coup, a number of people had been killed locally and their bodies dumped in the forest. They were found by a forester who reported to the police. No action was taken; he was told he had not seen any bodies and should keep his mouth shut. However, the story soon became common knowledge. We were glad not to have known before our visit.

Just before we left Uganda we spent a week-end at Paraa in the Murchison Falls National Park (now Kabalega). The Head Warden, Mr Bwami, kindly put us up in his guest house. To our delight Hugh Cott was staying at the hotel; he was continuing his research on crocodiles. He had located most of the crocodile nests in that part of the Nile and was studying the critical temperature and humidity of the nests for successful hatching.

The next day he took us in a launch with two African rangers he had trained, slowly making our way against the current towards the foot of the falls. He pointed out the nests, each marked by a numbered post and guarded by a female crocodile usually lying on top of it. According to his notes, he considered that on this particular day one nest was due to hatch. As we approached, the crocodile took to the water and we landed. On putting an ear to the ground we could hear the croaking of the young as they responded to the vibration caused by our feet! Digging at the compacted sand with a panga and using his hands one ranger exposed the nest about 18" below the surface while the other kept an eye on the mother, viewing us from a distance. Many of the eggs (about the size of a goose's) were cracked; from a few, the head was projecting. After taking photographs and removing samples of the soil for analysis of water content, the sand was quickly replaced and we left to allow the mother to return.

Further on, we had the good fortune to find a large cluster of recently-hatched crocodiles, probably two days old; they were grouped on a log jutting out into the river, just as they sometimes do on their mother's snout. Quietly letting the boat drift towards them we were able to take some unique photographs. Hugh was particularly excited and took 16! He had never seen this before.

We spent much time with Hugh over the week-end; the beginning of a long friendship which I greatly valued. He was a superb zoologist, particularly noted for his pioneering work on adaptive colouration in animals, writing the definitive book on the subject. He had led an expedition to the Amazon Forest and done research in many parts of the world, particularly Africa. When he retired from Cambridge University to Dorset I saw more of him; it was always a joy to visit his home, share his enthusiasm for travel and research and see his magnificent pen-and-ink drawings. He was a founder member of the Wildlife Artists' Association and I greatly treasure the fine collection of his pictures he gave me.

Both Hugh and Keith Eltringham used to accompany safaris to East Africa as guest lecturers for the tour company, Swan Hellenic, and on their recommendation I wrote to Mr Swan on my return offering my services. This was the start of many safaris to Kenya, Tanzania and the Seychelles with tourist groups - a wonderful way of getting back to Africa and becoming familiar with some of the finest national parks. Betty often accompanied me. My job was to give about ten informal talks, mainly about the ecology and behaviour of the animals we encountered. It was sometimes difficult to find a quiet place to give talks. One time I found an empty room which appeared to be ideal, but as soon as I began a strident chorus of bullfrogs started up just outside by way of opposition. Another time the only quiet place was the unoccupied laundry of the Lodge. However, on many occasions it was under a tree in the grounds or after a picnic when on a game run. I was learning all the time, and it was a privilege to help enthuse others about African wildlife and its conservation. I made many friends through these trips, including some of the African drivers.

I could fill a book with accounts of these visits, but will limit them to a few incidents which stand out in my memory. On one safari we met up at Heathrow as usual and the 'Jumbo jet' made its way towards the runway for take-off. Suddenly, clouds of black smoke came through the ventilation system; we had to return to base for a check. An hour later we tried again and the same thing happened, so we had to spend the night in a hotel, leaving on another plane early next morning. This, of course, affected our meticulously-planned schedule; we arrived in Nairobi in the late evening instead of the early morning. We were due to spend the first night at Lake Naivasha Hotel so were taken there by minibuses. On arrival after midnight, all was locked up; nobody appeared. I made a tour of the main building and found a sleepy guard huddled in a corner. He could speak little English, but I gathered that the manager lived some distance away, but that he would fetch him.

We were all tired and hungry; this was the last straw! While the group waited, surrounded by piles of luggage, I examined the building carefully; all doors were locked, but one window was not latched. I got in, and found myself in the kitchen; the group, including some elderly ladies, managed to follow. All the food was locked up except for cheese and biscuits. That was better than nothing. The manager eventually arrived to find us having a picnic in his kitchen! He was very understanding, gave us drinks and allocated rooms. We had a few hours sleep before the scheduled boat trip on the lake.

Another year, when preparing for a similar trip on Lake Naivasha, the boatman was over-zealous in filling the tank with petrol and some spilled into the bilge below the deck planking. The party was divided into two, Betty was in one boat and I in the other. Her boat went first, but the engine failed after about 20m; the battery was flat. Another boat went to help and the batteries were connected to get her started. The wrong connections were made, and the spark resulting, ignited the petrol floating on the bilge water! This was potentially a very dangerous situation; if the petrol in the tank were ignited it would blow up like a bomb. Two passengers, realising the danger, immediately jumped into the water, cameras and all, and waded to shore; others were quickly helped on to another boat, but it could not take everybody. Betty and the Tour Manager were the last to leave, wading with cameras and binoculars held high. Betty told me that the deck boards were very hot by the time she left. Soon after leaving, the boat was quickly enveloped in flames and was eventually completely burnt out. What saved it from being a major disaster was the petrol tank, which being completely full, contained no air to cause it to blow up. We spent the next few hours washing and drying clothes in the sun! Perhaps I had better add that these incidents occurred some time ago; the hotel is now much enlarged and very efficient.

One year on visiting Meru I planned a trip to the Tana River, but the Authorities were reluctant as Somali poachers had been very active in that neighbourhood using automatic weapons to kill elephants and the river to smuggle out the ivory. We did go, but a truck full of troops preceded us to see that it was safe. When we arrived we saw no troops, and to relieve ourselves, according to custom the ladies used the cover of bushes to the right and the men to the left. One lady was somewhat embarrassed to find she was being protected by a soldier with a rifle! They had formed an unseen ring around us. The trip was worthwhile, not least because we found a nesting colony of Madagascan bee-eaters in a river bank; they were feeding their young on dragonflies

Getting through luggage checks was sometimes a problem. Knowing I was going out, I was occasionally asked to deliver parcels. One was given me at Heathrow which contained an electronic ostrich egg! It was a device which looked like an egg, but contained the mechanism to measure the temperature when placed in a nest and incubated by an ostrich. It was the shape of a bomb! Fortunately its battery was packed separately. It was examined with considerable suspicion, but on being told what it was, it was passed without even a smile.

On another occasion a parabolic reflector for sound recording was regarded with great suspicion by Customs at Entebee. Further officials were consulted and although I tried to explain what it was I had no success, so I changed tack and laughingly told them it was a riot shield! A sense of humour is always appreciated by Africans and it was let through without further delay.

I also accompanied safaris to Zambia with Ecosafaris, run by Peter Moss. These were of particular interest as they included four or five days walking in the South Luangwa National Park. We would walk to a camp, stay two nights, make walks in the surrounding area next day, and then on to another camp and do the same. You see so much more detail when walking – you follow animal trails, examine their tracks and signs, try to interpret their activities, use fieldcraft to approach as near as possible to watch or photograph and have time to pause and examine insects and flowers. All senses are alert; you have a feeling of expectancy and excitement.

We travelled in single file as quietly as possible, the ranger leading with a rifle. He was rationed to two cartridges, one soft-nosed to be fired as a warning over the head of any unduly-aggressive animal and one hard-nosed for real. Usually there are no problems, although we did have one near miss when a bull buffalo lying on its own in long grass

Walking Safari in Zambia: watching elephants, 1983

was taken by surprise and leapt to its feet a few metres from us. Fortunately it charged off in the opposite direction.

On another occasion we were watching a herd of female elephants slowly grazing their way towards us. The wind was exactly right and they had no idea we were there. When about 20m away, one adult left the others and came straight for the huge, old termite mound on which we were standing; it appeared determined to feed from the vegetation which partly covered it. We kept quite still. It continued to advance. At 6m, it was too near for comfort and the ranger coughed twice to arrest its progress, but it took no notice, coming a few paces further. Elephants look very large when only a few metres away! Adrenalin started to flow as we wondered what the outcome would be. Then the ranger, speaking quite quietly, said "Go away elephant!". It tossed its head, shook its ears and quietly ambled off! We all relaxed. The ranger had certainly done the right thing; the elephant was disturbed by the human voice, but did not panic and charge as she might have done if he had fired a shot over her head.

That evening when we reached our camp we were shown the footprints of a lion at the door of one of the huts. The night before a lioness had visited the camp and chewed up one aluminium and two plastic wash-basins left outside! A return visit was possible, so we were asked to put a paraffin lamp outside our huts, close what passed for a door and tie it shut with string! A little inadequate, we thought! Just before dawn one of our party got up to go to the hut which acted as a loo. Having gone a few yards, he saw a white object moving up and down. This turned out to be the vest of our ranger who was signalling him to stop; he had been on guard all night, rifle in hand. He whispered "There's a lion by the loo!"

Soon after dawn, there were roars and squealings coming from the other bank of the river. The ranger took us across in a small boat; there was only a single paddle so a shovel was used in addition. Some of us were just in time to see a lion and lioness on a warthog kill not far away. Seeing a group of people, the lions rather reluctantly left the kill which we were then able to examine. No doubt they returned later.

A more beautiful sight was a breeding colony of carmine bee-eaters. Their nest holes were in the steep bank of the river, and on our approach they took to flight in their hundreds. However, by approaching slowly and then keeping quite still, the disturbed birds would quickly settle again, decorating their favourite trees with living patterns of vivid colour. It was a magnificent sight to see these gorgeous birds in such

On safari: Betty and the author on a tributory of the Zambesi, 1985

249

numbers at close quarters.

My last safari in 1990 was a celebration and very special. It was my 22nd to East Africa and anticipated by 6 months my 80th birthday. I worked out the itinerary myself and asked Ecosafaris to arrange the bookings and transport. I greatly wanted my sons, Keith and David, to come to Africa with me before I gave up (Andrew had been with me before in Uganda and Zambia and was also too involved with the BBC, and sadly, Betty felt unable to join us.) I also invited good friends, who had been on safari with me before and loved Africa, to make up the party of 14. These included Stephen and Barbara Curry who came from Western Australia where they had lived since leaving Kenya soon after our visit in 1962; they had not been back since.

We flew to Nairobi, but our main objective was the national parks of northern Tanzania, the highlight being two nights camping in the Ngorongoro Crater, something I had always wanted to do. Keith and David took the everyday arrangements off my shoulders and organised everything wonderfully well. You can seldom go on safari without unexpected problems, but all were dealt with efficiently and everybody enjoyed the trip greatly.

Camping in the Crater was a magnificent experience. From dawn to dusk there was plenty of time to watch and marvel at this microcosm of East African wildlife - one of the great wonders of the natural world. Soon after dawn, we watched the sun disperse the mist over the escarpment, and as we slowly explored the area it threw into relief the herds of herbivores: buffalo, wildebeest, zebra, gazelle and kongoni. There were also a few black rhinos and elephants, reminders of human pressures on any creature wearing an object of commercial greed. The predators were there too: a pair of courting lions oblivious of our presence, a large pride resting, following a kill made the previous night; a hyaena wandering along the lake's edge, apparently aimlessly, yet alert for any opportunity to dash into the water and take an unwary flamingo; golden jackals making the rounds of their territories for any small rodents, beetles or anything to scavenge. However, the majority of predators were resting, most of their hunting being done at night.

Early morning was the time of greatest activity for the birds. Eagles and vultures searched for prey or carrion as they soared; marsh harriers quartered the area for small birds or rodents; flamingoes,herons, egrets, cormorants and many species of duck were busily occupied in the water of lake and swamp, each employing its particular technique for finding food. Bustards, secretary birds and ground hornbills strutted the plains for insects, snakes or lizards. In the air, swallows and martins snapped up flying insects; cattle egrets, some perched on the backs of the buffalo, looked for insects disturbed by their movement; wagtails darted around the feet of these great beasts doing the same and oxpeckers busily explored every part of their anatomy removing ticks. Here was something marvellous to contemplate - a whole community living out its complex inter-relationships before our eyes. Humanity still desperately needs their message of inter-relationships.

At night, our camp was a small oasis of twentieth century activity surrounded by wilderness. All around us were countless animals, ignoring our intrusion into their domain, living their natural lives. For them for a short time the human species was irrelevant - this was their world. We saw little of it, but the sounds were tantalising indications of ceaseless activity: the chirping of crickets; the screaming of a tree hyrax high up in the fig tree under which we camped; the hooting of owls; the contact calls of hyaenas; the distant roar of a lion. The ancient voices of wild Africa were reminding us of a world which, long, long ago, had once been our ancestral home.

We left with much regret but with a renewed sense of wonder and delight and a greater determination to help conserve such areas for posterity.

We returned to Nairobi, via Serena Lodge, Amboseli, where we celebrated Keith's birthday. Africans love an excuse for a party, so when dinner was finished, the head chef, followed by a group playing various musical instruments, ceremonially entered the dining room carrying a birthday cake adorned with candles. This was duly presented after a most amusing 'happy birthday' song comprised of a number of humorous extempore verses. It was a complete surprise for Keith and appreciated by everybody.

Before our flight from Nairobi we had a last dinner at the Carnivore Restaurant. It was a particularly happy way of ending what was probably my last safari, having two sons representing the family and in the company of particularly good friends. I was immensely grateful for the warmth of their good wishes and the opportunity to share such a wonderful experience in their company.

Chapter Sixteen

The Bonus Years

By 1986 my lower back, which had given me pain for some years, was giving increasing trouble; I was getting muscular and neural complications in my legs. Betty and I were less able to look after the house and garden; increasingly we thought about the future. Our three boys were probably more realistic about this than we were and it was a complete surprise when David and Rachel invited us to join forces with them in Bedford. They needed a larger house as their family was growing up; we needed a smaller one with fewer physical demands. The idea was to buy a fairly large property together and adapt it so that we had a ground-floor, self-contained flat and they had the remainder. We could share the garden. To leave the West Country after 40 years was a difficult decision for me to make although Betty immediately accepted the idea with enthusiasm. However, the long-term advantages were obvious, and more importantly, we were sure the arrangement would work as we got on so well as a family; both parties would retain their need for privacy, we should see more of the grandchildren, and hopefully all three generations would benefit. Such arrangements either work or become disasters. We had no doubt about the outcome and gladly accepted.

It was becoming increasingly obvious that I needed to seek expert advice over my back. Ian Menzies (see p.78) was on the staff at St Thomas's Hospital in London and arranged for me to see a consultant orthopaedic surgeon. The problem was complex; a detailed investigation was necessary involving a long stay in hospital. I was found a bed in one of the oldest wards, shortly scheduled to be replaced. It was a sobering, fascinating and sometimes harrowing experience to be thrust into a community drawn from such diverse backgrounds and in such varying conditions: the dying and the almost cured, the victims of accidents and brutality, the young and the old and a few, like myself, undergoing tests before operations. Being able to wander about I was able to get to know several patients quite well. The physical and mental suffering of some of them helped to put my own problems in perspective. I found myself next to a West Indian who had water on the brain and was shouting madly most of the night. I was immensely impressed by the kindness and expertise of the sister and nurses.

My surgeon examined me and worked out a series of tests to determine the details of the problem. Unfortunately, I had had 'flu that autumn and was having bouts of giddiness. It was likely that the virus had affected my inner ear, but it could have been due to a neurological problem or restricted blood flow through the carotid arteries. As the surgeon pointed out, it was necessary to see that my head was alright before embarking on my back!

I learnt a lot about modern diagnostic techniques during the protracted period that followed. It was rather like being a medical student except that I was the victim as well as the learner. Each investigation occurred in a different department so I got a good idea of how the hospital ticked. It was difficult not to become frustrated by delays as each test had to be arranged with the department concerned and on some days nothing happened at all; what I hoped would be a matter of days turned into weeks. Betty helped to relieve the monotony by coming in every day - she was wonderful - and with Andrew's Sony Walkman I had hours of pleasure listening to tapes and the radio - something I had had little time for previously. At week-ends everybody who could, went home; I was glad to spend them with Andrew and Ghyslaine in Richmond where Betty was also staying.

The doctors were still worried about my giddy fits, so an angiogram was arranged to test the circulation to the head. The technique was to pass a long catheter up the artery in my arm until it reached the aortic arch; then dye was released which was swept up the carotid arteries in my neck making the vessels visible to X-rays. I was fascinated to see the whole process on the monitor.

However, my mind was soon switched to other things as David had found a possible house for sale in Bedford. Andrew drove up to see it and a roll of film was taken to give Betty and me some idea of what the house was like. Andrew agreed with David that it was just what we wanted and we were happy to accept their judgement. We had not sold our Milverton house, so a bridging loan was essential. A phone call to my brother, Bill, brought an immediate and generous response. Meanwhile I had to leave the arrangements to the family and return to the delights of St Thomas's.

The neurologist, after further tests and having seen the results of the angiogram, was convinced that my giddiness was not due to circulatory or nerve problems and the 'flu virus was almost certainly the cause. Now the other more relevant tests could be done.

My X-rays gave only limited information so I was booked into the newly-opened Churchill Clinic which had one of the few new MRI (Magnetic resonance imaging) scanning machines in the country. I had read about them in the National Geographic Magazine. I had to sign a statement that there was nothing metallic in my body as the machine was powerfully magnetic. I lay on a narrow aluminium bed with a small head cushion and was slowly shunted into a narrow tunnel about $2^1/_2$ft in diameter. It was disturbingly like being cremated before my time - all but the absence of the organ music! It was very claustrophobic lying quite still in that confined space for 45 minutes. I was warned it would be noisy; it was - rather like a road drill! The apparatus took pictures from all angles giving a three-dimensional computerised image on a monitor in another room from which photographs were taken.

My surgeon still wanted one more test - a radiogram of the base of the spine. This involved a local anaesthetic, a lumbar puncture and flooding the area around the lower vertebrae with dye and taking up to 40 X-rays with my body twisted in every possible position. It was extremely unpleasant. Back in the ward I had to sit up for 6 hours, not get out of bed for another 6 and drink as much water as I could.

The next afternoon my surgeon discussed the position. Two vertebrae were out of place causing severe compression of the set of nerves coming from the base of the spinal cord; surgery was essential. It would mean decompression, correcting the slippage of vertebrae, removing the disc between them and pinning them together. A second operation a week later from the front would be advisable to make the pinning more secure. I would be in a straight-jacket for 6 months. It was quite a shock and disappointment that the treatment was so long, but the alternative was worse. The sooner it was done the better.

The date was fixed for 16 February ready for the operation the following afternoon. As luck would have it the operation was delayed several hours as the theatre was still occupied by the previous surgical team, so I somewhat sleepily listened to tapes (as I had had my premedication) to while away the time. It was late that night that I was returned to the ward after a $5^1/_2$ hour operation. It was a relief to see Betty again the following day and feel the worst was over. Now I could concentrate on getting strong again.

However, that was not to be. Unfortunately, my previous partial gastrectomy had not been taken into account, and on my fourth night, lying flat on my back and with the bed tilted backwards, I regurgitated gastric fluid into my lungs. I regained consciousness a long time later to find myself in intensive care and in great pain. If it had not been for the immediate action of Sister Linley and the nurse, Louise, I would never have made it thus far. As it was, I was very ill with pneumonia, kidney failure and jaundice. Time seemed to stand still; all I could do was stare at the ceiling and out of the corner of my eye watch the pattern of my heart-beat on the monitor. I was 'wired up' with tubes to keep the life processes going and blood tests were taken regularly to monitor my chemistry. With hindsight it is likely that the trauma had caused a stone to pass down the bile duct and this was what was causing such excruciating pain. All I realised at the time was that the ceiling looked yellow and I began to doubt whether I could stand the pain for much longer. The next 24 hours were critical; my surgeon admitted afterwards that he thought I had had it, but that 'somebody upstairs must have thought otherwise'. I do not think I ever thought I was going to die - I had been too ill even to think about it. Everything that could be done, was done; the whole team was marvellous. I was enormously encouraged by visits from Betty and all the family; I knew I had turned the corner. Gradually I began to take a more intelligent interest in all the techniques and treatments.

I have no idea what drugs I was given, but one certainly caused hallucinations which intrigued me. With my eyes open things looked normal, but on closing them I saw geometric shapes in vivid colours which were added to incredibly fast to form a complex pattern. On opening my eyes again, normality returned, but on shutting them once more, the phenomenon was repeated with different patterns. Each time the design started with a simple form such as a triangle or a circle mainly made up of extremely vivid primary colours. I wondered whether this effect explained the 'help' or 'inspiration' some artists derived from drugs for their colour and form paintings.

After a week I was glad to be moved from intensive care to another ward where I could look out on the River Thames and the Houses of Parliament rather than just stare at the ceiling. I was incredibly weak as my muscles had become reduced to starvation proportions. I knew it would be a long haul, but I was obsessed with determination to get better however long it took; life had been given back to me; I was living on bonus time and was full of gratitude.

When very ill the world seems so small; all your thoughts are channelled into basic activities; it takes a real effort to think outwardly and positively. In this I was helped enormously by the great love and caring surrounding me; Betty visited every day and was a great source of strength and support, Ian Menzies came regularly to have a chat and keep an eye on progress and I had numerous visits from relatives and friends - some delightfully unexpected.

I had plenty of time on my hands. Flowers had always been a great joy to me, but now I was seeing them in an enhanced manner. I would gaze at a single flower near my bedside and see as never before the incredible beauty of its functional design, colour and texture. I kept recalling those inspirational lines of Masefield's 'The Everlasting Mercy' which seemed to mirror my feelings and aspirations:

> 'O lovely lily clean,
> O lily springing green,
> O lily bursting white,
> Dear lily of delight
> Spring in my heart agen
> That I may flower to men.'

After 7 weeks in hospital I had learned how to get out of bed without twisting my back, was able to walk around the ward and climb a few stairs. Progress had been very slow as initially my vertebrae had had no chance to fuse, the only food available having been used up in keeping me alive. I was longing to leave hospital, but was not yet ready for home, so I went into a nursing home near Manchester, not far from where Keith was living and where Betty was able to stay. I was taken there by ambulance from London lying on a stretcher. It was a very old vehicle which appeared to be wholly deficient of springs; Betty travelled with me. Strangely enough that five-hour journey was the last occasion I experienced those fits of giddiness - perhaps the bumps had done the trick for my inner ear!

I made good progress during the 4 weeks in the nursing home. There were two highlights. The first was receiving a huge 'get well' card signed by nearly all the members of the Mammal Society who had attended the Easter Conference - the first I had missed for many years. It had been extremely cleverly designed and painted by Graham Allen, a most talented artist in the Society. It portrayed a Council meeting with a number of mammals sitting round the table each recognisable to me as a member who did research on that particular species. It was a wonderful gesture and a real morale-booster. It remains one of my treasured possessions.

The second event was very different - the celebration of our Golden Wedding! Not quite the place we would have chosen for such a landmark, but Keith, Ruth and the three grandchildren were able to join Betty and me after school and we had a party in my room. The Sister gave us a magnificent bouquet of flowers done up with golden ribbon, and a celebratory cake had been baked specially. It was with great gratitude that I looked back on those 50 years with Betty. Her utter loyalty and loving support through good times and bad; the major part she played in bringing up the family with such understanding and selfless devotion; the way she testified through words and actions her own strong faith and ideals and how she gave so much for the benefit of others. It was good for me to ponder how difficult and sacrificial her part had been as the anchor-pin of the family, and on top of it all, married to me - not an easy assignment for anybody! I felt greatly blessed.

When the 4 weeks were up, I felt stronger, was walking quite well and was ready for the journey home. Keith brought me back to Milverton by car; it was great to be home again. By this time our house had been sold but we had until July before having to vacate it and move to Bedford. Meanwhile, David, Rachel and family had moved into our new house and were frantically busy getting the necessary alterations and decorating done. David had planned everything meticulously, so by the time we arrived the essentials had been carried out. I well remember our arrival - the heart-warming welcome of the family and the experience of seeing our new home for the first time! It had been a big responsibility for the family to make all the decisions; however, I never once doubted that they would be the right ones.

I write these memoirs more than 6 years on. The move to Bedford has undoubtedly been a great success for Betty and me. It has been a delight to feel part of a larger family and see the grandchildren grow up. Getting fit had its ups and downs, but I was soon able to drive a car again, get to London for meetings, attend a few conferences and even manage two more safaris to Africa. However, my back problems, a gall-bladder operation and *anno domini* imposed their limits and I began to spend more time at home.

I continued editing the 'Helm' Mammal Series. This kept me in touch with a number of authors, many of whom were friends from the Mammal Society; it also kept me informed of current research. However, what I enjoyed most was writing 'On Safari in East Africa - a Background Guide'. This book was written to supplement the Collins' Field Guides which catered mainly for identification; mine concentrated on ecology, behaviour and adaptations. It had been my experience that it was this kind of background knowledge that made safaris so much more rewarding for the visitor. The writing gave me the chance to re-live some of my more memorable experiences in Africa and in researching it, I added much to my own knowledge – one of the more satisfying aspects of writing books.

I have now nearly finished my memoirs and feel more than ever thankful for all the benefits of these bonus years. In my final chapter I shall try to draw together some of the experiences and beliefs that have been important to me throughout my life; they can be summed up by the term 'relationships'.

Badgers eat anything, including earthworms,

small mammals, roots,

and berries

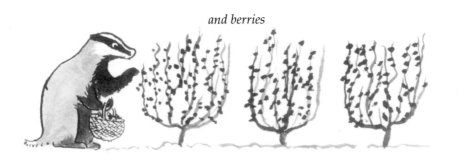

Towards Synthesis - a philosophy based on relationships

When you write your memoirs you try to remember what it was like to be 'you' at various times of your life. You become dimly aware of the importance of certain people, experiences and circumstances which have made an indelible impression on your developing personality. Life rushes by; periods of ceaseless activity make less impression on your conscious memory and recollections of these busy periods are difficult to recapture. Times of serious illness and enforced inactivity remind you how precious life is and how ridiculously insignificant any contribution you have tried to make has been.

I consider myself very fortunate that in my earlier years there were two major influences: the Christian home into which I was born with all its caring relationships and sense of purpose which gave me from the start a belief that I had a part to play, however insignificant, and secondly, my love of natural history and training as a biologist with special emphasis on ecology and behaviour. These strong influences brought nature and people together in many fundamental and significant ways.

As an ecologist I have come to realise the basic truth that all life is about relationships. 'No man is an island unto himself' is a fact that can be applied not only to humans but at all levels: between atomic particles, intracellular organelles, different kinds of cells, tissues, organs, organisms, societies and nations. All fulfil their functions in relation to each other. It is the relationships between these entities that are so significant, just as our human relationships are all-important in determining our niche in society and indeed our happiness and fulfilment.

A biological analogy I first thought about as a student has developed over the years into a parable which illustrates for me the overwhelming importance of relationships in everyday life. There are some lovely sandy beaches off the coasts of Brittany and Normandy - good for bathing and surfing. If you walk beyond the sun-tanned bodies and inspect the less frequented areas when the tide is out, you may notice that not all the sand is brown; some is darker where mud is mixed with it; other patches are strangely green. The latter are curious because as you approach the green reverts to brown. You wonder if your eyes have deceived you but further on you see more green patches which also disappear when you approach. If you take a handful of this sand and look at some of it under a lens you will discover a mass of tiny green flatworms which had been lying on the surface until the vibration of your feet caused them to burrow.

These flatworms, *Convoluta*, are green because they contain unicellular green algae living within their tissues. When the worms lie on the surface the algae can photosynthesise and make products that benefit the worms. In return the algae receive carbon dioxide and other waste products from which they make sugars and proteins. This is one of numerous examples of symbiosis - living together for mutual benefit. But there is a strange aspect of the *Convoluta* story. When the worms are growing everything goes well as at this stage they have rudimentary mouths and feed on diatoms and other small organisms whilst enjoying the additional resources supplied by the algae. However, when they near maturity they give up all external feeding, the mouth becomes non-functional, they lie on the surface less and no doubt they feel hungry so they digest a few algae inside their bodies. This makes matters worse and soon all the plants are digested and the worms die of starvation. Of course by this time they have laid their eggs, ensuring the presence of another generation which eventually will commit mass suicide once more.

When the balance between partners was right, all went well, when upset, disaster for the individual followed. This is a principle true for all life and true for us. All relationships involve give and take; when the emphasis is more on getting than giving, they may deteriorate and even collapse altogether.

We see so many examples of this all around us. The wanton exploitation of nature has upset that delicate balance within ecosystems. The removal of rain forests, the near elimination of certain fish stocks, desertification due to a combination of climatic factors with over-population, poverty and war are all reminders that if we ignore the parable of those patches of green sand, we do so at our peril.

Within society we have the same problems. Division of labour within the community is an example of right relationships between people, each making his or her contribution towards the family and community. Of course, the complexities are enormous, but basically when the emphasis is more on getting than giving, society begins to disintegrate - broken

The Neal Clan celebrating the author's 80th birthday, 1991. Standing: Alastair, Ruth, Keith, Ghyslaine, Andrew, Peter, Rachel, David. Seated: Betty, the author, Ghyslaine's mother. In front: Margaret, Robert, Hilary

marriages, injustices, crime, violence and even anarchy - all patches of green sand.

Those Normandy beaches are more famous for the Allied landings in the Second World War than for *Convoluta*. What sort of memorial is fitting for such an epic event? One to the greatest sea-borne invasion of all time? A memorial to the fantastic courage of the troops? Yes indeed! But also to the failure of people to live together in a balanced and right relationship of mutual giving - another patch of green sand.

During my university years I thought much about the relationship between science and religion. Most of my contemporaries considered the two were incompatible. However, the more I studied both the more I was convinced that many of the basic principles of each were complementary - different aspects of truth enhancing one another.

Science accumulates knowledge about the universe and everything pertaining to it; it deals with material things, but it also excites awe and wonder and widens our perception of beauty and art. Biology, being the study of life, makes a further contribution as it helps us to understand ourselves and the world we live in - who we are in the context of the whole of life. I have become more and more intrigued by the way religious and moral principles and attitudes are analogous with biological (and particularly ecological) fundamentals and behaviours. Later in this chapter I will enlarge on some of these which have particular relevance to relationships.

Religion on the other hand is an expression of belief in a supernatural power which affects our attitude towards life and our moral standards, embraces the spiritual side of our nature and adds a transcendental component which inspires, enthuses and brings purpose to living. That there is a God - some creative power behind the universe - is unprovable by scientific means. However, this does not invalidate the concept. Science can illuminate religion, but it has its limitations. Belief in God is an act of religious faith justified by the accumulated experiences of those who have put to the test their trust in such a power. From my own experience of life I believe this is true. Also, as a biologist, the more I contemplate the majesty, complexity and evolution of life on earth the more I am convinced of some power behind it all. Now, with modern research, including that of DNA and the human gene complex (genome), we know we are not just the product of genetic certainty modified by the environment in which we live; we also have the choice which allows us freedom to chart our own course and make our own decisions. As I look back I see clearly how sets of circumstances and the application of choice have been very significant turning points in my life.

God is a mystery. No language is adequate to express a power – a truth we cannot comprehend. For me, the greatest concept of what God is like which we can begin to understand is the Christian doctrine which affirms that Jesus Christ is the personification of God and that his life and teaching demonstrates in terms of practical living what God is like: God is love, God is spirit, God is within us, God is the spirit of love which works miracles in people's lives transforming mere existence into purposeful living, adding a new dimension to our relationship with others.

Unfortunately, the word 'love' in its modern context gives little idea of the immensity of the concept. Love is all-embracing and includes compassion, sacrifice of self and undemanding relationships; it is the ultimate expression of creative living, attained in all its fullness in the life of Christ. God becomes meaningful to me when I see love at work in the lives of people such as Mother Teresa with her selfless, caring devotion to the destitute and dying; in the serenity, compassion and laughter of the Dalai Lama in the context of disaster for his country; in the courage, devotion and sacrifice of parents of badly handicapped children and in those radiant people in every walk of life who appear to have something many others have not got, who make you feel better when in their company. I think of a West Indian tea-lady who dispensed far more than a somewhat dubious cup of tea when on her rounds in St Thomas's Hospital; day after day her caring, quiet cheerfulness and sensitivity shone out; you missed her when she was not on duty. God is everywhere within people demonstrating the power of love in a host of relationships. However, understanding is never complete; our concept of God is an evolving thing - 'Now we see through a glass darkly'.

Considering the modern scene with all its troubles, anxieties, uncertainties, tragedies, unpredictabilities and evil it is easy to come to the conclusion that society is sick and on a collision course towards extinction. Many times in previous generations people have probably thought along similar lines but the difference today is the scale of the problem, the population explosion is a relatively new factor and our ability to react is potentially far more catastrophic. It is only because I believe in the power of love working through people everywhere that I remain an optimist. It is too easy to look at one side of the coin and ignore the fact that life can also be good, happy, full of fun and laughter, creative, and fulfilling. I believe we can all live positively and lovingly in our own sphere of influence however limited that may be.

My Christian beliefs and their application to human relationships have evolved over the years. There were the simple beliefs I was taught as a child; their gradual evolution as I began to realise some of the deeper truths behind the literal interpretation of parts of the Bible and the realisation that these truths were personal recipes for living. My association with Moral Rearmament for a number of years helped to deepen the realisation that people mattered, that Christian principles when practiced could open the way to better understanding, that humility and refreshing honesty could revolutionise relationships between husbands and wives, parents and children, managers and workers, nation and nation - a moral and spiritual print-out for the future evolution of our species. But I also had to face up to the fact that my concepts of 'truth' were not absolute; life was a continuous search for truth; all aspects, whether religious or biological, had to be assessed critically, re-evaluated according to new evidence and modified or discarded if they were in any way incompatible. Some ideas that I had grown up to regard as certainties became doubts and many former peripheral beliefs became untenable; however, the basic ones became stronger and more and more important. One difficult hurdle was to have the humility to realise that my understanding and beliefs were not the only right ones - nobody has a monopoly of truth and there are many access roads which lead towards that objective. I came to realise that much could be learnt from other religions and that tolerance towards other people's beliefs was an essential bridge towards better relationships. Life has often been described as a pilgrimage. We all have our journey to make. My genome is what I have been given - I am in that sense unique with my own choices to make and my search for truth, a personal endeavour plagued by doubts and, if fortunate, at times blessed with hints of insight. The search is never complete, but I am utterly convinced that if love is your guide life is fulfilling and relationships rewarding.

I do not doubt the value of Christian fundamentalist beliefs for many people; I remember their influence on my early upbringing. However, for me they merely represent a stage in the search for truth, a stage before doubt, critical appraisement and personal (in contrast to traditional) belief becomes part of one's life. However, I am convinced that extreme fundamentalism is dangerously divisive, whether of Christian, Judaic, Muslim, Hindu or any other faith because it represents a closed-mind belief which stultifies the on-going search for truth. Extreme fundamentalism seems to flourish under conditions of insecurity and confusion. It appeals to those who long for certainty in a changing world. It is not an expression of the power of God but the power of certainty exerted against all those who disagree. One of its dangers is the power it has over its believers, something that has been highlighted on a large scale by the so-called 'religious wars' of history and those masquerading under religious banners raging today. On another scale it is shown in denominational rivalries, doctrinal wrangling and the fanaticism demonstrated by members of certain cults that have made the headlines in recent years. No wonder people are put off by religion when they see the results of these conflicts of power rather than the exercise of love and compassion.

Within society, law is essential and morality a necessary yardstick against which behaviour may be judged; both reflect a code of practice, which if followed, oils the wheels of good relationships. However, neither is 'carved in stone ' but evolves as society changes; neither are sufficient for every situation. Love always transcends law, tempering it with compassion, understanding and tolerance. In a rather similar way organised religion has an important role to play but its value stands or falls by the quality of life and creativity of relationships of its members.

Belief is one thing, acting on it is quite another matter. Looking back I realise much more clearly than at the time how often I have failed to apply the basic principles I know to be right to my relationships with others. Divided loyalties between home, work and interests have brought clash; blindness to the needs of others and a lack of humility have caused unhappiness. Relationships are always difficult to maintain as a synthesising partnership as *Convoluta* and a host of other symbiotic relationships in nature have so clearly demonstrated. In this country one in three marriages fail, none is perfect, some are merely tolerable partnerships of convenience. Good relationships do not come naturally, they have to be fought for; differences in personality, interests and ideas which, without a degree of selfless love, bring conflict, but with give-and-take, apology and forgiveness can produce a dynamic synthesis out of diversity. A right relationship between people is built on mutual giving and mutual understanding, and the latter leads to mutual respect.

When thinking ecologically, the magnificent diversity of living things falls into recognisable patterns – complex inter-relationships between habitat and the species which live there, making up dynamic ecosystems (which too are inter-related) where each species is linked to others both by essential and more obscure bonds to form a living whole. Within an ecosystem each species has its place - its niche - to which it is uniquely adapted through evolution to fulfil its particular role.

The concept of the niche not only applies to species within an ecosystem; many species as diverse as bees and mongooses have complex social systems where individuals play differing parts ensuring the smooth running of the society in which they live. In nature, survival depends on getting those relationships right. We are no different; we too have our niche to fill as individuals; what we make of our lives is dependent upon what our relationships with others are like. This is where I believe 'purpose in life' comes in - it is finding one's niche in society and forging the right relationships with our fellows. With such complexities in human society the niche is far more than conforming to a rigid mould like being a doctor, a builder or a shop assistant, it can vary, not only through life, but in different situations. Each person is unique, capable of making a particular contribution to many situations. I believe that each one of us has a part to play, dependent on our abilities, opportunities and the environment in which we are living. It is the parable of the talents all over again.

We can apply the analogy further to the ecology of nations. The interdependence of nations is a reality today - no nation can exist on its own. The links are comparable to the webs of species in an ecosystem, each nation making its own particular contribution to the life of the world. Just as in nature there are laws which determine relationships, so there are between nations: respect, tolerance, trust and a balance between giving and receiving. The great message that ecology gives to the world is that there is unity in diversity.

Biological principles also helped me to formulate ideas on our relationship with the natural world. Biologically speaking, we cannot escape the fact that we are part of nature not apart from it. The early chapters of Genesis have had a profound effect on Western philosophical thought; it has become ingrained in our society that the rest of creation was made for our benefit. This is a myth which I believe has given rise to a tragic and arrogant intolerance of other forms of life resulting in the destruction of many ecosystems for human need and greed and the ever-increasing pollution of the planet which threatens so many forms of life including our own.

Our power to manipulate nature is an awesome responsibility which we ignore at our peril. In the long term our only hope as a species is to use our new-found power, technology and ecological know-how to work with nature, not ride roughshod over it. We will have to take stock of natural resources and imitate nature's methods of renewing what is taken out, aiming only for sustainable growth and recycling in the widest sense.

Our privilege and responsibility is to be good stewards of the natural world. If we take this line, our attitude will lead to a genuine respect for other forms of life - a realisation that every species is an end-product of evolution beautifully adapted to fill a niche in the grand design of our living planet. We too are part of that design - we like to think an important part - but if we are to play our unique role, need will have to supplant greed. There is no doubt that conservation problems in developing countries are inseparably linked with overpopulation, poverty and starvation and will only be halted when wealth is more fairly distributed and population growth curbed. This will entail much sacrifice, compassion and greater respect for other races - a much-needed revolution in human relationships.

The problem of population control needs to be urgently addressed. It is basic to our survival. In animal populations, overcrowding leads to increasing stimulation between individuals, greater competition for resources and mounting aggression. Dramatic drops in numbers may result due to disease, including those which are stress-related. We see comparable conditions today in our over-crowded cities. Go to remote places where conditions are hard and people are few and you still find a basic caring between neighbours, each helping the other when difficulties arise; survival depends on this co-operation. These good relationships become more difficult in large communities.

I believe that one of the problems that faces humanity, especially in the western world, is that our way of life has become more and more divorced from nature. Our spiritual values and deep instinct to be part of nature has been replaced by an artificiality of our own making, materialistic attitudes suppressing religious awareness and the feeling of oneness with the natural world. In this respect I have been greatly impressed by the writings of Laurens van der Post with his remarkable insight into the spiritual world of the Bushmen of the Kalahari, his own attitude to nature and his philosophical conclusions. Indications of this unconscious longing to have relationships with other living things shows itself in our love of gardens, our attitudes to pets, the exodus from towns and cities for holidays (holy days - times when we have a chance to become whole again), our desire for the relative peace of the countryside for renewal of the spirit amid the beauty of nature's landscapes. Only a very few have the good fortune to experience the healing powers of wilderness in all its moods where the forces of nature make us feel insignificant, and like astronauts in space, we are filled with awe and wonder at the majesty of planet earth and the complexity of the web of life-forms inhabiting its vulnerable surface.

The subject of relationships leads one inevitably to education. Bringing up the next generation is an enormous responsibility shared primarily between parents and schools but also society in general. When I first went into teaching I had starry-eyed views of what education was all about. I believed strongly in the development of the whole person - body, mind and spirit; I wanted to help children discover their identity, realise their full potential, prepare them to fill their unique niche in society and learn how to make positive relationships with others. However, when faced with a lively class of youngsters, such thoughts fly out of the window and you are brought down to earth with a bump. Nevertheless, after 35 years of school teaching and falling far short of these ideals, I still feel that education needs that broad vision. I like the definition of education by Dominic Milroy: 'to foster the ability to react wisely to new circumstances which society challenges them with, involving spiritual, moral, intellectual and emotional components.' It is so easy to get bogged down in the minutiae of routine, administrative procedure and a mass of paper-work; if one is not careful, teaching merely becomes a matter of imparting knowledge, getting good examination results and maintaining discipline. The problem is keeping the vision bright, constantly reminding oneself what education is really about and having the courage to act on priorities whatever the cost to oneself.

In practical terms, my experience at Rendcomb and Taunton taught me much. Dealing with parents from many backgrounds and differing circumstances, remembering my own home background, having a family of my own and by studying animal behaviour, I realised the enormous importance of early learning, the interactions between members of the family and the quality of relationships within the home. Motivation towards learning is first fostered there; it is the place where the sense of wonder and discovery can be encouraged in the security of home surroundings. A child needs to feel safe when starting to explore. Home also provides the environment where discipline is experienced - an essential step towards the goal of self-discipline. In addition, the home background can foster the growth of morality, tolerance and mutual caring which are the roots of character-building and a responsible society. The child with such a start in life is indeed fortunate. Would that such a home was the norm instead of the exception! However, it is enormously encouraging that young children are so resilient and may develop so astonishingly well in spite of our many failures as teachers and parents.

By stark contrast, home background can have a devastating effect on a child's personality, bad relationships between parents, racial and religious prejudices, drug abuse and the general breakdown of morality can easily be passed on to the next generation to the detriment, not only of the individua,l but of society as a whole.

Much also depends on the quality of playgroups and early schooling. Far too little emphasis has been given to this critical stage which should widen horizons beyond the limitations of home, provide greater experience of other children, increase tolerance, enhance motivation, encourage self-expression and inculcate a measure of discipline which can be of the greatest value in later schooling; all are important factors leading to good relationships.

My own methods of teaching have developed over the years. Some techniques have worked, others have failed, but I believe one of the most significant factors is one's own attitude and example. In my experience, pupils seldom act on advice unless they actively seek it. This only happens when trust has been established and objectivity is taken for granted. However, they do take notice of example. Children are remarkably perceptive regarding their teachers; they are quick to notice whether you are trying to put precept into practice, whether you are honest or false, fair or show favouritism, consistent or weak, humorous or sarcastic. One's relationship with a class is of paramount importance and a responsibility of the greatest magnitude. Sadly, this is often borne out when one asks why a pupil is poor at a particular subject? A common answer is, "I cannot get on with the teacher".

Another reply to the same question is, "It is all so boring". This is a tragedy because children have a natural capacity to wonder and the art of teaching helps to develop this into the adults' ability to contemplate and solve problems. Having taught biology, I feel I have been particularly fortunate as it is a subject which is easy to enthuse about; pupils are usually intrigued by the natural world and an understanding of themselves. Of course teachers of other subjects would make the same claim, but it is this chance to enthuse that brings delight as well as enlightenment.

The gulf between teacher and taught is very wide when the child is young; the teacher is thought to know everything. However, with increasing age the relationship alters. Both teacher and taught have much to learn together even though they are at very different stages in the process. Admitting you don't know all the answers is an encouragement to the learners and helps to narrow the generation gap. I believe in most cases it is good to treat pupils as if they are slightly older and more intelligent than they appear to be; if you expect a lot, they usually rise to it. When you take a class and come to know its members, you tend to notice the good things about the better ones, the bad things about the rascals and the remainder attract less notice. However, each has facets of character and particular interests which respond to encouragement;

one's job as an educator is to find out what these are and help with their development.

Pupils have different abilities and some competition is very helpful in stimulating endeavour. However, others become depressed because they cannot do so well. These can be encouraged by measuring in various ways their own progress (a type of competition with oneself). Just as in athletics where you can measure your improvement over time with a stop-watch, so in class, comparable devices can demonstrate a pupil's progress.

My experience at Rendcomb convinced me that teaching should be a team effort, the ideal to aim for being good liaison between all staff concerned in relation to each pupil. In reality, especially in large schools, this is seldom possible - time is finite and teachers are human, nevertheless much can be done. Having had an enthusiasm for teaching biology I have had to ask myself many times,'Does the interest of this pupil come first or am I more concerned with my ambitions for him regarding a particular career or outcome?' Too often one sees pupils in the middle of a tug-of-war between teachers over early specialisation instead of concern for their best interests.

All teachers develop their own techniques, have their own strengths and weaknesses. Diversity is of enormous value in education just as it is in the natural world. A good headteacher fosters the strengths of his or her staff, encourages initiative and gives guidance and support. Teachers need just as much encouragement from those in authority as children do from their teachers. They need to feel they are valuable members of a team. When this happens a school becomes a place where good relationships flourish and a happy and successful society results.

For many of us our days become crammed with activities; time to think, contemplate and wonder becomes so limited that life rushes by and before we know where we are it is nearly over. Symptoms of stress are a common result and relaxation becomes essential but often difficult to achieve. There are many biological analogies which are relevant to this situation. Life processes in all organisms vary in efficiency according to a number of factors; success lies in maintaining these at optimal levels - the optimum being the level of greatest efficiency which is sustainable. Temperature is one of these factors. Many species of mammal, including ourselves, use a number of physiological and behavioural devices to maintain their temperature at optimal levels. However, under some circumstances greater benefits can be achieved by exceptional effort at the expense of raising the temperature above the optimal, but this can only be maintained for a short time, as when a predator on the hot

African plains pursues its prey. Then by resting, sweating and/or panting the temperature is soon reduced to the optimal once more. Nevertheless, temperature must not rise too high as brain damage may occur.

The philosophy for living derived from such an analogy is to aim for the optimum because it represents the most efficient level which is sustainable. Again, under special circumstances, a maximum effort is both necessary and desirable, but it cannot be sustained for long without adverse results - undue fatigue, stress and so on. Each person according to his or her physical and mental capacities has an optimum for a wide range of activities which may differ greatly according to many variables. For example when driving a car there is an optimal speed which varies with age, driving competence, type of road and traffic conditions; exceed this and stress results. Again, workaholics often burn themselves out at an early age because they are exceeding their optimum most of the time and the same applies to the young sports achiever. Incidentally, this may bring stress to others as well as themselves; relationships suffer. The capable, willing person can fill the days and weeks with useful activities with no let-ups, but when too much is attempted, as I found during my last few years of teaching, effectiveness suffers. Emphasis on priorities then has to be made and it is necessary to say "no" to some requests.

Optimal use of time is a main reason why some people achieve so much without the stress that is so common in other 'successful' people. This is because the day is planned, priorities are identified, work is carried through in an unhurried manner and others concerned are given the impression that if a matter is important there is always time for it. This leads to good relationships and is the art of successful management. Again, in many situations optimal efficiency varies with the time spent on the job, shorter spells often resulting in better work with less stress. This is well illustrated by the length of lessons in schools (very variable with age), the amount of homework set and the time given to recreation. It also applies to the hours truck-drivers, pilots and doctors work, to name a few examples where the principle, if ignored, can bring obvious perils.

Striving for the optimum also underlies the ecological/economic theory of sustainable growth in the use of natural resources such as timber from forests and fish stocks in the oceans. It raises monumental questions of a political and personal nature which, if put into practice, would alter the life-style of people world-wide. This can only be considered against the background of the future of the human race. Have we got a long-term future at all? If so, what can be said about it? Evolution is not just something that has happened in the past; it is still occurring.

In nature, evolution does not occur suddenly. It comes about through genetic variations in individuals which are helpful under changing conditions and which gradually spread throughout a population bringing about progressive adaptation. In this way a minority may become strong enough to supplant a previously dominant species. The evolutionary record is littered with species which were well adapted to a particular habitat but could not cope when conditions changed too rapidly. Change is always the opportunity for some and the undoing of others. Does this apply to us?

Our evolution has been rapid, spectacular and unique. There have been anatomical changes, in particular, increase in brain size and structures concerned with manipulative skills. However, natural selection acts just as much on aspects of behaviour as on advantageous anatomical characteristics. For example, a caterpillar resembling a twig only gains from the likeness when it remains still, and thus it confines its feeding to night-time.

Behaviour has also played a major part in human evolution. Our early ancestors were curious, adventurous, aggressive and increasingly social; brain development gave rise to greater intelligence, increasing dexterity in the making and use of tools led to more control over the environment. This in turn made possible a greater choice of food, and there was a gradual change to a scavenger/hunter/gatherer way of life in an increasing variety of habitats. This opened up greater opportunities, allowing our more recent ancestors to spread all over the world and even become adapted to the most hostile environments. In recent times our control over nature has become so great that little remains of true wilderness and we increasingly live in artificial habitats of our own making.

Today we have many of the characteristics of our ancestors, but we are now faced with a problem of immense magnitude; we have become so numerous that society is increasingly showing signs of breakdown. Aggression, which served the human race so well during its early evolution, is still with us and is now a hindrance to our future evolution if uncontrolled; violence, crime and war are some of its consequences.

It seems unlikely that physical evolution will help us, only a change in the way we live and our attitudes to others will assure our future. Thus our evolution will not just depend on our technical know-how, but on moral and spiritual factors which affect our behaviour and hence our relationships.

In a colony of bees the queens, drones and workers have different parts to play but are of equal importance for the survival of the colony. We still have a long way to go in applying this principle to ourselves in terms of colour, gender, class and nationality.

During our evolution, the sexes have evolved characteristics which fulfil different functions in society; by being complementary, they have helped survival. Male and female sex hormones are present in both men and women; in men there is an over-riding concentration of the male hormone, in women the opposite occurs. However, the proportion differs from one person to another. The male hormone influences aggressive behaviour and the urge to dominate, the female, a more caring attitude towards others. It would be false to suggest that behaviour is governed by hormonal factors alone; this is not so; but there is no doubt that they play a part. Within each of us whatever our gender there are signs both of aggression and caring, but historically, with male-dominated societies, the former has played the major role in influencing international affairs and social behaviour in most parts of the world. If we are going to learn to live together, caring behaviour will need to supplant aggression. This does not necessarily mean that the world will have to change to being female-dominated but that we shall have to exploit fully the complementary contributions made by both sexes, not only in personal relationships but within all levels of society, particularly where decisions of national and international importance are made.

In human society, cultural as well as genetic inheritance plays an important part in evolution. We learn from each other's behaviour especially when we are very young, and later through the spoken and written word and the power of the media. Society is changing rapidly. The clue to the future is which of these changes will have survival value? It is a terrifying, sobering and challenging thought that our future evolution depends on the changes now occurring in us and the society in which we live. Some of these behaviours will lead to evolutionary dead-ends, others to advances towards a new kind of person.

There are obvious instances of the importance of behavioural patterns in this respect. History gives us many examples of how pursuit of power, wealth, ideologies and intolerance of the beliefs of others have led to wars; the same is happening today. Now, with nuclear weapons we could end human evolution altogether. However, there are more subtle aspects of behaviour which may effect human evolution, one example being the spread of Aids. By the end of 1993, it was calculated by the World Health Organisation that the number of estimated cases of Aids had reached 4 million while the number of people infected with the human immunodeficiency virus (HIV) numbered about 17 million, new infections during that year occurred at a rate of about 10,000 a day. By the end of the century it was estimated that between 30 and 40 million would be infected. Many of those who contract the disease are the innocent victims of the behaviour patterns of others. In some developing countries family structure and whole villages are being destroyed as thousands of children become 'AIDS orphans' left with elderly relatives. We shall not know for many years how much this fast-spreading disease will affect the future of the human race.

However, it is enormously encouraging that history also gives us many examples of dynamic minorities, initiated by individuals of great vision and courage, who have seen the need, lived out their beliefs and caused humanity to take a great leap forwards in its moral and spiritual evolution.

I believe the greatest example of the effect of a dynamic minority in history is the Church of the First Century with Christ as its origin. It was a minority which 'turned the world upside down'. It reflected a new belief and way of life which could not be suppressed and spread to all corners of the earth. The Church over the years has lost much of its dynamic nature; it has become bedevilled by controversy over matters of secondary importance, is tragically divided, and to the layman appears to be an institution rather than an instrument of God's power working through people united in their determination to live as true followers of Christ. Nevertheless, there is a dynamic minority who, as individuals in all walks of life and in their own unique ways, are devoting their lives to improving relationships through the power of love.

Speaking biologically, Christ to me is the prototype of the new kind of person. To be more like him is the road towards our moral and spiritual evolution. It is not easy to be optimistic about the future when all around us relationships seem to be worsening. However, there is a positive side to every situation. Never before have there been so many from different races and backgrounds who are selflessly making their contributions towards healing the ills of society in ways large and small. They are bound together by an affinity of spirit - a faith in the power of love - these will be the survivors when selection of the fittest takes place.

Let us return once more to those Normandy beaches. Dawn has broken. We are quite alone. The tide is out and the sand is still wet. As the day gets brighter, patches of green appear as those tiny flatwoms come to the surface in their millions in response to the light, and in the stillness, into one's consciousness come those words from down the Ages which are the key to good relationships: "Freely you have received, freely give".